Engineering:

principles and problems

Lee H. Johnson

Tulane University

Engineering:

principles
and
problems

McGRAW-HILL Book Company, Inc.

New York   Toronto   London   **1960**

THIS BOOK HAS BEEN SET IN JANSON,
A VERSION OF A TYPE FACE

This book has been set in Janson,
a version of a type face
of about 1700, probably Dutch
in origin. Heads are in Vogue Bold.
The line illustrations are by Joseph Halus.

To

Mary McKay *and* **Millbrook**

Preface

One purpose of this book is to introduce the student of engineering to basic ideas, principles, and methods underlying the profession of engineering. It is to serve as a guide in the development of his ideas and attitudes, and also to provide a foundation of elementary knowledge on which to build as he pursues his career in college.

Another purpose is to develop in the engineering student the capacity to meet new situations and to solve new problems with confidence. The very term "engineer" is related to the word "ingenious," meaning clever, resourceful, or able to think creatively in evaluating situations.

The book has yet another purpose. Beginning students in engineering often complain that they do not really "get any engineering" during the first year or two in college. This text attempts to provide immediate stimulation and motivation for engineering students by calling on them to evaluate situations from an engineering viewpoint during the first year of college.

The following topics are treated in some detail: the role of the professional engineer and the types of problems which face him; estimating costs and quantities; derivation of equations; dimensions and units; measurements and accuracy; energy and power, with separate chapters on potential and kinetic energy, internal energy, heat, and electric and magnetic energy; and project or design problems. One chapter is devoted to report writing and the presentation of problem solutions, and another emphasizes the importance of geometry in engineering. The appendixes provide reference material for current and future use, including dimension systems, standard abbreviations, conversion factors, geometrical formulas, and illustrative reports.

The book offers two new approaches to the subject: (1) discussions and original problems to develop in the engineering student the capacity to meet new situations and to solve new problems with confidence, i.e., to introduce the beginning student to the truly professional type of problem, which has no unique solution and which requires him to exercise his ingenuity and creative capacities, and (2) an introduction to engineering theory from the standpoint of energy and power, their various forms, and their conversion and transfer. The purpose here is to give the beginning student a broad foundation of knowledge which will lead to a better understanding of the relationship between the various branches of engineering and will provide a greater capacity for solving the unknown problems of the future. Again, some original problems are introduced.

The author is particularly indebted to the following colleagues at Tulane University for their assistance and suggestions: D. H. Vliet, J. A. Cronvich, R. V. Bailey, R. M. Rotty, and E. H. Harris. He expresses appreciation to others of his colleagues for helpful information: W. E. Blessey, M. M. Gilkeson, H. N. Lee, J. L. Martinez, J. H. Peebles, C. A. Peyronnin, C. J. Sperry, W. T. Tucker, and A. D. Wallace. He is grateful for advice from R. G. Folsom, President, Rensselaer Polytechnic Institute, and N. A. Hall, Head, Department of Mechanical Engineering, Yale University. Appreciation is also expressed to the Engineering Department of E. I. du Pont de Nemours & Company, Wilmington, Delaware, for valuable assistance to the author, especially in the chapter on report writing. And finally, the author wishes to thank his wife, Eulalie M. Johnson, for her helpful assistance in preparing the manuscript.

Lee H. Johnson

Contents

Engineering:

principles and problems

ONE

The profession and its problems

Students decide to study engineering for a variety of reasons. Some like to tinker with television or monkey with machinery. Some have fathers who are engineers or perhaps some have worked summers on construction jobs, or some have heard that engineers make high salaries or that engineers are in demand. Whatever the reason, each student has in his own mind some picture of what an engineer does and would like to try his own hand on some real engineering problems as soon as possible. It is fitting that these problems be the subject of the opening chapter of the book.

Types of problems

The student is right when he thinks of problems. An engineer's entire career from his freshman days to retirement is mostly the solution of problems one after another with no two exactly alike. On the other hand, he may think that the practice of engineering involves primarily the use of handbooks to supply formulas and the substitution of numbers into these formulas. It is highly important that the student realize that this is not true. Only a portion of an engineer's work involves such methods and such tools. It may come as a surprise to be told that his problems are not all mathematical in nature and that many of them

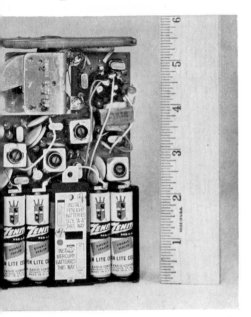

FIG. 1.1. Pocket-sized radio circuit using transistors. *(Courtesy of the Zenith Radio Corporation.)*

involve human characteristics and most of them have *more than one answer*.

There are two extremes in engineering problems. One type is mathematical in nature and has a unique solution. This type can be specifically numerical such as substituting numbers for letters in formulas, or it can be general in nature such as the theoretical derivation of a formula. The following represent problems of this type and could be either derivations in terms of letters or numerical solutions with numbers: (1) the calculation of the transfer of heat in a radiator, (2) the calculation of the current in an electric circuit (Fig. 1.1), and (3) the calculation of the bending stresses in a structural beam.

If we stop and think, we realize that all these problems have unique solutions because they are set up that way by making certain assumptions and by selecting dimensions, materials, loads, and such. But we can also readily see that these problems are parts of much larger problems.

The radiator, the electric circuit, and the beam may be respective parts of an automobile, a radio, and a bridge, all of which serve human beings in one way or another. These "engineered" finished products must be comfortable, safe, appealing to the eye, economical, durable, or in a phrase, generally satisfactory. Yes, somewhere along the line we human beings with all our frailties must be considered in designing and building these products. People have to "live" with what the engineer designs; people have to "keep it up."

For example, an engineer does not necessarily succeed by building an automobile engine which runs smoothly and efficiently. He fails if the mechanic in the garage down the street has to tear the motor apart to change spark plugs or if the filling station attendant has to remove the oil filter to check the oil.

An engineer has not necessarily succeeded when he has calculated the sizes of the members of a bridge to span the Mississippi River at New Orleans (Fig. 1.2). He fails if the bridge is too low to allow merchant vessels and warships to pass. He fails if the location of the bridge snarls the traffic pattern of the city streets. He fails if the approaches to the bridge are too steep and dangerous for automobiles in wet weather.

These are failures to solve the other type of engineering problem, the *nonmathematical* kind which requires judgment, imagination, and experience, and which has *more than one possible solution.*

The engineer fails also if he does not consider costs in most of the problems which are brought to him. Those engineers who perform as designers or consultants on projects involving construction, production, maintenance, and operation must certainly be aware of costs. It is true that many engineers work on specific problems in which costs are not directly involved, perhaps more so in research than in any other phase of engineering work. Young engineers at the outset of their careers are frequently assigned problems which are limited in scope and which do not include directly the factor of economy. Yet it is

FIG. 1.2. Bridge across the Mississippi River near the heart of the business district in New Orleans, Louisiana, showing the approaches on the east bank. (*Courtesy of the New Orleans Times-Picayune.*)

FIG. 1.3. Sequence photographs of the launching of an Atlas intercontinental ballistic missile from the Air Force Test Center at Cape Canaveral, Florida. [*Courtesy of Convair (Astronautics) Division, General Dynamics Corporation.*]

difficult to find any engineering problem whose solution will not ultimately have some bearing on the cost of the project or design in which it is used.

The importance to industry of the engineer's ability to combine the dollar sign with the integral sign cannot be overestimated, confronted as industry is with many taxes on the one hand and the demands of labor on the other. His success as a consultant depends upon how many dollars he can save his clients through the application of his professional knowledge and skill. Therefore, it is most important that the student of engineering become cost conscious at the beginning of his college career.

A word of caution is needed at this point. The student must not conclude from the foregoing discussion that basic science and engineering theory play an insignificant part in engineering as compared with judgment and ingenuity; nor that one need not try to master physics, mathematics, engineering mechanics, thermodynamics, electrical theory, and such. Far from it! These theoretical subjects are becoming ever more necessary as a foundation. It is virtually impossible today in many areas of engineering for a person to understand what is being done unless he has mastered them.

Thus, professional engineering is a combination of theory and practice, or we might say a combination of the science and the art of engineering. In the early days of engineering, there were fewer scientific tools and more reliance had to be placed on the artful use of judgment and experience. But scientific discoveries and mathematical developments along with more extensive application of classical scientific theory have changed this picture tremendously so that engineering is quite scientific. The advent of such developments as nuclear reactors, electronic computers, jet and rocket engines (Fig. 1.3), soil mechanics, plastic design of structures, automation, synthetic materials, and many others makes it imperative that engineering curricula place proper emphasis on the *basic sciences* and their close relatives, the *engineering sciences*. This latter group of subjects includes the mechanics of solids, fluid mechanics, thermodynamics, electrical theory (including fields, circuits, and electronics), rate and transfer mechanisms (including energy and material balances), and the materials of engineering.

Definition of engineering

It may occur to the reader that we have been discussing engineering, its theory and practice, but have not tried to define engineering. From the preceding discussion there are certain implications which lead to a definition. However, it would be very difficult to find a definition upon which all engineers would agree. One might say that engineering is the application of scientific knowledge and of judgment to practical problems involving the forces and materials of nature. A more extensive definition might be given as follows: "Engineering is the scientific utilization of the forces and materials of nature in the design, construction, production, and operation of works for the benefit of man." *

Engineering might also be explained in terms of the instrumentalities

* C. C. Williams and E. A. Farber, "Building an Engineering Career," 3d ed., chap. 2, McGraw-Hill Book Company, Inc., New York.

which it uses in such a way as to imply a definition. The instrumentalities are called the four M's of engineering,* as follows:

Methods. Primarily the applications of the principles of mathematics, physics, and chemistry to the problems of the engineer, or in a phrase, the artful application of the engineering sciences.

Materials. The knowledge of the physical and chemical properties of an ever-widening range of materials, both natural and synthetic.

Money. Knowledge and experience in estimating and balancing costs to determine the most economical solutions.

Men. A knowledge of human experience and human relations to enable the engineer to work effectively with individuals and organizations.

The artful use of all four of these instrumentalities makes for success in engineering practice.

Procedure in solving problems

Now that the student has some idea about the theory and practice of engineering, it is time to turn professional and to try his hand at some elementary problems. Before doing this, however, he should have some idea about how to proceed. One might say that professional engineers use, in general, a procedure which involves the following steps:

1. Definition of the problem
2. Selection of methods and procedures
3. Collection of data
4. Application of methods and procedures
5. Conclusions and recommendations

This arrangement of the various phases in solving problems and the choice of words in describing them represents but one of several possible statements of procedure. Some might be given in more detail. However, it is believed that the above procedure broadly interpreted is representative of all basic steps.

Definition of the problem. Defining the problem is frequently not so simple as might be imagined. If it is only the calculation of the deflection of a steel beam of given size and material under a given load using a formula which has been derived and verified, yes, it is a simple matter

* *Ibid.*

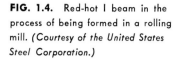

FIG. 1.4. Red-hot I beam in the process of being formed in a rolling mill. *(Courtesy of the United States Steel Corporation.)*

to state the problem. But can the problem of designing a steel mill to make the beam be stated so simply? Unless the engineer knows all the factors to be considered in solving the problem, can he present a good solution?

What is to be its production capacity? What kind and size of various pieces of equipment are to be purchased or designed and built outright? How many different steel shapes shall it produce (Fig. 1.4)? What types of controls and instrumentation shall be installed? What voltage shall be required for the electric power? How much maintenance is anticipated? What is the estimated unit cost of production? The initial statement of the problem, therefore, must frequently include a broad survey of the many factors which could conceivably influence the design, construction, and operation. A decision must be made as to which must be included and which may be ignored.

It is highly important that the engineer state clearly the assumptions that he has made, if any, in defining the problem. There are few problems where assumptions are not made, either implicitly or explicitly. Some of the assumptions which might be made in designing the machinery for the steel mill might be (1) the size of the ingot to be heated for rolling, (2) the specific heat of the steel, (3) the time required to raise the temperature of the ingot, (4) the speed of the rolling mills, (5) the precision to which the dimensions of the shapes are to be rolled, and (6) the method of cooling the rolls themselves and their maximum permissible temperature.

It will probably be necessary to make assumptions at other stages in solving a problem which follow its definition. This is particularly true whenever adequate data cannot be obtained. We shall discuss this more at length in the section on the collection of data.

Selection of methods and procedures.   The methods and procedures which are used by professional engineers to solve the problems presented to them by their clients or colleagues include those precise methods of engineering science used for theoretical analysis, calculation, and theoretical design as well as the more intangible use of common sense and ingenuity. Judgment and experience are elements of common sense which along with ingenuity are necessary in determining how a problem is to be approached. A small specific problem may involve only the theory to be applied and the extent to which calculations are to be made. A major project could involve not only theory but also the creation of an organization to carry out the work, the assigning of responsibilities, and the coordination of activities.

Many engineers work primarily on theoretical analyses and would make use principally of the science of engineering. Other engineers are engaged mainly in the nontechnical phases of an engineering project. However, some engineer or team of engineers must be responsible for bringing together all of these factors to determine the methods and procedures to be used in attacking the problem. For example, let us consider two problems in the design and manufacture of electric circuits for instruments or radios.

The assembly of components into a circuit involves manufacturing procedures which are the concern of the mechanical and industrial engineers. Several methods might be used to solder connections. One is an assembly-line method in which a particular person in the line will solder a particular connection in each set as it passes by him. Another procedure is to solder all connections simultaneously. This is done by manually or automatically inserting the various components into position on a chassis or frame and dipping the connections as a group into a bath of molten solder. Still a third procedure would be to have one man assemble and solder all the components for the entire circuit. Each has its respective advantages and disadvantages. For instance, the third method might be used for the manufacture of a small number of special-purpose instruments or radios.

A second problem faces the designer of a radio circuit which involves a number of component parts such as vacuum tubes, capacitors, resistors, transformers, and such. He might use one of several methods for his calculations such as the method of equivalent circuits, the graphic method in which tube characteristics are plotted as curves, or the method of linear approximations. The operating characteristics of the circuit would have some bearing on which method to use, such as the degree of amplification, the extent of the elimination of static, and the range of frequencies.

Collection of data. It should be pointed out that sometimes data must be collected before methods and procedures can be determined. Accordingly, the placing of this item as third on the list of steps in the solution of an engineering problem is not necessarily in order. The collection of data might also be necessary in order to define the problem. Data, therefore, may be needed at several stages in the solution of an engineering problem.

Gathering data frequently presents the greatest difficulty in solving a problem because it is not always possible to obtain complete or adequate data. Often engineers have to solve problems with incomplete data by making assumptions. This is one reason why judgment, experience, and ingenuity are so important to an engineer. For example, offshore drilling operations on the continental shelf are relatively recent (Fig. 1.5). Structures had to be built under absolutely new conditions

FIG. 1.5. A self-contained drilling platform located in coastal waters 95 ft deep in the Gulf of Mexico near Grand Isle, Louisiana. (*Courtesy of the Continental Oil Company and J. Ray McDermott and Company, Inc.*)

in a major body of water. At first there were not sufficient data to guide the designers in estimating wave forces or probable maximum wave heights in a given depth of water. Accordingly, the first designs had to be made on the basis of inadequate data with the use of judgment, ingenuity, and whatever experience could be brought to bear in making the necessary assumptions.

FIG. 1.6. Main span of the Tacoma Narrows Bridge in vigorous single-noded torsional motion a few minutes after this kind of motion developed for the first time in the life of the bridge. The roadway structure collapsed and fell 70 min later. (*Courtesy of Professor F. B. Farquharson, the University of Washington.*)

Another example is the Tacoma Narrows suspension bridge, which was dubbed "Galloping Gertie" because of its excessive movement in high winds. Although the bridge was perfectly safe on the basis of conventional analysis, i.e., the analysis for the bridge as a static or motionless structure resisting lateral wind pressures, there were not available adequate data on the aerodynamic characteristics of the bridge. The side walls of the floor system were designed as flat plates instead of trusses. As a result strong cross winds produced severe aerodynamic effects which led to its destruction (Fig. 1.6). A noted scholar of aerodynamics, Theodore von Kármán, described the failure as follows:[*]

> Unfortunately these (flat plates) gave rise to shedding vortices, and the bridge started torsional oscillations, which developed amplitudes up to 40° before it broke. The phenomenon was a combination of flutter and resonance with vortex shedding (Fig. 1.7).

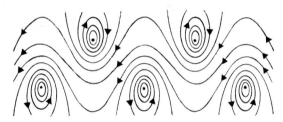

FIG. 1.7. Instantaneous stream velocities of the von Kármán vortex street.

The term "vortex street" in Fig. 1.7 is used to describe a particular pattern of vortices in the flow of a fluid. The vortices in this pattern are formed alternately, first on one side and then the other of an object in the path of flow. They also alternate in direction, one clockwise, the next counterclockwise. This characteristic of alternating directions and positions has a tendency to produce oscillation of the object from side to side, i.e., at right angles to the direction of flow.

Although the main cables and suspender cables withstood the unusual stresses to which they were subjected, the floor system in the center span was completely wrecked and a large portion broke loose and fell into the Tacoma Narrows.

This again shows the importance of including all factors in a design which can conceivably affect the performance of a structure and of having *adequate data* or making *reasonably correct assumptions*.

Application of methods and procedures. The actual solution can involve much or little work. Frequently, the major task lies in setting

---

[*] Theodore von Kármán, "Aerodynamics," p. 72, Cornell University Press, Ithaca, N.Y., 1954.

FIG. 1.8. Siamesed free-piston compressor being lowered onto the chassis of XP-500, the General Motors experimental free-piston engine-powered automobile. The compressor, which has two sets of opposed free pistons, "pumps" hot gases to a turbine in the rear of the car. This eliminates the customary drive shaft. *(Courtesy of the General Motors Corporation.)*

up the problem, and when this is done, there remains only to apply well-known mathematical or theoretical relationships. The answer to such a problem may be unique and require only numerical computations which are routine in character. Even very complicated and difficult computations have now been made routine by the advent of the electronic computers.

On the other hand, the solution may involve the complete design of a complicated product which may be a machine, a structure, a process, a measuring or controlling device, or such. This will require much more than routine computations. For example, the problem of developing a new automobile engine, say the free-piston engine (Fig. 1.8), is extremely difficult. This involves not only the design of component parts of the engine considering innumerable factors such as the relation of horsepower to size and speed, combustion rates and temperatures (Fig. 1.9), relation of gas turbine to free-piston mechanism, power take-off, and cooling system. It also calls for estimates of the cost of manufacturing for a particular design, costs of installation and maintenance, and economy of operation for various potential fuels such as gasoline, kerosene, and crude oil. Also to be considered are the potential sales appeal and markets, availability of particular fuels along the highways, safety features, and many other factors.

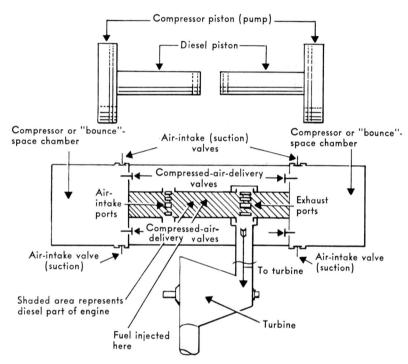

FIG. 1.9. Diagrammatic view of the free-piston engine mechanism. (*Courtesy of the General Motors Corporation.*)

All of these are interrelated. Not only must fuel economy be considered in determining sales appeal, but also such factors as time of "warm-up" and acceleration on "getaway." These latter factors in turn are related to the combustion rates, power take-off and transmission, cooling system and such, all of which have an effect on the design and related cost of manufacturing. Thus it becomes quite a problem to achieve a delicate balance among all of these factors to give the best solution from all points of view. Here is where the engineers really earn their salt.

Conclusions and recommendations. From the results that he obtains, the engineer reaches his conclusions with regard to the problem and presents his recommendations in the form of a report accompanied by plans, drawings, specifications, models, or whatever is necessary to give complete information about his solutions. Frequently, he will present alternative solutions, pointing out the respective advantages and disadvantages of each.

For example, an engineer might report on various methods of extracting the salt from sea water in order to make it potable. In his conclusions he might discuss the relative advantages and disadvantages of the various methods which he has studied such as distillation, filtration, or sedimentation. Distillation would remove all the mineral content of sea water, whereas filtration and sedimentation might remove only part of it. Distillation would require heat energy as compared with the others which might require only chemicals. In discussing distillation processes, he would have to compare the various types of stills used and the sources of available energy such as gas, oil, coal, electricity, or solar energy. He would weigh such factors as the quantity of water produced per hour, the availability of fuel at the place where the still is to be used, the cost of manufacturing the equipment or the first cost, the cost of operation and maintenance, and other such factors. He would then conclude which is the most suitable method considering all factors and make his recommendations.

The engineer should be careful to include all significant information in his problem solution or report, to state what assumptions he has made, and to defend his judgment in making these assumptions. His presentation should fit the scope of the problem and might consist of a one-page calculation in answer to a specific question about one particular component of a machine. In this case there would be no conclusion beyond stating a numerical answer. On the other hand, the greater the responsibility which the engineer normally assumes as his career progresses, the greater is the scope of the professional problems which confront him. Sooner or later he will be faced with the task of presenting a more or less comprehensive report in which his conclusions and recommendations will have to be well supported at length.

Suggested references

Clement C. Williams and Erich A. Farber, "Building an Engineering Career," 3d ed., McGraw-Hill Book Company, Inc., New York, 1957. Orientation in the profession of engineering, its history, branches, and achievements, and specific suggestions on how to study engineering.

Ralph J. Smith, "Engineering as a Career," McGraw-Hill Book Company, Inc., New York, 1956. The history, branches, and functions of engineering plus previews of engineering curricula and the engineering sciences.

Willy Ley, "Engineers' Dreams," Viking Press, New York, 1954. Ideas and proposals of engineers that stretch the imagination and border on the fantastic.

Engineers' Council for Professional Development, Definition of Engineering, *J. Eng. Educ.*, vol. 49, no. 7, p. 624, March, 1959. A carefully conceived definition accompanied by brief discussions of each of the major elements.

H. J. Gilkey, Definition of Engineering: A Counter Proposal, *J. Eng. Educ.*, vol. 50, no. 3, p. 257, December, 1959. A simple 27-word definition.

Problems

1.1 Characterize the types of engineering problems. Which type is the beginning engineer likely to meet? The research engineer? The consulting engineer?

1.2 Give a definition of engineering. Can you make up one of your own?

1.3 What are the four M's of engineering?

1.4 What are the five steps which are presented in this chapter for solving problems?

1.5 What factors would you include or what things would you consider in defining the problem of building a portable conveyor-belt machine for transporting building materials between the ground and the second and third stories of a building under construction? Make a sketch of the general configuration.

1.6 What factors would you include in defining the problem of designing a coil spring for smoothing out the "ride" of a streamlined railroad passenger car?

1.7 What data would you obtain and what assumptions would you make in designing the layout of a multistory parking garage with inclined ramps for access between stories? Make a sketch of the general layout.

1.8 What data would you obtain and what assumptions would you make in designing a fork-lift truck for use in a storage warehouse?

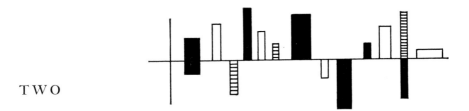

TWO

Estimating costs and quantities

One may wonder why the subject of estimating costs and quantities is considered so early in a book on the theory and practice of engineering. There is good reason for this. It is possible to give the beginning student certain types of problems involving costs and quantities which are solved by the engineering method, but which do not require much of the theory of engineering. In solving them he is exposed to the full experience of the engineer, from defining the problem to drawing conclusions.

The engineering method

It is highly important that the student master what might be termed the "engineering method" in college, and the earlier the better. This engineering method is the essence of engineering. Thomas K. Sherwood has characterized the situation very clearly in the following quotation:[*]

The "engineering method" is more than a catch phrase. It involves the evaluation of a situation—a process seldom required in the solution of a

[*] T. K. Sherwood, Should Engineering Schools Teach Engineering? *J. Eng. Educ.*, vol. 43, no. 7, pp. 383–386, 1953.

typical ten-line problem assignment. It involves the selection of the appropriate tools—those applicable to the assigned home problem or quiz are usually indicated, or obvious from the context of the course. Very often it requires economic balances of a type which the student meets only in the most elementary form as an undergraduate. It usually involves the handling of situations without adequate data and without unique answers, in which conclusions based on judgment must be made and defended. These are so foreign to undergraduate instruction that students feel ill-treated when sometimes given an assignment with missing data, or one without a definite answer. These protected students experience a rude awakening in the cold world of engineering practice.

Accordingly, the purpose of this chapter is to introduce the student to a professional type of problem at the outset of his career so that he may avoid this rude awakening upon entering professional practice. Each student is expected to set up his own problem, make his own assumptions, collect his own data, and reach his own conclusions. The answers to these problems are not unique and can conceivably vary over a wide range of values, depending upon the conditions and quantities which are assumed and the data which are collected from different sources by different students.

As a matter of fact, this chapter consists principally of problems. The student may ask how he can solve these problems if he is not given any data or any definition of the problem. The answer is that the professional engineer must define the problem for his clients in much the same way that the physician analyzes and determines the ailments of his patients.

The value of these problems is largely lost if the student should be given specific instructions for solving them beyond the suggestions in Chap. 1. To specify procedures, outline conditions, give data, and suggest methods of evaluation and presentation would defeat the purpose of these problem assignments. Here is the opportunity for the student to use judgment and ingenuity and to develop his capacity for creative thinking. It is hoped that he will approach these problems with the enthusiasm of a consulting engineer who is undertaking his first professional work. Although these problems may be different from any with which he has come in contact in his previous experience, at least he is starting his professional career in earnest; he is using the engineering method.

Estimates

Another reason for this chapter is to introduce the student at an early opportunity to the importance of cost estimates and quantity estimates in engineering practice. Considerations of economy are paramount throughout many phases of engineering practice. Furthermore, the solution of many engineering problems frequently depends heavily on the engineer's best estimate of the quantities involved—quantities of material or manpower as well as of money. Sometimes quantities have to be estimated before further steps can be taken in solving the problem. In designing floor loads produced by people in public buildings, some estimate must be made of the number of people on a given area and the average weight per person before the engineer can begin his calculations. The loading in Fig. 2.1 indicates what can occur.

What is involved in planning an alumina refinery (Fig. 2.2)? Some estimate of the amount of aluminum to be extracted per ton of bauxite ore, the size and cost of the equipment and machinery, the amount of power required to run the plant, and the cost of the plant structures is necessary in order to determine the feasibility of the plant. These are more complex problems worthy of the mettle of experienced engineers.

FIG. 2.1. Bird's-eye view of 36 persons in a box of inside dimensions 6 by 6 ft. The average floor load here is 165 lb per sq ft, and the range of weights per person is from 95 to 215 lb.

FIG. 2.2. Alumina refinery, rated at 800,000 tons of product annually. Visible in the picture are ten 250-ft rotary kilns, a bank of 80-ft-high precipitator tanks, a bauxite storage building, and dock and unloading facilities. *(Courtesy of the Kaiser Aluminum and Chemical Corporation.)*

Introduction to the problems

The problems which follow this section are chosen to be worthy of the mettle of the beginning student of engineering and are based upon his previous experiences and present state of knowledge. He should approach these in the spirit of the professional engineer who is applying the "engineering method." Although these problems may be relatively simple, they serve as a foundation for the knowledge and experience yet to come that will enable the engineer to handle much more complex problems.

In presenting the solution of these problems, the student should be sure to state every assumption which is made, every source of data, and every step used in solving the problem or arriving at a conclusion. The answers should not be simply wild guesses.

The student should also read Chap. 14, Submitting Problems and Reports, before beginning his solutions. This chapter presents techniques and rules which will serve as a guide in solving problems throughout the book and in presenting their solutions. Some instructors may wish the solutions to problems in this chapter to be presented in simple report form. Chapter 14 also suggests the steps to be followed in writing a report along with the essential elements.

Now, let us consider an illustrative application of the engineering method. Estimate the length and width of a rectangular school building to provide instruction for 1,800 high school students.

The definition of the problem requires decisions with regard to the factors to be considered. Many possible factors can be included and the purpose of the estimate will usually have a bearing on the number. In this case we will decide to include only a few in order to keep the problem from becoming too complicated. In addition to the number of students we shall consider the number of teachers, the space required for typical classrooms, offices, rest rooms, and hallways, and the number of floors.

Data to guide us in selecting the numerical values to be assigned to the foregoing quantities might be obtained by examining existing buildings, by talking to teachers, principal, or architects, from sets of building plans, and such. In this case the author will draw upon his own experience and make the following assumptions:

1. A student-teacher ratio of 30 to 1.

2. Students are seated 3 ft apart with aisles 4 ft wide on sides and back and a teaching space 12 ft wide in front.

3. Classrooms designed to hold 36 students.

4. Average office size 10 by 12 ft.

5. Rest rooms to be 15 by 30 ft, two to each floor.

6. Halls to be 10 ft wide.

7. Building to have three floors.

The method of solution is apparent from the assumptions. We shall determine the number of teachers and the total office space for them. We shall also calculate the total number of classrooms and total area required for these rooms. If we add this area and divide by the number of floors, we have the space per floor for offices and classrooms. Add the area for rest rooms and hallway per floor and this gives the total building area. The length and width must be determined to yield this area.

Let us now proceed to the calculations and analysis. Area of one classroom:

Assume the students seated in six rows of six seats each, all seats being 3 ft apart. This gives an area which is five seat spaces square, or $5 \times 3 = 15$ ft on a side.

Seating area $= (15)^2 = 225$ sq ft

The side aisles are 4 ft wide, which makes the total room width $15 + (2 \times 4) = 23$ ft.

Side aisles	$= 2 \times 4 \times 15$	$= 120$ sq ft
Back aisle	$= 4 \times 23$	$= 92$ sq ft
Front area	$= 12 \times 23$	$= 276$ sq ft
Total area (one classroom)		$= 713$ sq ft
No. of classrooms	$= \dfrac{1,800}{36}$	
	$= 50$ rooms	
Total classroom area	$= 50 \times 713$	$= 35,650$ sq ft
No. of teachers	$= \dfrac{1,800}{30}$	
	$= 60$ teachers	
Area of one office	$= 10 \times 12$	$= 120$ sq ft
Total office area	$= 60 \times 120$	$= 7,200$ sq ft
Total offices and classrooms		$= 42,850$ sq ft
Office and classroom area per floor	$= \dfrac{42,850}{3}$	$= 14,300$ sq ft

Note that the result is rounded off to three significant figures because this is sufficient for the purposes of the problem, which calls only for a rough estimate.

Rest-room area per floor is $2 \times 15 \times 30 = 900$ sq ft.

Total floor area exclusive of hallway is $14,300 + 900 = 15,200$ sq ft. When we begin to compute the area of the hallway running the length of the building, we meet a difficulty. How long is the building? If we say the length is L and the width W, the hallway area is $10L$, and is unknown at this point.

The next step is, then, to see if we can decide on a building width. We envision a hall with classrooms on each side, so that the combined width of these areas would be

$$W = 23 + 10 + 23$$

$$= 56 \text{ ft}$$

We now set up the relationship for the total floor area as follows:

$$WL = 15,200 + 10L$$

or

$$56L = 15,200 + 10L$$

$$46L = 15,200$$

$$L = 330 \text{ ft}$$

These estimates, of course, are too precise on the basis of the approximations which were used in obtaining them. In conclusion, we can more reasonably say that the building dimensions should be either about 55 by 300 ft or else 60 by 300 ft.

Note that we need not have considered the hallway area in the calculation. The width of the building space allocated just to classrooms, offices, and rest rooms was selected to be 46 ft. We could have set up directly the relationship $46L = 15,200$.

If we reexamine our estimate critically, we find several factors which might call for a reevaluation. The building is rather long and narrow, in fact, too long to fit into the usual city block, which is about 300 ft square. Another question is whether or not the offices 10 by 12 ft and the rest rooms 15 by 30 ft can be fitted into the 23-ft width on each side of the hallway without leaving any dead space. It is obvious that this cannot be done because there is no combination of dimensions of offices and rest rooms which adds to 23 ft. Some of these difficulties can be resolved by changes in the assumptions of room sizes and by using various sizes to meet different situations.

Other factors which might be considered in a more refined estimate might include a reception room and larger office for the principal, teachers' rest rooms, lateral hallways across the building on the first floor, stairs at other positions than at the ends of the halls, space for utilities and maintenance, wall thicknesses, site limitations, bookstore, cafeteria, and such.

Suggested references

Dennistoun W. Ver Planck and B. Richard Teare, Jr., "Engineering Analysis," John Wiley & Sons, Inc., New York, 1954. Detailed examples of the application of the engineering method. Although the theory in general is advanced, beginning students will be able to recognize the factors involved in the solutions to most of the problems.

J. C. L. Fish, "Engineering Economics," 2d ed., pp. 71–75, McGraw-Hill Book Company, Inc., New York, 1923. A brief and specific presentation of various methods of estimating.

John B. Wilbur, An Excursion through Exactitudes, *J. Eng. Educ.*, vol. 48, no. 3, pp. 182–187, December, 1957. A strong plea for a balance between theory and practice.

Problems

2.1   *a.* Estimate the annual cost in dollars of owning and operating a low-priced automobile driving 12,000 miles per year.

b. On the basis of your estimate, what is (1) the total cost per mile to own and operate this car, and (2) the cost per mile for gas and oil only?

2.2   Same as Prob. 2.1 except that the car is driven only within a city for 3,000 miles per year.

2.3   Compare the cost to an off-campus student of using his own car purchased new and sold after four years with the cost of using public transportation including buses, taxis, and drive-it-yourself cars as the occasions demand. Make the comparison on the basis of the academic year of nine months.

2.4   Estimate the cost of flunking one three-semester hour (or quarter hour) course in an engineering curriculum, assuming that the course cannot be made up during subsequent regular semesters (or quarters).

2.5 *a.* Estimate the total cost of a four-year college education in engineering at your institution, excluding the summer months.

b. On the basis of your estimate in (*a*) make another estimate of the average cost per hour in classroom and laboratory.

2.6 Estimate your total gross income in your engineering career from graduation to retirement. Estimate your total gross income to the same retirement date, assuming that you had not gone to college but started to work after being graduated from high school. Considering the total cost of your college education, how much has it been worth to you in dollars and cents to attend college? (Please note that the values of a college education go far beyond mere dollars and cents.)

2.7 Suppose that a city has a population of about 600,000 people. The city must supply each of these persons with fresh water for daily domestic use.

a. Estimate the complete *per capita* use in gallons per day, itemizing each use such as drinking, bathing, etc. It is important that you show all assumptions and all calculations made in arriving at the estimate for each item.

b. If the city should be faced with a water shortage, estimate how many gallons of water would be saved per day if an ordinary brick were placed in the reservoir tanks of the water closets (toilets) in every home?

2.8 Ordinary gravel has a specific gravity of about 2.65 (i.e., is 2.65 times as dense as fresh water). Gravel shoveled loosely into containers occupies about 67 per cent of the volume of the containers, the rest of the space being filled with air. Loose gravel will stand in a pile whose side slope is about 30°.

A medium-size gravel shovel has a blade with over-all dimensions of 12¼ in. width and 15¾ in. length. The blade curves sharply upward where it joins the handle to a height of about 5 in. forming a back side. This side sweeps around the edges of the blade with diminishing height which becomes zero at the front edge of the blade.

A small gondola car on a railroad has the following inside dimensions: length 40 ft 4 in., width 9 ft, and depth 4 ft 3 in. Its maximum load is about 65 tons of dry gravel.

A fully loaded gravel car is to be unloaded by hand at a siding in a small town. Estimate the number of man-hours required to unload this car by shoveling gravel over the side into storage piles on the ground.

2.9   *a.* Assume that a football stadium (capacity 80,000 seats) is surrounded on all sides by the standard square pattern of blocks and streets in a city (Fig. 2.3). If the stadium is completely filled to capacity and cars are parked solidly but properly parallel to the curbs, estimate how many blocks from the stadium it would be to the first available parking space on the streets.

   b. Estimate the total amount of money in dollars which these cars represent.

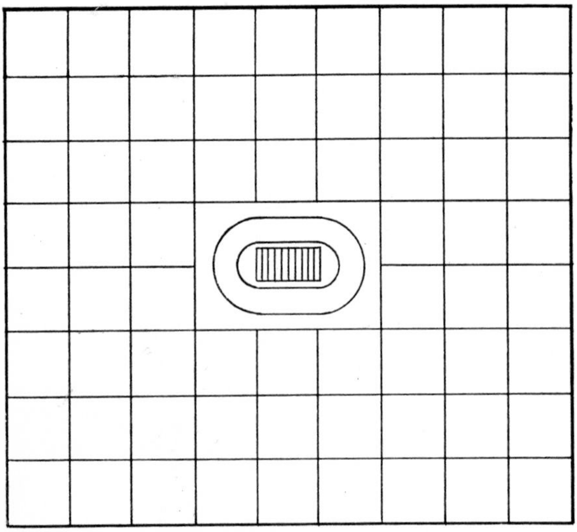

FIG. 2.3.

2.10   *a.* Estimate the area in square miles of the paved and surfaced streets either (1) in the city in which you are attending school or (2) in your home town.

   b. This area would be the equivalent of a two-lane highway of approximately how many miles long?

   c. If a street contractor were given the job of starting from unpaved surfaces and paving all of these streets with macadam ("black-top") within one year, estimate how many persons he would have to have in his entire force. Assume that this is his only work for the year.

2.11   *a.* Estimate the percentage of paper saved in the average textbook if the margins were reduced by one-half inch on all four sides of the page.

FIG. 2.4. Dormitory in the traditional architectural style, left, and in the modern architectural style, right.

b. Estimate the total area of paper in square feet saved in the average text.

c. This method of saving paper was used during World War II. Why do you suppose it was not continued after the war, since it would apparently reduce publishing costs?

2.12 *a.* Estimate the volume of exhaust gases in cubic feet produced daily by automobile and truck traffic in a city of a million people.

b. If some practical device were invented that could be installed in the exhaust system of an automobile to remove toxic gases from the exhaust, estimate how long it would take for automobile mechanics in the city to make installations on all cars and trucks working full time (but not overtime) on just this job.

2.13 *a.* Estimate the number of gallons of gasoline consumed daily by automobiles and trucks (exclusive of diesel trucks) in a city of 300,000 people.

b. Estimate the average gross daily income per filling station in this city from the sale of gasoline only.

c. How many persons would be required to supply and operate the filling stations in this city?

2.14 *a.* Estimate what per cent of the floor space of an office building does not bring in revenue, i.e., halls, washrooms, elevator areas, and such.

b. Estimate what per cent of the floor and wall area is saved by constructing a university dormitory in the modern architectural style rather than in the traditional style (Fig. 2.4). Compare the relative advantages and disadvantages of these two styles of dormitories.

2.15   Estimate how many persons are required to man the freight and passenger carriers of all kinds which daily come into and go out of a city of 200,000 people. Do not consider intracity transportation.

2.16   *a.* Estimate the total number of persons, working full time, necessary to provide adequate instruction and auxiliary services for an undergraduate college with an enrollment of 2,400 students in three divisions, Arts and Sciences, Business Administration, and Engineering. Assume that the college is in a small community so that it must provide facilities for housing and feeding most of the students.

b. What would you estimate the annual expenditure for salaries and wages to be?

THREE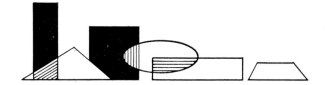

Geometry in engineering

Professional practice requires a certain amount of basic information. A working knowledge of geometry is definitely part of this information because every material thing in the world has linear dimensions, area, and volume. These are quantities which constantly confront the engineer. The purpose of this chapter is to give the student some idea of the many places in which geometry is used in engineering and to give him practice in applying it to a few elementary problems. He will realize early in his college career the necessity of having basic geometric data at his finger tips and of having a ready reference for more complex geometric shapes.

The importance of geometry

There are many ways in which one might approach the subject of the place of geometry in engineering and there are innumerable examples which he might use. It has been said in effect that one picture is worth a thousand words and for this reason the author has chosen to build his approach around pictures. He has selected a few pictures accompanied by brief discussions to bring out the importance of geometry in engineering. These are illustrative of the almost infinite variety of geometric applications.

The automotive engineer is always seeking to improve engine per-

FIG. 3.1. Piston for 348-cu-in. V-8 automobile engine. *(Courtesy of the General Motors Corporation.)*

formance and frequently does this through changing the geometry of engine parts. Originally pistons and cylinder heads were designed with flat tops so that the compression chamber in which the gas-air mixture was ignited was in the form of a right cylinder. However, research has shown that this does not always make for the most efficient combustion of the fuel. Note the double bevel of the piston and the matching slope of the cylinder head in a late model V-8 engine in Fig. 3.1. The more complex combustion chamber is designed to give better control of the combustion process and a more effective spread of the flame front.

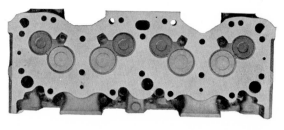

FIG. 3.2. Engine head for 348-cu-in. V-8 engine. *(Courtesy of the General Motors Corporation.)*

Figure 3.2 shows the underside of one of the heads of the same V-8 engine. We see in this illustration the arrangement of the intake and exhaust valves, openings of the channels for circulating cooling water, holes for bolts, threaded holes for spark plugs, and other features. Note the complex geometry of the perimeter of the head where it fits the engine block. The geometry must take into account not only the arrangement of the various holes and ducts but also the strength of the metal to avoid excessive concentrations of stress.

FIG. 3.3. Tilting bridge, designed to operate at different elevations of the water surface of the river.

The geometry of a three-dimensional structural problem is evident in Fig. 3.3. This is a unique bridge designed for loading and unloading

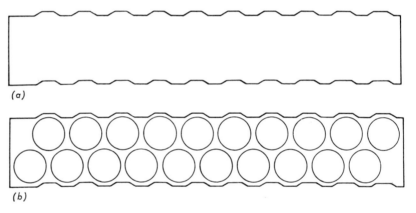

(a)

(b)

FIG. 3.4. (a) Sheet-steel plate after being cut by a scroll shear to a pattern designed to reduce the amount of scrap metal. (b) "Skeleton" of plate in (a) after circular end units for cylindrical cans have been punched. (Courtesy of the Continental Can Company.)

bulk cargo from vessels on the Mississippi River. The illustration shows the river end of the bridge mounted on rollers which rest on curved steel runways attached to a moored barge. The curved runways are designed to make the end of the bridge self-centering when the barge rises and falls with the surface of the river, and they also permit movement to avoid excessive stresses and possible damage when there is impact between vessels and the barge during berthing operations. The barge support is designed for an 11-ft rise or fall from the level position of the bridge and also for a small amount of upstream or downstream movement. The crane support at the top of the illustration is pivoted so that it can be leveled by hand at different elevations. The shore end of the bridge is not shown, but it is mounted on a universal-joint arrangement to permit tilting and a small amount of swinging.

A different problem is involved in the manufacture of tin cans. The thin steel plate coated with tin in Fig. 3.4a has been cut from a long rectangular strip by a scroll shear. Its particular design was dictated by economy and was developed to give the largest number of circular end units (tops and bottoms) for cylindrical cans from the original rectangular strip with the least waste of material. The cutting edge of the scroll shear is shaped to cut the plates to this particular pattern. The design of the various parts of the mechanism to operate the cutting die, to feed the plates into the machine, and to eject and pile them after cutting is a dynamic problem involving timing as well as geometry.

The plates go from the scroll shear to punches which punch out

FIG. 3.5. Condenser bushings for circuit breakers and transformers. (Courtesy of the Westinghouse Electric Corporation.)

FIG. 3.6. F-101 Voodoo fighter-bomber. *(Courtesy of the McDonnell Aircraft Corporation.)*

circular end units for cans and eject a "skeleton" (Fig. 3.4*b*), which is the waste material from the process.

High-voltage bushings or insulators (Fig. 3.5) with their tapering concentric rings of glazed ceramic material present a striking picture. Their design is relatively simple, and yet, as we frequently find, there is beauty in simplicity. They are made in one piece which is designed to provide a long sinuous path from the point where the conductor leaves the bushing back to the casing of, in this instance, a circuit breaker. This prevents a "dielectric breakdown," or breakdown of the insulation. The bushing in the center of the picture is being installed on a 230,000-kv circuit breaker.

The fighter-bomber plane in Fig. 3.6 presents problems in geometry quite different from those of the bushing. Here sleek streamlining of a jet plane to fly faster than a thousand miles per hour is of paramount importance. The wing span is relatively small, about 60 per cent of the length of the plane, as is customary with high-speed planes. Both the wings and the stabilizer are swept back for better aerodynamic characteristics. The fuselage is streamlined in its unusual shape to provide for the intake and exhaust of the jet motors, an unusually large fuel supply, and other features.

The steam-turbine rotor in Fig. 3.7 is a study in concentric circles and radial blades pitched at an effective angle. Note that each circular impeller is composed of separate groups of from five to six blades which are built as a unit. High-pressure steam enters around the circumference of the rotor at the center and flows outward in both directions. As the steam pressure drops, each successive set of blades is made larger in order to transfer as much energy as possible from the steam to the turbine rotor. Note that the blades are pitched in opposite directions on each side of the center so that the thrusts on the blades will produce rotation in the same direction.

FIG. 3.7. Steam-turbine rotor. *(Courtesy of the Westinghouse Electric Corporation.)*

A gantry tower used to prepare the Atlas intercontinental ballistic missile (Fig. 3.8) presents a complex framing problem in geometry. It provides work platforms at eleven different levels, of which seven have folding components which can be lowered to surround the missile completely by working space. Access is quickly gained by elevators on each leg. Note also the launcher arms which clutch the missile during

FIG. 3.8. Atlas intercontinental ballistic missile on launching pad with gantry tower moved back. *[Courtesy of the Convair (Astronautics) Division, General Dynamics Corporation.]*

final fueling and engine ignition and then spring clear for the take-off.

A striking departure from traditional structures is the geodesic dome (Fig. 3.9) composed of steel pipe, rods, and sheet metal. It is approximately one-quarter of a sphere and is constructed as a three-dimensional curved truss about 4 ft deep designed as a unit cell system of octahedra. The sheet-steel surface material in hexagonal units serves as the inner-member tension system and also as the weathering surface. The outer hexagonal array is composed of steel pipe sections held in position by steel tension rods. Note the jigs for fabricating the sheet-metal units in the foreground and the view of the far side of the interior of the dome through the doorway. It was the largest circular structure in the world without internal supports at the time of its erection. The inside diam-

FIG. 3.9. All-steel geodesic dome building. *(Courtesy of the Union Tank Car Company.)*

FIG. 3.10. Over-all and close-up views of piping in an oil refinery. *(Courtesy of the Esso Standard Oil Company.)*

eter is 375 ft and it covers over 2½ acres. This type of structure provides complete utilization of space without interference from interior columns. This particular dome was erected in Baton Rouge, Louisiana.

The geometry of pipes to transport liquids is by no means as simple as a student may imagine. If a pipe is to transport liquid from one place to another, he may say at first thought, "Run it in a straight line, which is the shortest distance between two points. If something is in the way, just bend the pipe a bit and go around it." But there are processes

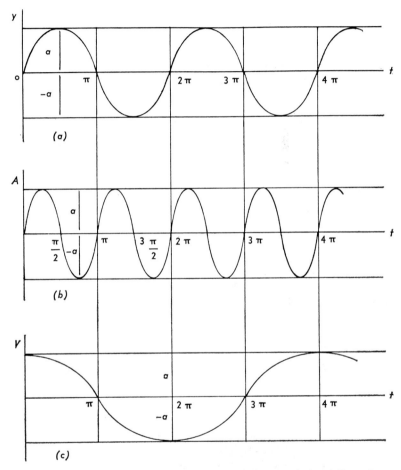

FIG. 3.11. Sinusoidal curves: (a) $y = a \sin t$, (b) $A = a \sin (2t)$, (c) $V = a \sin (t/2 + \pi/2)$.

which involve a coordinated flow of many different liquids in differing quantities to and from many pieces of equipment. More than that, many of the pipes in such a process must be interconnected and all must be laid out so as not to interfere with access for plant operation, maintenance, and repair. The sizes of the pipes, transition sections, valve locations, and general arrangement can present a very complicated problem in geometry as well as in calculation as seen in the over-all view of a pipe still in a petroleum refinery in Fig. 3.10. Details of the lines on pipe bands and exchanger equipment are clearly shown in the close-up view where some of the interconnections may be seen.

Finally, there is one set of geometric elements which is of considerable importance to almost all engineers, the group of curves which are called *sinusoidal* (Fig. 3.11). They are representative of many phenomena in engineering such as electromagnetic waves, alternating currents and voltages, sound waves, and other waveforms. They express simple harmonic motion, which occurs time and time again in the design of rotating machinery. Many forms of mechanical vibrations are sinusoidal in character. Furthermore, their usefulness does not end with phenomena which follow the simple sinusoidal curve. Many more complex periodic curve forms which occur in engineering can be closely approximated by a series of sinusoidal curves with the proper amplitudes and periods. The engineering student will meet these curves in their graphical and mathematical forms many times in his career.

Geometric problems

The problems in this chapter are intended to give the student a variety of experiences in solving situations which involve geometry. Not all of them are straightforward computations of areas and volumes, for some are designed to test the student's ingenuity and capacity to reason. Since geometry is the principal element, the student should make full use of carefully drawn sketches either with instruments or freehand. Clear and reasonably accurate sketches are an invaluable aid to the engineer and are equally important to those who study or check his work. Many hours of time can be saved by devoting a small amount of it to making good sketches at the outset. The ability to make good rapid freehand sketches is a great asset to an engineer and every student would do well to practice these sketches on every problem which involves geometry while he is in college.

Most students are familiar with the properties of the common geometric shapes such as circles, parallelograms, triangles, spheres, and cylinders. However, it is well to repeat these, and Appendix B includes the properties of these shapes along with others which are more complex. This appendix is intended to serve as a useful reference for the student throughout his college and professional careers.

Suggested references

Ovid W. Eshbach (ed.), "Handbook of Engineering Fundamentals," 2d ed., John Wiley & Sons, Inc., New York, 1936, Geometry, pp. 2–48 to 2–70. Geometric concepts, mensuration, and geometric constructions.

Bruce E. Meserve, "Fundamental Concepts of Geometry," Addison-Wesley Publishing Company, Reading, Mass., 1955.

Felix Klein, "Famous Problems of Elementary Geometry," Dover Publications, New York, 1956. A reprinting of an old book which includes the problems of the duplication of the cube and the trisection of an angle.

Daniel T. Sigley and William T. Stratton, "Solid Geometry," The Dryden Press, Inc., New York, 1956.

Problems

See Appendix D for abbreviations of units of measure.

3.1 A concrete measuring tank is 5 ft wide by 8 ft long and is 4 ft 6 in. deep, outside dimensions. The walls are 5 in. thick and the bottom is 6 in. thick. When the tank is filled with water, the total combined weight of tank and water is 16,400 lb.

How much does the concrete weigh per cubic foot?

3.2 Twelve steel balls or spheres of diameter $1\frac{3}{4}$ in. are cut from a bar of steel $2\frac{1}{8}$ by $2\frac{1}{4}$ in. by 1 ft $11\frac{1}{2}$ in.

What volume of steel is wasted in this process?

3.3 An irregular piece of cast iron is believed to have some cavities on the inside which occurred during the casting operation. Its weight in air is measured on scales to be 1,196 lb. It is immersed in a cylindrical container of water 3 ft 3 in. in diameter and raises the water level therein $3\frac{3}{4}$ in. Iron weighs 490 pcf.

What per cent of the total volume of the cast iron is occupied by the cavities?

3.4   A piece of cast iron has a very irregular shape and its volume is to be determined. It is submerged in water in a cylindrical tank having a diameter of 2 ft 2 in. The water level is raised $3\frac{5}{16}$ in. above its original level. Iron weighs 490 pcf.

a. How many cubic feet are in the piece of cast iron?

b. How much does it weigh?

3.5   A canal on level land with locks at each end is 19 miles long, 16 ft deep, and has a trapezoidal cross section. The distance across the canal at the top is 106 ft and across the bottom is 40 ft.

a. How many cubic yards of dirt were removed to complete the canal?

b. What was the total profit to the excavating contractor if his unit profit was $3\frac{1}{2}$ cents per cu yd?

3.6   A swimming pool is 150 ft long and 50 ft wide with a straight sloping bottom. The pool is designed so that when it is filled the water is 3 ft deep at one end and 10 ft at the other. Fresh water is pumped continuously into the pool at the rate which would completely fill it in two days. What is this rate in gallons per minute?

3.7   A hopper for fine sand is in the shape of the frustum of a cone with the larger end uppermost. The inside diameter of the top of the hopper is 7 ft 6 in. and of the bottom 6 in. The hopper is 14 ft high. When the gate at the bottom is opened, the sand flows out at an average rate of 32 lb per sec. Assume that the sand weighs 125 pcf.

a. If the hopper is level full of sand when the gate is opened, how many minutes will it take to empty it?

b. What per cent of error is introduced by assuming that the hopper is a perfect cone 14 ft high?

3.8   A cylindrical water tank is constructed with wooden strips and steel hoops. It has an inside diameter of 6 ft and an inside height of 12 ft. It is to be filled with water to a depth of 10 ft through an overhead pipe of 2 in. inside diameter in which water is flowing at a velocity of 3 fps. Before the wooden sides swell, the tank leaks at an average rate of 4 gpm.

If the depth of water in the tank is 4 ft in the beginning, how many minutes will be required to fill the tank to the desired depth, considering the average leakage?

3.9 A lamp shade made out of a parchment-type paper is in the shape of the frustum of a hexagonal pyramid. The top of the shade measures 9 in. across flats, i.e., the distance between two opposite sides (not vertices) of the hexagon. The bottom of the shade measures 12 in. across flats, and the vertical height is 11 in.

  a. Compute the dimensions and the angles of one side or face of the shade and show them on a dimensioned freehand sketch.

  b. If the shade were conical in shape with diameters of 9 in. and 12 in. at top and bottom, respectively, and the same height, what would be the inner radius and the outer radius for laying out the shade on a flat sheet?

3.10 A horizontal cylindrical drum 6.9 ft long with an inside diameter of 19 in. has hemispherical convex ends. The wall thickness is $\frac{3}{16}$ in. throughout. The drum is filled with air at a pressure of 100 psi.

  How many cubic feet would this air occupy at atmospheric pressure (14.7 psi) with no change in temperature? (For any given mass of gas, the volume varies inversely as the pressure, i.e., as the pressure goes up, the volume goes down in proportion, if the temperature is kept constant.)

3.11 A plain concrete sidewalk of a certain mix weighs 192 lb per ft of length. It is 4 ft wide, 4 in. deep, and is not reinforced with steel. A reinforced concrete beam of the same mix has a cross section 12 in. wide and 2 ft deep. It is reinforced with 16 round steel bars each $\frac{1}{2}$ in. in diameter which extend the full length of the beam. Assume that steel weighs 490 pcf.

  How much does the reinforced concrete beam weigh per foot of length?

3.12 A cylindrical block of iron 3 in. in diameter and 1 ft long has conical holes reamed in each end. These conical holes are 2 in. in diameter at the ends and are 4 in. deep to the apex of the cone. The holes are completely filled with lead. Iron weighs 490 pcf and lead weighs 708 pcf.

  What is the apparent or average density of the iron-lead block in pounds per cubic foot?

3.13 *a.* Calculate the approximate volume of water on the earth's surface in cubic miles based on your estimates of the various quantities involved. Give your answer in powers of ten. Be sure to list all assumptions which are made.

b. Considering the relative height of the highest mountains on the earth and the irregularities on the skin of an ordinary orange, which is rougher?

c. Approximately how deep would a depression on the earth's surface be in proportion to the depression in an orange where the stem has been removed?

3.14   An open aluminum kettle in a chemical plant is lined with glass of equal thickness to contain a 40 per cent sulfuric acid solution by volume. The kettle is cylindrical in shape with a hemispherical bottom. The outside diameter of the kettle is 3 ft 0 in. and the thickness of the combined glass and aluminum is ⅜ in. throughout. The kettle is to hold 1,400 lb of the solution and still have the cylindrical walls project 2 in. above the mixture's surface. Pure sulfuric acid (100 per cent) weighs 1.83 times as much as water. Glass and aluminum may both be assumed to have a density of 168 pcf.

a. What must be the over-all height of the kettle to meet these specifications?

b. What is the weight of the kettle itself? (Use wall thicknesses and average radii.)

3.15   Determine the over-all dimensions of a cylindrical glass-lined aluminum kettle with a flat bottom to contain a sulfuric acid solution to meet the following specifications: The kettle is made out of aluminum ⅛ in. thick with the glass lining of the same thickness. No cover on top. Ratio of inside dimensions: diameter = ⅔ height. Sulfuric acid solution: 40 per cent pure sulfuric acid, 60 per cent water by weight. Quantity to be contained: 453 lb of solution when level full. Pure sulfuric acid weighs 1.83 times as much as water. Glass and aluminum have equal densities of 168 pcf. Over-all dimensions are to be specified in feet and inches.

3.16   A steel spherical water tank has an inside diameter of 28.3 ft. It is filled with water by means of a pump which produces a constant flow into the tank of 120,000 gph.

a. How long will it take for the pump to fill the tank completely if it is empty at the start?

b. What is the rate at which the water surface is rising in feet per minute when the depth of water in the tank has reached 4.15 ft?

3.17 A 7.60 by 15 automobile tire measures 29 in. in outside diameter when new and on the wheel.

a. If this tire is rolled along the highway under no load, how many revolutions will it make in half a mile?

b. If ³⁄₁₆ in. is worn off of the tread uniformly around the tire, (1) how many revolutions will it make in half a mile and (2) what is the per cent of change in the number of revolutions?

Some automobile speedometers are made to operate from the transmission of an automobile such that the speed registered is directly related to the average rate of revolution of the rear wheels. Suppose that the speedometer on a certain model car is calibrated to read correct ground speed for new 7.60 by 15 automobile tires inflated to an air pressure of 26 psi.

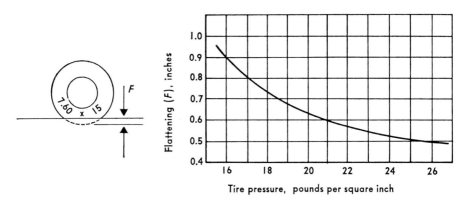

FIG. 3.12. Graph of the relationship between tire pressure and amount of flattening of tire.

c. What is the speed of the car on the highway if the wheels are turning at the rate of 700 rpm with new tires at 26 psi (Fig. 3.12)?

d. What is the error in the speedometer reading in mph if the wheels are turning at the same rate of 700 rpm, but the tire pressure is 20 psi (Fig. 3.12), and ¼ in. has been worn uniformly off the treads?

3.18 An excavation in level ground has a level floor 38 ft by 66 ft with side slopes on all sides of 30° with the horizontal and a depth of 9 ft 0 in. A heavy rain resulting in blocked storm sewers causes an overflow of water into the excavation to a depth of 3 ft 6 in. The contractor starts to pump out the water with equipment that can remove 340 gpm. Illustrate your problem with a well-drawn freehand sketch. Note that the excavation is not in the shape of the frustum of a pyramid.

a. Assuming that 11 per cent of the water is absorbed into the ground, how many hours are required to empty the excavation? Compute the volume precisely.

b. Compute the volume of water approximately by multiplying the depth by the median width and median length (i.e., the width and length at mid-height). What is the per cent of error with respect to the precise volume?

c. This difference between the volumes which are computed by the precise and the approximate methods is not constant for all such excavations with constant and equal side slopes. Under what condition will this difference be greatest and what is the maximum per cent of error for this case?

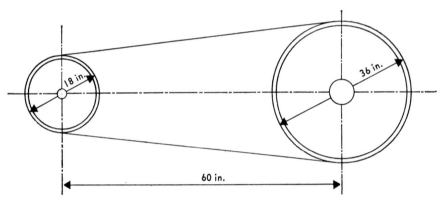

FIG. 3.13.

3.19 Two pulleys are connected by a flat belt as shown in Fig. 3.13. One pulley is 36 in. and the other is 18 in. in outside diameter. The center-line distance between the shafts of the pulleys is 5 ft 0 in.

a. Compute the precise length of the belt in inches. Slide-rule accuracy is sufficient. Neglect the effect of the thickness of the belt. Some students may think that a satisfactory approximation to this length may be obtained by using half of the circumference of each pulley plus twice the distance between center lines of the shafts.

$$L(\text{approx.}) = 18\pi + 9\pi + (2 \times 60)$$

Such an approximation gives a length of belt which is about 1.3 in. in error. The question arises as to whether or not this would be a significant difference.

b. Is the length of the belt computed by the approximate method longer or shorter than the true length? Answer first on the basis of a visual examination of the sketch and check this by calculation.

c. Approximately how much must the distance between centers of the pulleys be altered for the belt of approximate length to fit the pulleys?

d. Could the approximate length be used for the belt when one considers the practical aspects of a belt drive of this type? Give reasons for your answer.

e. The belt drive can be installed so that the pull is on either the lower part of the belt or the upper part. Which arrangement would be better, if either, and why?

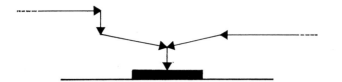

The engineer derives equations

It is important for the engineer to be able to set up basic equations and to derive fundamental relationships for a problem or a situation. This ability is frequently more valuable in professional practice than to be able to make the actual calculations because there are available today many aids for mathematical calculations. Also, it is frequently the case that after equations or relationships have been derived for particular problems, the numerical solution of these problems becomes a routine matter in industry or professional practice which can be set up in standard form and carried on by subprofessionals. Accordingly, it is difficult to overemphasize the importance of being able to derive equations and relationships.

Prose versus symbols

All of us are accustomed to reasoning in terms of words put together in sentences. By means of sentences we express our thoughts and observations, we develop relationships between things and reach conclusions. And yet few of us recognize the fact that there is basically no difference between using mathematical equations or relationships and corresponding word sentences.

Equations are merely sentences which express in symbolic form some particular relationship between things. Most students have already learned this subconsciously or implicitly, but they frequently fail to understand the simplicity of the relationships when they are confronted with the task of writing a mathematical equation for some new relationship or concept. The very mention of the word "derivation" is apt to strike fear into the hearts of many students who immediately visualize some complex and abstruse phenomenon which they do not understand and which by a mysterious process is to drop out some equation in mathematical form through the magic of derivation.

Such fear is not justified. Every student has already derived equations before coming to college, although he may not have been aware of it at the time. These equations were derived and used in terms of words rather than symbols. But there is a very good reason for using symbols in engineering because they simplify greatly the handling of mathematical and engineering quantities.

Let us begin at the beginning with some simple examples. Students have used equations many times in their childhood and in early youth without realizing what they were doing and without expressing the equations in symbolic form. A child soon learns that for some mysterious reason, one small dime has the same purchasing power as two larger nickels. Now if we let D represent the purchasing power of a dime and N represent the purchasing power of a nickel, we have the equation

$$D = 2N$$

An older boy is given a weekly allowance which provides for a movie, for a haircut every two weeks, for lunch at school, and for miscellaneous expenses. Suppose that he wants to determine what he has to spend for miscellaneous items daily. He estimates how much he spends daily for lunch and multiplies by five. Since haircuts come every two weeks, he divides the cost of a haircut by two. He subtracts these and the cost of the movie from his weekly allowance and the balance is for miscellany. He divides this by seven to see how much he can spend daily.

If we assign symbols to these quantities, weekly allowance A, movie m, haircut h, lunch L, and miscellany Z, we find that he has been using unknowingly the equation

$$Z = \frac{A - m - \dfrac{h}{2} - 5L}{7}$$

Another example might be that of a young man who is planning to drive an automobile from one town to another. He and his companion will stop for lunch en route and he knows that he will drive at about a certain average speed. He and thousands of others every day estimate the time that will be required by dividing the speed into the distance and adding the time for lunch. He uses the following equation:

$$t = \frac{s}{v} + t_L$$

where t = total time required

s = distance between towns

v = average speed

t_L = time for lunch

These are examples of simple equations expressing equality in relationships. We find similar equations in engineering expressing the equality of forces, or of stresses, or of electric currents and such. There can also be other expressions which do not express equality. For example, relationships might be indicated by any one of the following symbols:

Symbol	Meaning
$=$	Equal
$\neq$	Unequal
$\cong$	Approximately equal
$>$	Greater than
$<$	Less than

How many times have persons compared the weights of two objects by holding them in their hands to find that their weights are not equal, i.e.,

$$W_1 \neq W_2$$

or that they weigh approximately the same, i.e.,

$$W_1 \cong W_2$$

Other comparisons may be made. This particular line is longer than that one, i.e.,

$$L_1 > L_2$$

or this number is smaller than that one, i.e.,

$$4 < 7$$

Expressions such as the last two which use the symbols for "greater than" or "less than" are called *inequalities*.

There is, of course, no limit to the symbols which can be used to express relationships, but for practical purposes the symbols are limited to those which have been adopted and are recognized by everyone. This is necessary in order for people to be able to understand each other in the use of these symbols and to avoid undue confusion.

There are distinct advantages in mathematics, engineering, and science in the use of standard symbolic forms of expression. To attempt to solve even some of the simpler problems in mathematics and engineering in the form of English prose would become quite involved. To illustrate this, the solution to a very simple problem will be derived first in English prose. Then an equation expressing the same relationships will be derived in terms of symbols for purposes of comparison. The problem is to derive an expression for the number of gallons per hour which

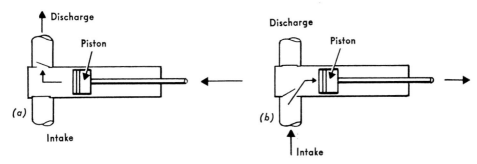

FIG. 4.1. Diagrammatic sketch of single-acting pump. *(a)* Discharge stroke—discharge valve open, intake valve closed. *(b)* Intake stroke—intake valve open, discharge valve closed.

are delivered in a single-acting pump which has a certain internal diameter in inches, a certain length of stroke in inches, and which pumps at the rate of so many strokes per minute (Fig. 4.1).

Prose derivation. The effective volume of the cylinder in cubic inches is equal to the square of the diameter multiplied by pi and divided by four, all times the length of stroke. This volume is in cubic inches and must be divided by two hundred and thirty-one (the number of cubic inches in one gallon) to convert the volume to gallons. It must then be multiplied by the number of strokes per minute and in turn by sixty (minutes in an hour) to give the required answer in gallons per hour. This answer is then: pi times sixty divided by two hundred and thirty-one divided by four, all multiplied by the square of the diameter in inches times the length of the stroke in inches, times the number of strokes per minute. This can be more simply stated by combining the numerical quantities to give two hundred and four thousandths, times the square of the diameter in inches times the length of the stroke in inches times the number of strokes per minute, gallons per hour.

Derivation with symbols. Let D be the diameter in inches, S the stroke in inches, n the number of strokes per minute, and Q the quantity in gallons per hour.

$$V \text{ (cu in.)} = \frac{\pi D^2}{4} S$$

$$V \text{ (gal)} = \frac{\pi D^2 S}{4 \times 231}$$

$$Q \text{ (gph)} = \left(\frac{\pi D^2 S}{4 \times 231}\right) 60n$$

$$= 0.204 n D^2 S$$

The derivation of this equation is a two-stage process of assigning symbols and then expressing and simplifying the proper relationship between the symbols in the form of equations. Note that both the numbers and the physical quantities are expressed symbolically.

Number symbols

It should be helpful to the student to understand that there is nothing magical or mysterious about symbols and that he has been using them for years. He has become so accustomed to using symbols for numbers that he is not aware that he does this daily. There is no reason other than historical and physical for our commonly used system of numbers. We derive our symbolic forms from the Arabic and our unit probably comes from the number of fingers on our two hands. If human beings had been so constituted as to have only four fingers on each hand, we might have had a number system based on the number eight instead of the number ten. Let us compare these two systems.

Assuming that human beings had been constituted with only four fingers on each hand, the symbol 10 would then stand for *one* complete set of *eight* fingers and the symbol 20 for *two* complete sets of *eight* fingers. These symbols in this case would not mean sets of ten fingers as is the case in our decimal system. Moreover, there would have been no need for separate symbols for the quantities eight and nine, such as 8 and 9. These quantities would now be represented by

Quantity	Symbols, based on a unit of ten	Symbols, based on a unit of eight
One	1	1
Two	2	2
Three	3	3
Four	4	4
Five	5	5
Six	6	6
Seven	7	7
Eight	8	10
Nine	9	11
Ten	10	12
Eleven	11	13
Twelve	12	14
Sixteen	16	20
Sixty-four	64	100
One hundred	100	144

10 and 11. We could have expressed all numbers with just seven quantity symbols, i.e., 1 to 7, and zero.

The binary system of numbers which is based on a unit of two is of special interest to engineers because it has been the basis for the design of various types of modern electronic digital computers. The binary and the decimal systems are compared in the following table:

Decimal system	Binary system
1	1
2	10
3	11
4	100
5	101
6	110
7	111
8	1000
9	1001
10	1010
11	1011
12	1100
13	1101
14	1110
15	1111
16	10000

The relationship between these number systems may also be shown in another way. The system based on a unit of eight is included for purposes of comparison.

Symbol	Decimal system	Decimal system equivalent	Eight system	Decimal system equivalent	Binary system	Decimal system equivalent
10	$(10)^1$	10	$(8)^1$	8	$(2)^1$	2
100	$(10)^2$	100	$(8)^2$	64	$(2)^2$	4
1000	$(10)^3$	1000	$(8)^3$	512	$(2)^3$	8
10000	$(10)^4$	10000	$(8)^4$	4096	$(2)^4$	16

At first glance the binary system appears to be altogether too cumbersome. But it does have one very simple characteristic, namely, only two symbols, 1 and 0, are required to express any number. This has great significance when we think in terms of electricity and magnetism. The current in a circuit may be either *on* or *off* and depending upon this, a relay contact may be either closed or open, a thermionic tube may be either conducting or not conducting, or a ferrite core may be magnetized in either one of two directions or the other. The relay closed may correspond to the "one" state and open to the "zero" state. The speed with which these operations may be carried on is related to the speed with which electricity flows through a conductor, almost 186,000 miles per second (mps).

Engineers have taken these simple fundamentals and from them developed ingenious circuits and devices for processing thousands of bits of data per second in the form of binary numbers which represent instructions to a machine as well as numbers used in computations. It is this fantastic speed of operation which enables the digital computer to solve many problems in hours which would otherwise require months or years using any other previously developed calculating devices or methods. This does not mean, however, that computers will replace mathematical techniques because these are still needed in order to tell the computer what to do. Also there are many problems which are solved more efficiently with mathematical techniques than on computers.

We have become so accustomed to writing the symbols 1, 2, and 3 for the numbers one, two, and three that we almost regard them as absolute. If we stop and think, we do recognize the fact that we use to a lesser extent the Roman system of numbers in which one, two, and three are represented by I, II, and III. However, most people are not aware that we could just as well set up an entirely new system of symbols to represent one, two, and three such as ∠, ∫, and ┼. But these new symbols would not be very useful unless everyone adopted them, and this is not likely. There is no reason to abandon a system which has been in use for centuries and prevails throughout the literature in almost every language.

Functional relationships

We have seen that symbols are used to express relationships as well as to represent things. The most widely used symbol which expresses a relationship is the equals sign. Other symbols expressing relationships are those which appear in the following equations:

$y = \sqrt{4x}$; the square-root symbol and the equals sign express a certain relationship between y and $4x$

$y = (3 + x)^4$; here the $+$ sign, the parentheses, the exponent, and the equals sign are used to express a certain relationship between y, x, and the number 3

A more complicated equation illustrates another combination of relationships using additional symbols:

$$y = \frac{4x^2 - \log x}{\sqrt[3]{5x}}$$

These are all particular relationships using particular symbols. If we wish to indicate some general relationship, we can say in everyday language that y depends on x in some general way, or we can use the customary mathematical language, y *is a function of* x. This can be written symbolically as

$y = f(x)$

There is no magic in the use of the letter f to represent a function. One can also write, and indeed, will do so in many college courses in mathematics and engineering,

$y = g(x)$

or

$y = \phi(x)$*

* See Appendix A for Greek alphabet.

The last expression makes use of a Greek letter, phi, but the meaning of the symbols in all three equations is identically the same, simply that y depends upon or is a function of x in some way in each case. For example, we might write the particular expressions and indicate the general functional forms as follows:

Particular	General
$y = \sqrt{4x}$	$y = f(x)$
$y = (3 + x)^4$	$y = g(x)$
$y = \dfrac{4x^2 - \log x}{\sqrt[3]{5x}}$	$y = \phi(x)$

or we could use subscripts to indicate the functional forms, such as $y = f_1(x)$, $y = f_2(x)$, and $y = f_3(x)$.

If y is related in some particular way to two variables x and z, such as in

$$y = 4x^2 + 2xz + z^2$$

this can be stated in general form as

$$y = f(x,z)$$

All of the relationships which we have discussed so far may be called *explicit relationships*. In functions of the kind $y = f(x)$ and $y = g(x,z)$ in which the equation is solved for y in terms of other variables, we say that y is an *explicit function*, respectively, of x or of x and z. The distinguishing feature of these relationships is that we have the single variable y by itself on one side of the equation and all the other variables on the other side. We speak of these quantities as variables because they can have different values. In the preceding equations y is called the *dependent variable* and x and z are *independent variables*. The value of y depends upon whatever values are assigned to the other variables, x and z.

Note that y does not always have to be the dependent variable. We could just as well write

$$x = f(y)$$

or

$$x = g(y,z)$$

or

$$z = \phi(x,y)$$

Equations and relationships can also be written in forms which are not explicit in terms of any variable. For example, suppose that we have

$$y^3 - 2xy^2 - 3x^2 = 0$$

In this form the equation represents an *implicit* relationship between x and y. In functional form this is written as

$$F(x,y) = 0$$

which is called an *implicit function*. This equation defines y as an implicit function of x, and x as an implicit function of y.

This implicit function can be expressed in explicit form by solving the equation for x in terms of y or for y in terms of x. The equation is a quadratic in terms of x which can be solved easily for $x = \theta(y)$. It is a cubic equation in terms of y which involves a slightly more difficult solution to obtain $y = \phi(x)$.

For example, let us determine $x = \theta(y)$. First rewrite the equation as

$$3x^2 + 2y^2x - y^3 = 0$$

This is in the form of the general quadratic

$$ax^2 + bx + c = 0$$

for which the general solution is

$$x = \frac{-b \pm \sqrt{b^2 - 4ac}}{2a}$$

In our particular equation we have

$$a = 3$$
$$b = 2y^2$$
$$c = -y^3$$

Now we obtain x as an explicit function of y, or $x = \theta(y)$, by substituting in the general solution

$$x = \frac{-2y^2 \pm \sqrt{4y^4 + 12y^3}}{6}$$

Another simple example is the equation of a circle in rectangular coordinates with its center at the origin and with radius r:

$$x^2 + y^2 = r^2$$

or

$$x^2 + y^2 - r^2 = 0$$

This represents an implicit function $F(x,y) = 0$. It can be easily solved for y as an explicit function of x, $y = f(x)$,

$$y = \pm\sqrt{r^2 - x^2}$$

or for x as an explicit function of y, $x = g(y)$,

$$x = \pm\sqrt{r^2 - y^2}$$

There are other relations between x and y which are not so simple. Consider the equations

$$x \sin x - y = 0$$

and

$$x^5 + x - y^2 = 0$$

These are easily rewritten in explicit form for y as a function of x,

$$y = x \sin x$$

and

$$y = \pm\sqrt{x^5 + x}$$

However, there are no simple or elementary forms in which x can be written as a function of y although we say that x is given *implicitly* as a function of y by each equation.

Derivations

Let us make now a few simple derivations of the kind that might be used in engineering.

The surface of a right circular cylinder of radius r and height h can be written in functional form as

$$A = f(r,h)$$

Suppose now that the student is asked to derive an expression for this surface area of the cylinder represented by A. This simply means to obtain an expression for the area A in terms of r and h, the two dimensions of the cylinder. This requires expressing the area of the ends of the cylinder and the lateral area of the cylinder in terms of these dimensions (Fig. 4.2). We have

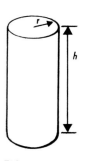

Area of one end $= \pi r^2$

Area of both ends $= 2\pi r^2$

Lateral area equals the circumference times the height $= 2\pi r h$

Total area $A = 2\pi r^2 + 2\pi r h$

$$= 2\pi r (r + h)$$

FIG. 4.2.

which is the required answer in its simplest form. Thus $f(r,h) = 2\pi r (r + h)$. What the f stands for, then, is 2π times the radius times the sum of the radius and the height, which is more easily expressed and understood in symbols than in words.

The surface area of the cylinder in the preceding example can also be expressed in terms of other quantities. For example, if $D =$ diameter and $V =$ volume, derive an expression for

$$A = f(D,V)$$

We express the area and volume in terms of the dimensions in order to begin the derivation. These are known to us:

$$A = 2\left(\frac{\pi D^2}{4}\right) + \pi D h$$

$$= \frac{\pi D^2}{2} + \pi D h \tag{1}$$

$$V = \left(\frac{\pi D^2}{4}\right) h \tag{2}$$

What we have done is to write down everything that is likely to be useful to us in solving the problem. This is not all that we know about the cylinder because we could write another equation

$$c = \pi D$$

where c is the circumference, but this is not likely to be useful in itself.

What now is the next step? The expression which we seek is in terms of D and V. The preceding expression for A has an h in it which we must eliminate. Let us try substituting for h in terms of V and D; so we go to Eq. (2) for V:

$$h = \frac{4V}{\pi D^2}$$

Substituting for h in Eq. (1),

$$A = \frac{\pi D^2}{2} + \pi D \left(\frac{4V}{\pi D^2} \right)$$

$$= \frac{\pi D^2}{2} + \frac{4V}{D}$$

$$= \frac{\pi D^3 + 8V}{2D}$$

Either of the last two expressions would be a suitable answer.

As another example consider the extraction of excess water from a mixture of bagasse and water in the manufacture of various types of wallboard. Bagasse is the waste pulp from sugar cane. It is mixed with large quantities of water at the beginning of the process and emerges with but little moisture at the end. Let p_1 be the per cent of water with respect to the combined weight of the mixture of water and bagasse solids at the start of the process and p_2 be the per cent with respect to the combined weight of the mixture at the end. If p is the per cent of water removed during the process and *is with respect only to the weight of the bagasse solids*, derive an expression for

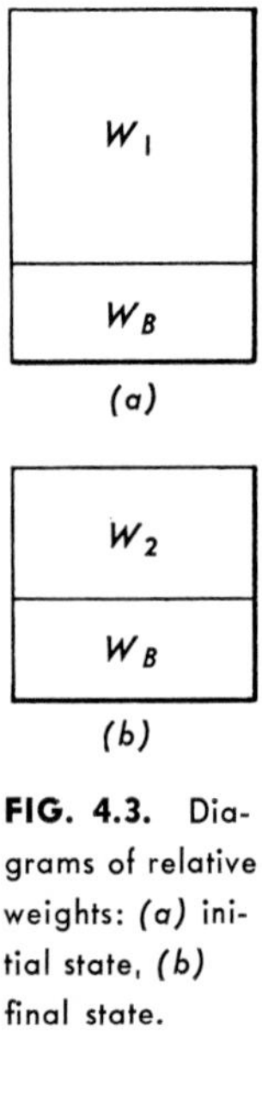

$$p = f(p_1, p_2)$$

It is desirable to introduce some other symbols in making this derivation. Let W_1 be the initial weight of water, W_2 the final weight of water, and W_B the weight of bagasse solids (Fig. 4.3).

Also use the percentages in decimal or fractional form rather than in per cent form.*

Initially

$$p_1 = \frac{W_1}{W_1 + W_B}$$

which we solve for W_1 in terms of W_B.

$$p_1 W_1 + p_1 W_B = W_1$$

$$W_1(1 - p_1) = p_1 W_B$$

$$W_1 = \frac{p_1 W_B}{1 - p_1}$$

FIG. 4.3. Diagrams of relative weights: *(a)* initial state, *(b)* final state.

---

* Per cent form: 25 per cent.
Decimal form: 0.25.
Fractional form: ¼.

Similarly

$$W_2 = \frac{p_2 W_B}{1 - p_2}$$

The weight of water extracted is equal to $W_1 - W_2$. We express this as a per cent of the weight of bagasse solids:

$$p = \frac{W_1 - W_2}{W_B}$$

We now substitute for W_1 and W_2 to obtain

$$p = \frac{\dfrac{p_1 W_B}{1 - p_1} - \dfrac{p_2 W_B}{1 - p_2}}{W_B}$$

W_B can be factored out of the equation, leaving

$$p = \frac{p_1}{1 - p_1} - \frac{p_2}{1 - p_2}$$

$$= \frac{p_1 - p_1 p_2 - p_2 + p_1 p_2}{(1 - p_1)(1 - p_2)}$$

or finally

$$p = \frac{p_1 - p_2}{(1 - p_1)(1 - p_2)}$$

This is an interesting derivation because it shows that sometimes it is desirable to introduce additional symbols or quantities to assist in making the derivation although they do not appear in the answer. The physical significance of the result is that the relationship between the percentages does not depend upon the actual quantities of water or bagasse involved but only upon their relative proportions.

Find the thickness t for the lining of a given open rectangular box (Fig. 4.4) of square base a and height h, inside dimensions, to reduce the volume of the box by a fraction p. At first glance this may appear to be another simple derivation of the form

$$t = f(a,h,p)$$

The initial equation is quite easy to set up. The new dimensions are $(a - 2t)$ and $(h - t)$ and the new volume is $(1 - p)a^2h$, from which we have

$$(1 - p)a^2h = (a - 2t)^2(h - t)$$

However, when we expand the preceding equation in terms of t, we have

$$(1 - p)a^2h = (a^2 - 4at + 4t^2)(h - t)$$

$$a^2h - pa^2h = a^2h - 4aht + 4ht^2 - a^2t + 4at^2 - 4t^3$$

which reduces to

$$4t^3 - 4(a + h)t^2 + a(a + 4h)t - pa^2h = 0$$

In functional form, this is

$$f(t,a,h,p) = 0$$

In this case, t is expressed implicitly in terms of the other variables. The determination of t as an explicit function of a, h, and p requires the use of methods for solving cubic equations.

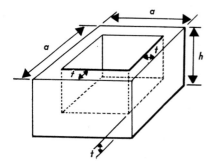

FIG. 4.4.

Derivations in general. There is no standard procedure for making derivations other than assigning symbols and setting up the proper logical relationships between the unknown quantity or quantities and the known quantities. The mathematical manipulation of these expressions in order to secure a suitable expression is frequently a matter of ingenuity.

A student should not permit himself to feel lost after he has assigned symbols and finds that he does not see how to obtain a result at once. He should begin with known facts and relationships between the symbols and work from those with the confidence that if he keeps trying different logical procedures, one will lead him to the desired result. In high school algebra the student was told to let x equal what was to be found and then to find x in terms of the known quantities. This applies generally to derivations although the symbol x is not necessarily used.

The choice of quantities to be used or to be designated by symbols sometimes affects the complexity of the derivation. For example, a derivation which involves a circle might be simpler in form if the radius of the circle were used instead of the diameter. Derivations which involve certain plane curves might be easier to obtain if the points on the curve were expressed in polar coordinates instead of rectangular coordinates. The equation of a circle of radius a in polar coordinates is $r = a$, and in rectangular coordinates is $x^2 + y^2 = a^2$. For certain other curves, the reverse might be true. There are no general rules which can be given with regard to the choice of variables or quantities. However, it is helpful if the student will be alert to the possibility of simplifying the mathematical form of various expressions with the proper choice of variables and symbols.

Introduction to the problems

The problems in this chapter are intended to give the student experience in making simple derivations to get answers to specific problems in engineering. The problems are not intended to introduce the student to any new concepts but rather to develop his capacity to choose quantities, assign symbols, and manipulate equations to obtain a particular relationship. The student should try to set up relationships in as simple a mathematical form as possible and should reduce his answers to the simplest possible expressions.

It is suggested that a neat sketch be made first for each problem and that the quantities involved be clearly designated on this sketch. A careful study of this pictorial representation of the problem may be of great value in suggesting a procedure for setting up relationships and deriving the required expression.

The student must beware of trying to save time and paper by doing algebraic operations in his head. It has been the author's experience that this "short cut" too frequently leads to mistakes which require much time and much scratch paper to discover. There is no substitute for writing out each operation term by term and step by step.

Suggested references

Silvanus P. Thompson, "Calculus Made Easy," The Macmillan Company, New York, 1944. An elementary approach to calculus in the language of laymen.

Lancelot Hogben, "Mathematics for the Million," W. W. Norton & Company, Inc., New York, 1940. A popular and interesting account of the historical beginnings of the various topics in elementary mathematics, their applications, and their influences upon civilization.

Helen A. Merrill, "Mathematical Excursions," Dover Publications, New York, 1933. Interesting problems and properties of numbers.

John S. Murphy, "Basis of Digital Computers," John F. Rider, Publisher, Inc., New York, 1958. An elementary and well-illustrated explanation of digital computers.

Edmund C. Berkeley, "Giant Brains: or, Machines That Think," John Wiley & Sons, Inc., New York, 1949.

Tobias Dantzig, "Number: The Language of Science," The Macmillan Company, New York, 1954. A nontechnical book on numbers and symbols.

Problems

4.1   *a.* Derive the total surface area A of a right circular cylinder of diameter D, height h, and volume V in terms of the diameter and of the ratio of height to diameter.

$$A = f\left(D, \frac{h}{d}\right)$$

b. Derive an expression for

$$A = f(h,V)$$

4.2   The frustum of a pyramid has a square base of sides a_1, a height h, and sides a_2 on the upper square. Derive an expression for the volume V of the frustum in its most reduced form.

$$V = \phi(a_1,a_2,h)$$

4.3   A pedestal is in the shape of the frustum of a right cone. The height of the frustum is h and radius of the base is r. The radius of the top of the frustum is a fraction p of the radius of the base. Derive an expression for the volume

$$V = f(r,h,p)$$

4.4   The equation of an ellipse with its center at the origin is

$$\frac{x^2}{a^2} + \frac{y^2}{b^2} = 1$$

Derive the equation of an ellipse from this in terms of the polar coordinates r and θ, the minor axis b, and the ratio of the minor axis to the major axis R, where $R = b/a$:

$$r = f(\theta,R,b)$$

4.5   An irregular solid mass weighs W_1 lb when weighed in air and W_2 lb when weighed completely immersed in water. There is a difference in weights because the mass is buoyed up by a force equal to the weight of water which it displaces. If δ_0 is the density of water, derive an expression for the density of the mass δ:

$$\delta = f(W_1,W_2,\delta_0)$$

4.6   The cooling system of an automobile has a volume of V qt and contains a mixture of water and antifreeze. The amount of antifreeze in the mixture is Q qt. It is desired to drain a certain amount of the mixture, x qt, from the radiator and replace it by the same amount of pure antifreeze in order to increase the percentage of antifreeze to a value p with respect to the total capacity of the system. Derive an expression for

$$x = f(p,Q,V)$$

4.7   A certain amount of water, W_w by weight, is to be removed from a mixture of water and wood-pulp solids in order to produce a pressed wallboard having a resulting moisture content p with respect to the weight of the solids alone W_s. If the initial water content is p_i, which is with respect to the combined initial weight of water and solids, derive an expression for

$$W_w = g(p_i,p,W_s)$$

4.8 The density of water may be taken to be 1 g per cu cm. Let the density of a liquid which is heavier than water be S and the density of a mixture of the liquid and water be d.

a. Derive an expression for $d = f(p,S)$, where p is the per cent by volume of heavy liquid in the mixture.

b. Derive an expression for $d = f(p,S)$, where p is the per cent by weight.

c. Determine which method gives the greater density by comparing the results of (*a*) and (*b*) or by any other reasoning.

4.9 A gearbox is used to reduce the speed of an electric motor. It consists of three sets of small gears (diameters D_1, D_3, D_5) which drive larger gears (diameters D_2, D_4, D_6) as shown in the diagrammatic representation (Fig. 4.5). Gears 2 and 3 are both on the same shaft and gears 4 and 5 are both on another shaft.

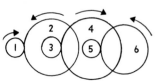

FIG. 4.5. Schematic diagram of gear train.

If the speed of rotation of the motor attached to the shaft for gear 1 is ω_1, derive an expression for the take-off speed ω_6 at gear 6 in terms of the motor speed and the gear diameters.

4.10 A vertical cylindrical water tank of inside diameter D is filled through a pipe of inside diameter d in which the water moves with average velocity v. If the initial depth of water in the tank is h_i, derive an expression for the depth of water h at any time t thereafter.

$$h = \theta(D,d,v,t,h_i)$$

4.11 A man is driving an automobile on a trip through the countryside. He wishes to drive at a certain speed S and also to average that speed for his trip. Whenever he has to slow down to any slower speed W, he counts to himself the number of seconds T at which he drives at that speed. Then when he is free of traffic he goes at a set maximum speed Z, which is greater than S, for the required number of seconds t to make up his loss and bring back his average speed to S. The speeds S and Z are set for the trip, i.e., are constants for a particular trip, and W varies depending upon traffic conditions. Derive the equation which he used for computing t:

$$t = F(S,W,T,Z)$$

4.12   A public park is located in a residential area of a city which is subdivided into square blocks. The park itself is square, measuring a certain number of blocks B on each side. Automobiles can be parked on both sides of the streets surrounding the park and in the residential area but not inside the park. The number of cars which can be parked on one side of a street in one block is n.

A large political rally is held in the park and a large number of cars N are parked centrally around the park completely occupying the available space bordering and inside of a larger square area of blocks. Derive an expression for the distance d in blocks from the edges of the park to the closest available parking space:

$$d = f(B,n,N)$$

4.13   A thick-walled kettle is in the shape of a hemisphere of inside radius r and wall thickness t. The kettle has no top (Fig. 4.6). The true volume of the wall V_t may be found by subtracting the volumes of the inner and outer hemispheres. An approximate volume V_a may be found

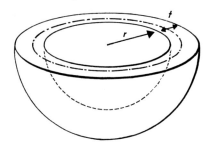

FIG. 4.6.   Thick-walled hemispherical kettle.

by multiplying the average surface area (taken at the center of the wall thickness) by the wall thickness. The latter method has the advantage of being more accurate for slide-rule calculation since it does not involve a small difference between relatively large numbers.

   a. Derive an expression for $V_t = f(r,t)$.
   b. Derive an expression for $V_a = g(r,t)$.
   c. Compare these by arranging the expressions in similar terms so far as is possible. Does the approximate method give a larger or smaller value than the true method? What is the maximum possible error in using the approximate method and under what condition does it occur?

d. What is the ratio of wall thickness t to inner radius r at which the error in using the approximate method becomes equal to or greater than 1 per cent? This will give some idea about the limits within which the approximate method may be used for practical purposes.

4.14   A spherical water tank has an inside radius R ft and is supplied by a water pipe of internal diameter d ft through which water is pumped at a velocity of v fps. Determine the rate z at which the water surface is rising in feet per second when the depth of water in the tank is h ft.

$$z = f(R,d,v,h)$$

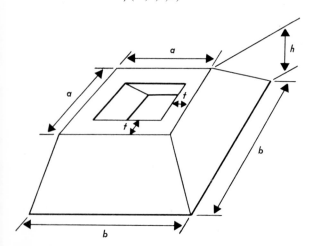

FIG. 4.7. Hollow pedestal.

4.15   A hollow pedestal is in the shape of the frustum of a right pyramid with a square base (Fig. 4.7). The pedestal is open at top and bottom. The sides are all of the same thickness t, which is measured horizontally. The density of the material from which the pedestal is made is δ. Derive an expression for its weight W:

$$W = g(a,b,h,t,\delta)$$

4.16   A closed cylindrical container has an inside radius r and inside height h. It is desired to insert lining material of sufficient thickness t to reduce the volume of the container to a fraction p of its original volume. Derive an expression for the implicit function $f(t,r,h,p) = 0$. Write the expression in terms of powers of t with the coefficients in terms of r, h, and p.

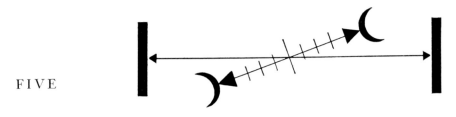

FIVE

Dimensions and units

The engineer works with the forces and materials of nature as stated in the definition of engineering in Chap. 1. These forces and materials are both physical and chemical quantities and vary from the simple to the most complex in their composition. It is necessary for the engineer to know the nature of these quantities and the units in which they are expressed. Since it is not the purpose of this book to concern itself with chemical quantities, this chapter is devoted only to the consideration of the nature and units of physical quantities.

Dimensions

The word "dimension" has two meanings which are used throughout the theory and practice of engineering. The *first meaning* is the more common one, namely, the space measurements of a box, or a room, or an object such as length, width, and height (Fig. 5.1). These dimensions designate measurements of distances in different directions and accordingly differ from each other in this respect. However, they have one thing in common. They are all measurements of a distance between two points.

In the terminology of engineering each of these space dimensions, length, width, and height, can also be designated simply as length in general. The standard notation for this general dimension of length or distance is $[L]$. Thus we have this *second meaning* of the word "dimension," *to designate the fundamental character of a physical quantity.* The dimension of the height of a box which may be 6 in. is $[L]$, the dimension of the width of a stream which may be 120 ft is $[L]$, and the dimension of the length of a highway which may be 40 miles is $[L]$. Notice that this dimension is *independent* not only of the *direc-*

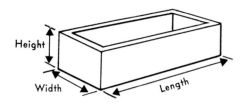

FIG. 5.1. Basic space dimensions.

tion of the distances but also of the *units* in which the distances are expressed. A distance is a distance whether it is measured in inches, feet, or miles.

Other physical quantities involving the fundamental quantity of length $[L]$ are areas and volumes. All areas are determined as the product of two lengths. For example, let us compare the areas of the three plane geometric shapes shown in Fig. 5.2.

Rectangle:

$$A = ab$$

$$[A] = [L][L]$$

$$= [L]^2$$

Triangle:

$$A = \tfrac{1}{2}bh$$

$$[A] = [L][L]$$

$$= [L]^2$$

Circle:

$$A = \frac{\pi d^2}{4}$$

$$[A] = [L]^2$$

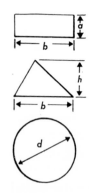

FIG. 5.2. Simple plane figures.

The dimensions of all three areas are identical, i.e., $[L]^2$. Note that the numbers 2, 4, and π are pure numbers which are characteristic of the particular shape of a geometric figure but which do not have any dimension. Such quantities are called *dimensionless constants*.

Correspondingly, the dimension of any volume must be $[L]^3$ or the product of three lengths. It makes no difference whether the shape is spherical, cylindrical, conical, or irregular. The volume of each must have the same dimension $[L]^3$.

There are two other fundamental quantities in the dimension system for mechanics which is called the *physical system*. These fundamental quantities are mass $[M]$ and time $[T]$. Other physical quantities than mass, length, and time are of such a nature that they can be expressed

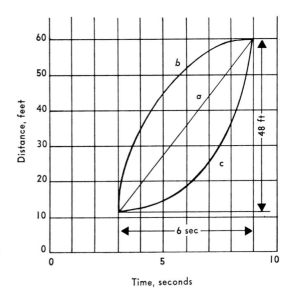

FIG. 5.3. Variations in velocity which yield equal average velocities.

in terms of these three elementary quantities (Appendix C). For example, in the study of motion, velocity depends upon distance and time. We speak of velocity as so many feet per second or so many miles per hour, meaning that a distance of so many feet is covered in one second or a distance of so many miles in one hour. Velocity is then the rate of change of distance with respect to time. If the position of an object changes by a distance of 48 ft in a time interval of 6 sec, the rate of change or the velocity is 48/6, or 8 fps. The object could move with constant velocity, in which case the velocity at any particular time would be 8 fps. Or it could move with varying velocity, in which case the rate of 8 fps would be an average velocity. Three general cases are shown in Fig. 5.3. The velocity in case *a* is constant throughout the time interval. In case *b* the velocity is continually decreasing and in case *c* it is continually increasing.

To measure velocity, we measure the time which it takes to go a certain distance and divide the distance by the time to get what is properly an average velocity. The distance and time may be very small so that the velocity approaches an instantaneous value. Yet it is still an average velocity for this very small interval. We say then that velocity is equal to distance divided by time, or in equation form,

$$\text{Velocity} = \frac{\text{length}}{\text{time}}$$

In terms of dimensions, we write the equation of velocity as

$$[v] = \frac{[L]}{[T]}$$

or

$$[v] = [L][T]^{-1}$$

Thus we might say that fundamentally velocity is made up of the quantities *L* and *T* as indicated.

Acceleration is the rate of change of velocity with respect to time. For example, if an object is moving initially with a velocity of 10 fps and 4 sec later is moving with a velocity of 20 fps, we say that the acceleration *a* is the change in velocity divided by the time in which this change occurs:

$$a = \frac{20 - 10}{4} = 2.5 \text{ fps}^2$$

Again, this represents an average value for the time interval, an average acceleration in this case which is similar to the average velocity in the preceding example. Possible variations of the acceleration during this interval of 4 sec are shown in Fig. 5.4. Case *a* is for constant acceleration, case *b* for a constantly decreasing acceleration, and case *c* for an acceleration which is first increasing and then decreasing.

Basically, the nature of acceleration is equal to velocity divided by time. Expressed in a dimensional equation,

$$[a] = \frac{[L][T]^{-1}}{[T]}$$

or

$$a = [L][T]^{-2}$$

Force is a more complex physical quantity which involves mass and acceleration. A simple definition of force is that which can be replaced by an equivalent muscular push or pull. In our physical system, however, force can be expressed in terms of the motion which it produces in acting on an object. This concept will be discussed at length in Chap. 7. Force is equal to the product of the mass of an object times the acceleration which the force produces on that object in the direc-

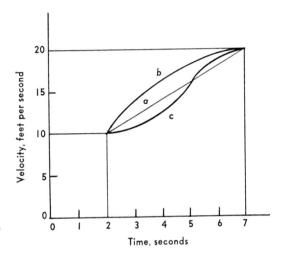

FIG. 5.4. Variations in acceleration which yield equal average accelerations.

tion in which the force acts. If we designate force by the letter F, the relationship in equation form is

$$F = ma$$

The dimensions of force are then

$$[F] = [M][L][T]^{-2}$$

There is no end to the number of examples which might be used to illustrate the relationship between force, mass, and acceleration. Figure 5.5 shows a dummy being used to test the runway ejection system of a jet fighter plane. The system is designed to exert a force much greater than the combined weight of pilot and seat in order to throw them high enough in the air for a parachute to open effectively. Thus we have a larger force acting on a smaller mass to give it a large acceleration during the small time that the force acts. A man pushing an automobile in which the engine is stalled on level ground illustrates the opposite condition. Here we have a small force acting on a large mass to give it a small acceleration. The chances are that the man will have

FIG. 5.5. Runway ejection system using rocket catapult being tested with dummy. Complete parachute opening is at height of about 100 ft. (*Courtesy of North American Aviation, Inc., Columbus Division.*)

to push for quite a distance in order to build up an appreciable velocity, assuming that he can keep applying a constant force. However, all forces whether great or small are basically the same physical quantity whose dimensions are $[M][L][T]^{-2}$.

There are other dimension systems which can be used in mechanics, such as the system in which force $[F]$ is used as one of the basic dimensions. This is called the gravitational or technical system and has as its elements $[F]$, $[L]$, $[T]$. Then there is the energetical system which is based on energy $[E]$ along with $[L]$ and $[T]$. For example, the dimension of mass in the technical system is $[F][L]^{-1}[T]^{-2}$ and in the energetical system $[E][L]^{-2}[T]^{-2}$. These systems are included in Appendix C.

However there is no law which requires that a dimension system for mechanical quantities be based upon three, and only three, elements. Engineers frequently find it desirable to use more elements in a dimension system to simplify their work in a particular field. Such a system might be based on four quantities, $[F]$, $[M]$, $[L]$, and $[T]$, or even more. It might also be based on such quantities as momentum and acceleration along with other suitable quantities.

On the other hand it should be emphasized that three is the *minimum* number of dimensions which can be used to describe quantities in the mechanical system, and that these cannot be chosen at random. For example, the dimensions $[M]$, $[L]$, and $[T]$ form a proper set, as do the dimensions $[F]$, $[L]$, and $[T]$. However, the dimensions $[v]$, $[a]$, and $[T]$ do not form a proper set because not one of them contains mass. Consequently, it would be impossible to express mass or force, for example, in terms of these quantities.

There are also several dimension systems for heat and for electromagnetism, as might be anticipated. The most widely used dimension system for heat is the "thermophysical" system, which is based upon $[M]$, $[L]$, and $[T]$ with addition of a fourth fundamental dimension, temperature $[\theta]$. The mechanical quantities are the same as in the dimension systems previously discussed but this system also includes such quantities as thermal capacity, thermal conductance, transmittance, entropy, and specific heat, all of whose dimensions include temperature $[\theta]$ as well as $[M]$, $[L]$, and $[T]$. This system is also included in Appendix C along with the "thermotechnical" and the "energetical" systems.

There are many dimension systems of electromagnetic quantities. The "electrophysical" system is based upon $[M]$, $[L]$, and $[T]$ with the addition of a fourth dimension, the electric charge $[Q]$, and is extensively used. However, another electromagnetic dimension system is also used in engineering literature. This is called the "practical" system and has the fundamental dimensions length $[L]$, time $[T]$, electric current $[I]$, and electric resistance $[R]$. This system is useful because convenient standards are available for the two electrical quantities of current and resistance. One disadvantage of the practical system for electrical quantities is the difficulty of combining it with the mechanical dimension systems based on $[M]$, $[L]$, $[T]$, and $[F]$. Another system known as the "definitive" system is based upon $[Q]$, $[L]$, $[T]$, and power $[P]$. These are included in Appendix C.

A knowledge of the dimensions of physical quantities is not only necessary to a more complete understanding of their nature but is also very useful in deriving and working with relationships among them. It is possible for the student to begin now to make use of the dimensions of physical quantities to check the correctness of equations. For example, suppose that he should be told that the volume of a sphere was given by the following equation:

$$V = \frac{4\pi r^2}{3}$$

where V is the volume, r is the radius, and $4\pi/3$ is a dimensionless constant. Dimensionally, this is written as $[V] = [L]^2$. Obviously, this is incorrect because the dimension of a volume must be $[L]^3$.

Again, examine the expression for the volume of the water tank (Fig. 5.6) which is composed of portions of a cylinder, a sphere, and a cone. The volume is given by

$$V = \frac{\pi r^2 d}{3} + \pi r^2 h + \frac{2\pi r^3}{3}$$

Again, the numbers are dimensionless constants and are characteristic of the various shapes. Note that each one of the three terms in this expression contains the dimension of length cubed: the dimension of

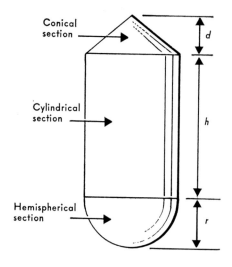

FIG. 5.6. Water tank composed of three geometric elements.

r^2d is $[L]^3$, of r^2h is $[L]^3$, and of r^3 is $[L]^3$. If any of these expressions should not have the dimension $[L]^3$, the equation would obviously be incorrect.

Such expressions are said to be *homogeneous*, which means that the dimensions of each quantity in the equation are the same and that the dimensions of the quantity on one side of the equation are the same as those on the other side. This is necessarily true of the relationships between physical quantities, since obviously apples cannot equal apes although both begin with the same letters.

However, a word of caution is necessary at this point. The fact that the dimensions of the quantities in an equation are consistent is not sufficient in itself to establish the correctness of the equation Although it might be dimensionally correct, there could be an error in one or more of the dimensionless constants which would make the equation incorrect in a numerical sense. For example, we could write the area of a circle as $A = \pi D^2$. This is dimensionally correct because $[A] = [L]^2$ but it is numerically incorrect. The dimensionless constant should be $\pi/4$ instead of π.

A knowledge of the dimensions of physical quantities is also useful in deriving equations. For example, one might be interested in how the surface area of cylindrical containers of constant volume varies with the h/r ratio (Fig. 5.7). Even though the cylinders in Fig. 5.7 might contain equal volumes, their surface areas will be different. It can be shown that the minimum surface area to contain a given volume occurs when the height is equal to twice the radius. A student might be

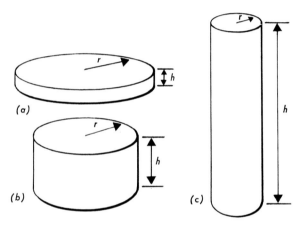

FIG. 5.7. Various shapes of cylinders: *(a)* $h/r = 1/3$, *(b)* $h/r = 1$, *(c)* $h/r = 8$.

tempted to write the functional relation for the total area of the cylinder as

$$A = f\left(\frac{h}{r}\right)$$

Is such a relationship possible? The ratio h/r has the dimensions of a length divided by a length, or $[L]/[L]$, which cancel in the same way as 7/7. In other words the ratio h/r is a pure ratio or a dimensionless quantity. We cannot express any area which by definition is of the dimension $[L]^2$ in terms of a dimensionless quantity, i.e., we cannot have $[L]^2$ on one side of an equation and no dimension on the other side. So it is not possible to obtain an expression for the explicit function $A = f(h/r)$.

Any one of the following relationships, however, would be theoretically possible:

$$A = f\left(r, \frac{h}{r}\right)$$

$$A = f\left(h, \frac{h}{r}\right)$$

$$A = f\left(r, h, \frac{h}{r}\right)$$

For example, the total surface area of the cylinder is

$$A = 2(\pi r^2) + (2\pi r)h$$

$$= 2\pi(r^2 + rh)$$

We wish to find $f(r, h/r)$. The second term in the parenthesis contains h and if we divide this by r^2, we would convert it to rh/r^2 or h/r.

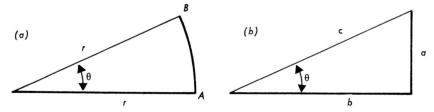

FIG. 5.8. (a) Arc $AB = r\theta$, $\theta = $ arc AB/r; (b) $\sin \theta = a/c$.

Accordingly, multiply and divide the expression on the right-hand side by r^2 to obtain

$$A = 2\pi r^2 \frac{r^2 + rh}{r^2}$$

$$= 2\pi r^2\left(1 + \frac{h}{r}\right)$$

and we have the desired explicit expression. The student should test his ingenuity now and see if he can derive expressions for the other two functions. Note that the above expression is dimensionally correct with $[L]^2$ on both sides.

Pure numbers, including such constants as π and e (the base of natural logarithms), are dimensionless. Conversion factors are dimensionless quantities since they represent the ratio between like quantities. For example, we use the factor 12 to convert feet to inches since 1 ft = 12 in. The conversion factor is expressed as 12 in. per ft or $12[L]/[L]$. Rates such as strokes per minute or revolutions per second are not dimension-less but have the dimension $[T]^{-1}$. Angles are dimensionless since they represent only a change in direction rather than a distance or a length itself. They are measured either directly by change of direction or indi-rectly by the ratio of two lengths. This is true both of angles and of functions of an angle. From Fig. 5.8, we see that

$$\theta = \frac{\text{arc } AB}{r} = \frac{[L]}{[L]}$$

or

$$\sin \theta = \frac{a}{c} = \frac{[L]}{[L]}$$

However, there are some constants which do have dimension, and these are called *dimensional constants*. For example, the fundamental law of universal gravitation might be stated as follows: the force of attraction between two masses is proportional to the product of the masses divided by the square of the distance between their centers of mass.* In equation form this is

$$F \propto \frac{m_1 m_2}{r^2}$$

This is an observed natural law. However, in order to be able to use it for a particular case, we must introduce the gravitational constant G and write

$$F = G \frac{m_1 m_2}{r^2}$$

This constant G must necessarily have the dimensions $[M]^{-1}[L]^3$ $[T]^{-2}$. The student can make use of his present knowledge to verify these dimensions of the gravitational constant. On the other hand, the nature of problems which involve G might well be such that it would be more desirable to express the dimensions of G in other than the three basic dimensions. For example, it might be better to include the element of force and to write

$$[G] = [F][L]^2[M]^{-2}$$

or if energy is involved to write

$$[G] = [E]^2[M]^{-2}[F]^{-1}$$

* Sir Isaac Newton, *Philosophiae naturalis principia mathematica*, 1686. Trans-lation: "Every particle of matter in the universe attracts every other particle with a force which is directly proportional to the product of the masses of the particles and inversely proportional to the square of the distance between them."

We find a simple example in experiments on rolling friction. This is the resistance to the motion of a wheel rolling over a surface or a rail such as a steel rail. There is a force of resistance R to the motion which is called *rolling friction*. This is found to be closely proportional to the combined weight W of the wheel and its load and inversely proportional to the radius r of the wheel. Thus we have

$$R \propto \frac{W}{r}$$

For particular materials such as steel on steel, we write

$$R = a\frac{W}{r}$$

where a is the *coefficient of rolling friction*. This coefficient is not dimensionless, as is seen from the dimensional relationship in which we use $[F]$ as one of the basic dimensions:

$$[F] = \frac{[a][F]}{[L]}$$

or

$$[a] = [L]$$

We see that the coefficient of rolling friction a has the dimension $[L]$. It depends upon deformation in the surface material under the concentrated load imposed by the wheel (Fig. 5.9) and would be expressed in the same units as the radius of the wheel, usually in inches. The deformation in Fig. 5.9 is exaggerated for the sake of clarity. The same condition is not true of coefficients of sliding friction which are dimensionless constants.

There are also empirical equations which are derived from particular experiments under special conditions and which hold only within the range of data collected in the experiments. Such equations are not necessarily homogeneous. For example, in the flow of water through a pipe of a certain roughness, the loss in head h_F which corresponds to a length might be determined by experiment to be

$$h_F = 0.6\frac{V^{1.95}}{D^{1.25}}L$$

where V represents the velocity of flow of the water in the pipe, D the inside diameter of the pipe, and L its length. The student can see that this equation is not homogeneous and could never be regardless of the exponents because the left side of the equation has only length and the right side of the equation has velocity, which includes time. The coefficient 0.6 therefore is a dimensional constant, and in this case a rather complicated one because of the nonintegral exponents of D and V. It must be emphasized that the usefulness of empirical equations is limited strictly to the specific conditions of the particular experiments from which they were obtained.

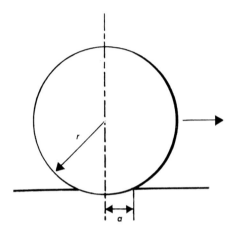

FIG. 5.9. Surface deformation under rolling wheel.

Units

Units are used for measuring the number or the amount of physical quantities. These quantities are measured only by comparison with like quantities. In order to make such comparisons, some distinct amount of a physical quantity must be defined as a unit or a reference amount. It is obvious that there are any number of possible units which might be selected for measuring a particular physical quantity and that all of these units for this physical quantity must be related by purely numerical factors.

Thus although a physical quantity is represented uniquely in a dimension system, it can be measured in many different systems of units. For example, in the United States length may be measured in the English system in which a foot is the fundamental unit; or it may be measured in inches or yards. In Europe and South America length is measured in the metric systems, in which the meter and the centimeter are fundamental units of length.

Frequently it is necessary to convert units to larger or smaller units within the same system, or to units in another system. The ratios which are used for this purpose are called *conversion factors*. For example, there are 12 in. in 1 ft, and thus the conversion factor of 12 is used to convert feet to inches. Likewise there are approximately 454 g in 1 lb so that a conversion factor of 454 is used to change pounds to grams.

It is highly important for the engineer to be aware of the units of the physical quantities with which he is dealing in any particular problem. Some rather bizarre answers can be obtained if he neglects the units. For example, no one would question the following numerical statements:

$$2 + 2 = 4$$
$$2 \times 2 = 4$$

On the other hand, everyone would deny the truth of the following numerical statements:

$$2 + 2 = 22$$
$$2 \times 2 = 48$$

The student tells himself that these statements are obviously false. Yet if we add 2 cm and 2 mm, we do obtain 22 mm. Furthermore, if we multiply 2 ft by 2 in., we do obtain 48 sq in. Or we could state that 2 ft times 2 in. equals 4 ft-in.

It is apparent that such numerical statements can be correctly written only by stating the units with each number, such as

$$2 \text{ cm} + 2 \text{ mm} = 22 \text{ mm}$$
$$2 \text{ ft} \times 2 \text{ in.} = 48 \text{ sq in.}$$

This is a cumbersome and impractical method of handling the measurements of physical quantities and is not generally used by engineers, mathematicians, or scientists.

Students who are beginning the study of engineering should be especially alert to avoid mixing units in solving problems. Very frequently the same physical quantity in a problem will be expressed in different units, as the dimensions of a box may be given as 6 in. by 8 in. by 4 ft. The student must decide whether to compute the volume, if that is what is requested, in terms of cubic inches or of cubic feet and make the necessary conversion before multiplying the three dimensions. Note the use of the word dimension here in the more commonly recognized sense of the word.

Occasionally a formula will be developed which is dimensionally correct but where the quantities are expressed in different units. This usually occurs with respect to commercial equipment for which the dimensions and other characteristics are specified in certain units but the rating or performance is in different units. For example, the formula for the quantity delivered by a single-acting pump which was derived in Chap. 4 gave the quantity in gallons per hour, whereas the pump dimensions were in inches and rate of pumping was in strokes per minute. This was found to be

$$Q = 0.204D^2Ln$$

where D is diameter of cylinder in inches, L is length of stroke in inches, n is number of strokes per minute, and Q is gallons per hour.

The customer wants to know how many gallons are delivered per hour but the manufacturer may specify his pumps in inches and strokes per minute. Such formulas are dimensionally homogeneous and can be verified, but the constant 0.204 involves the numerical conversion factors, 231 cu in. per gal and 60 min per hr:

$$[L]^3[T]^{-1} = \text{constant } [L]^2[L][T]^{-1}$$

or

$$[L]^3[T]^{-1} = [L]^3[T]^{-1}$$

Note again that the conversion factors are always dimensionless quantities.

The engineer always states the units of every physical quantity which he calculates at every stage in the solution of a problem. This is highly important. This can be illustrated by a very simple statement, "I spent thirty-five in town yesterday." Thirty-five what? It could be dollars, cents, or minutes. Any calculation of the amount of a physical quantity in a problem is incorrect unless the units accompany the resulting number, such as 15 lb, 25 fps, or 14 cu in. Factors for converting from one unit to another are given in Appendix E.

It will be helpful to students, especially in the early stages of study, if they will write out the units with the quantities in their equations. Some instructors will insist on this and others may suggest that this be done on the margin of the paper. Although this practice is not generally followed in later years by engineers by actually writing the units in the calculations, it is still necessary to do it mentally or on scratch paper. The following examples illustrate the ideas.

A rectangular block of concrete measures 6 ft by 2 ft by 4 in. and weighs 576 lb. What is its density in pounds per cubic foot?

$$\text{Density} = \frac{576 \text{ lb}}{6 \text{ ft} \times 2 \text{ ft} \times \dfrac{4 \cancel{in.}}{12 \dfrac{\cancel{in.}}{ft}}}$$

$$= \frac{576 \text{ lb}}{6 \text{ ft} \times 2 \text{ ft} \times \dfrac{1}{3} \text{ ft}}$$

$$= \frac{576}{4} \frac{\text{lb}}{\text{ft}^3}$$

$$= 144 \text{ lb per cu ft}$$

What is the acceleration of an automobile which speeds up from 10 to 60 mph in 12 sec?

$$a = \frac{60 \text{ mph} - 10 \text{ mph}}{12 \text{ sec}}$$

$$= \frac{50}{12} \frac{\text{mph}}{\text{sec}}$$

$$a = 4.17 \text{ mph per sec}$$

or

$$a = 4.17 \text{ miles per hour per sec}$$

Here is an example where the result might be more useful in mixed units of hours and seconds rather than entirely in terms of hours or of seconds. It might also be obtained in terms of feet and seconds by using the relationship that 60 mph is equal to 88 fps.

$$a = \frac{50 \dfrac{\cancel{mi}}{\cancel{hr}} \times \dfrac{60 \dfrac{ft}{sec}}{88 \dfrac{\cancel{mi}}{\cancel{hr}}}}{12 \text{ sec}}$$

$$= \frac{\dfrac{50 \times 60}{88} \dfrac{ft}{sec}}{12 \text{ sec}}$$

$$= \frac{50 \times 60}{88 \times 12} \frac{ft}{sec^2}$$

$$a = 6.11 \text{ ft per sec}^2 \text{ (or fps}^2\text{)}$$

or

$$a = 6.11 \text{ ft per sec per sec}$$

The result would not be practically so useful if expressed in miles per hour per hour or in other combinations. For example, in miles per hour per hour we would have

$$a = 4.17 \frac{mi}{hr \times sec} \times 3,600 \frac{sec}{hr}$$

$$= 15,000 \text{ mi per hr per hr}$$

On the other hand, if instead of an automobile we had some other device or system where low speeds were involved, other combinations of units might be more useful. Suppose that we have a situation where the speed changed from 0.030 fps to 0.040 fps in 2 min, and we wish to convert these speeds to feet per minute and find what change occurs in an hour.

$$a = \frac{(0.040 - 0.030) \frac{ft}{sec}}{2 \text{ min}}$$

$$= \frac{0.010 \frac{ft}{sec}}{2 \text{ min}}$$

Applying the conversion factors, we have

$$a = \frac{0.010 \frac{ft}{sec} \times 60 \frac{sec}{min}}{2 \text{ min}}$$

$$= \frac{0.60 \frac{ft}{min}}{\frac{1}{30} \text{ hr}}$$

$$a = 18 \text{ ft per min per hr}$$

An alternative way to check the units might be as follows:

$$\frac{\dfrac{\text{ft}}{\text{sec}} \times \dfrac{\text{sec}}{\text{min}}}{\dfrac{\dfrac{\text{min}}{\text{min}}}{\text{hr}}} \qquad a = \frac{0.010 \times 60}{\dfrac{2}{60}}$$

$$= \frac{0.010 \times 3,600}{2}$$

$$\frac{\text{ft}}{\text{min} \times \text{hr}} \qquad = 18 \text{ ft per min per hr}$$

The choice of units in solving a problem is also important. Few students ever learn the multiplication table beyond 12 in school. Few engineers extend their mental arithmetic beyond this other than to learn the squares of numbers up to 20 or perhaps 25. They generally have to stop and work out such products as 19×16, or 21×17. Also, we are accustomed to using numbers in general between 1 and 1,000. Most of us do not deal much with numbers below 1 or with numbers greater than 1,000. One reason for this is that numerical computation can be confined to this usual range of numbers by the proper choice of unit. For example, the distance between two communities would be normally expressed as 25.2 miles rather than as approximately 132,100 ft or 1,585,000 in. Also, the width of a room would normally be measured as 31 ft 4 in. rather than as 376 in. or 0.00593 mile. Accordingly, the student should be conscious of this at the outset of his college career and choose his units so as to get the most practical numerical answers.

Sometimes we are forced to use quantities that are very large or very small or we may wish to use certain units for special reasons which give very large or very small numerical answers. In such cases, the manipulation of these numbers can be simplified by expressing them in powers of 10. For example, coefficients of thermal expansion and contraction are generally quite small, such as 0.0000065 in. per in. per °F. This can more easily be used in a numerical computation as 6.5×10^{-6}. Again a computation might involve the velocity of light, which is approximately 186,000 miles per second or 30,000,000,000 centimeters per second. These could be more handily used in the computation as 1.86×10^5 miles per second or 3×10^{10} centimeters per second.

Introduction to the problems

The following problems are for the purpose of giving the student experience (1) in determining the dimensions of common physical quantities and in checking the correctness of dimensional relationships between them and (2) in solving problems where it is necessary to select units and to convert units in order to avoid mixing them. In working the problems in dimensions, it will be helpful to write the given relationship first and then to write individually the dimensions for each quantity involved on separate lines. These dimensions may then be substituted into the original relationship and manipulated algebraically to determine whether or not the relationship is dimensionally correct. The symbol g for the acceleration of gravity occurs in many of the dimensional problems. It is noted here and will not be redefined in those problems.

The problems in units are of two general types, one in which the units in the required answer are not specified, and the other in which they are specified. Both types give the student an opportunity to make a decision about units, either for the answer or for the intermediate calculations to obtain the answer. Frequently the conditions of the problem are such that it is better to make the intermediate calculations in terms of one set of units and to make a final conversion to another set of units for the answer. It would be better to make a series of calculations of volumes of excavation every 50 ft for a highway in cubic feet and to make a single conversion to cubic yards after the total is obtained. It is a waste of time to convert each volume for each 50-ft length into cubic yards.

Suggested references

Percy W. Bridgman, "Dimensional Analysis," Yale University Press, New Haven, Conn., 1931. A classical elementary presentation on the subject.

Robert L. Sutherland, "Engineering Systems Analysis," Addison-Wesley Publishing Company, Reading, Mass., 1958.

Henry L. Langhaar, "Dimensional Analysis and the Theory of Models," John Wiley & Sons, Inc., New York, 1951.

Ovid W. Eshbach (ed.), "Handbook of Engineering Fundamentals," 2d ed., John Wiley & Sons, Inc., New York, 1952, Unit Systems, pp. 3–12 to 3–35. An introduction to units and the various systems of units.

Problems

Check the following relationships to determine whether or not they are dimensionally correct.

5.1 Volume of frustum of cone: volume V, radii r_1 and r_2, height h.

$$V = \frac{\pi h}{3}\left(r_1{}^2 + r_2{}^2 + \sqrt{r_1 r_2}\right)$$

5.2 Area of truncated right circular cylinder: total surface area A, radius r, maximum height h_1, minimum height h_2.

$$A = \pi r\left[h_1 + h_2 + r + \sqrt{r^2 + \left(\frac{h_1 - h_2}{2}\right)^2}\,\right]$$

5.3 Area of a segment of a paraboloid of revolution: lateral area A, height h, diameter of base of segment l.

$$A = \frac{2\pi l}{3h^2}\left[\left(\frac{l^2}{16} + h^2\right)^{3/2} - \left(\frac{l}{4}\right)^2\right]$$

5.4 Area of a cylinder in terms of the volume and the dimensions: total surface area A, volume V, radius r, height h.

$$A = 2\pi r\sqrt{\frac{V}{\pi h^2}}\left(\frac{h}{r} + 1\right)$$

5.5 Period of oscillation of a conical pendulum (Fig. 5.10): time of one oscillation t, length of pendulum L, angle with the vertical θ.

$$t = 2\pi\sqrt{\frac{L\cos\theta}{g}}$$

5.6 Velocity of surface wave in deep water: velocity v, wavelength (distance between successive crests) λ.

$$v = \text{constant }\sqrt{\lambda g}$$

5.7 Freely falling body: height h, velocity v, time t, initial velocity v_0.

$$h = v_0 t + \frac{1}{2} g t^2$$

$$v^2 = v_0^2 + 2gh$$

$$t = \sqrt{\frac{v - v_0}{g}}$$

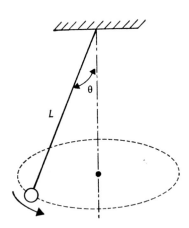

FIG. 5.10. Conical pendulum.

5.8 Motion of a projectile (Fig. 5.11); horizontal range R, initial velocity v_0, angle of elevation θ_0.

$$R = \frac{v_0^2 \sin 2\theta_0}{\sqrt{g}}$$

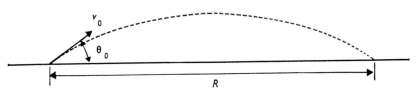

FIG. 5.11. Simple ballistic trajectory.

5.9 Centrifugal force: centrifugal force F, mass of object m, radius r, angular velocity (radians per unit of time) ω.

$$F = mr^2\omega^2$$

5.10 Measurement of the earth's mass: mass of the earth m_E, radius of the moon's orbit R, time of revolution of the moon about the earth T, gravitational constant G.

$$m_E = \frac{4\pi^2 R^3}{GT^2}$$

5.11   Theoretical loss of head in flow of water through pipes: loss in head in equivalent height h_F, coefficient (dimensionless) depending on pipe roughness f, length of pipe L, inside diameter D, velocity of flow V.

$$h_F = \frac{fLV^2}{2D^2g}$$

Problems in units

5.12   One cubic yard of concrete for a pavement requires 1.2 tons of gravel, 1,400 lb of sand, and 4.5 sacks of cement. A sack of cement weighs 94 lb.

Estimate how many railroad cars of each material are required for 8 miles of pavement 26 ft wide and 8 in. thick.

5.13   A conveyor belt (Fig. 5.12) is used to transport gravel from a railroad siding to a construction site 3 miles away. The belt runs on

FIG. 5.12.   Conveyor belt transporting coarse aggregate from a pit to the site of a dam project in Arkansas. *(Courtesy of the Goodyear Tire and Rubber Company.)*

horizontal rollers beneath it and also on rollers on each side set at an angle of 30° with the horizontal. The belt may be said to approximate a trough 3 ft wide at the bottom with side slopes of 30° and a depth of 2 ft.

What is the rate at which gravel is transported if the gravel fills the belt to an average depth of 20 in. and the belt moves at the rate of 15 mph?

5.14 A circular concrete water tank has an outside diameter of 62 ft and a depth of 18 ft. The wall is 10 in. thick. The intake is an overhead pipe through which water is pumped from a treatment plant. Discharge is through a 3-in. pipe (inside diameter) near the bottom. When the depth of water in the tank is 9 ft, the flow in the discharge pipe is at a velocity of 9.82 mph, and the flow in the overhead supply pipe is 373 gpm.

What is the rate at which the water is rising in the tank?

5.15 A farm has a small pond in the shape of an inverted cone which is 66 yd in diameter. It is 10 ft deep at the center, i.e., at the apex of the inverted cone. The drainage area for the pond, or the area from which rainfall drains into it, may be approximated by an equilateral triangle which has an area of 52 acres. Fifteen acres of the drainage area are in forest and the remainder is in pasture. When it rains, the forest portion absorbs and retains 30 per cent of the rain which falls upon it and the pastures retain 20 per cent of the rain falling upon them.

  a. How many inches of rainfall on the drainage area will it take to fill the pond completely? Assume that the pond is empty.

  b. Is it likely that the empty pond would be filled occasionally in one day?

5.16 The specifications for the construction of a 17-mile stretch of highway call for a compacted gravel base 26 ft wide and 5 in. thick. The contractor who was awarded the job on the basis of competitive bids had agreed with the owner of a nearby gravel pit on a price of 54 cents per cu yd for gravel loaded at the pit to build the compacted base. For hauling the gravel, he uses trucks whose capacity is 6 cu yd each.

Gravel loaded in trucks at the pit is in a loose state weighing 110 pcf. However, the gravel when compacted weighs 120 pcf. The average length of haul from the pit to the road under construction is 19.5 miles.

The average cost of operating a truck, whether loaded or empty, is $0.11 per mile.

a. How much money does the contractor lose if his construction crews are so careless in preparing a smooth subgrade and laying the gravel that they place a compacted gravel base which averages 5½ in. in thickness?

b. Suggest a reasonable method that the contractor might use as a guide to avoid placing a gravel base which is too thin or too thick.

5.17   Suppose that a sprinter runs the 100-yd dash in 9.2 sec, a miler does a mile in 3 min 58 sec, a race horse runs 6 furlongs in 71 sec, and a diesel streamliner train does half a mile in 16 sec. Convert these to miles per hour for purposes of comparison.

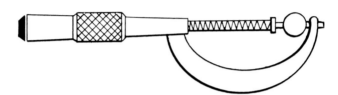

SIX

Measurement and accuracy

The engineer is constantly making measurements of physical quantities and using these measurements in the solution of his problems. The character and extent of these measurements, the errors in them, and their relative accuracy are important in professional practice. The purpose of this chapter is to give the student a clear understanding of the nature of measurements and accuracy and of their practical significance. This will enable him to judge and to use data more effectively and to avoid carrying calculations to an extent which is sometimes ridiculous.

Measurements

There is one outstanding fact about measurements which the student should grasp firmly at the outset. The numbers obtained by these measurements are always approximations as contrasted with integral numbers which are used in counting objects. Although one can say that there are exactly 35 students in a classroom, can he also say that a particular student weighs exactly 161 lb? The 35 students can be *counted* and there are no more, no less. The weight of a student, on the other hand, has to be *measured* and if it is measured to be 161 lb, that means that it is closer to 161 lb than to 160 lb or 162 lb (Fig. 6.1).

Strictly speaking, therefore, there is no such thing as an exact measurement because this would mean determining the measurement to an infinite number of places. If the weight of a boy is measured to the nearest one-thousandth of a pound to be 161.231 lb, there are still undetermined the ten-thousandths or hundred-thousandths of a pound, or less. Obviously, there are practical limits to the extent to which measurements can be made.

This does not mean that measurements are never used as exact quantities, because sometimes they are. For example, the motorist pays for exactly 10 gal of gasoline, say at 35.9 cents per gal, which amounts to exactly 359 pennies or its equivalent in dollars and cents. However, it could be safely stated that no one ever receives *exactly* 10 gal of gasoline so far as can be determined by actual measurement.

The extent to which measurements can be made depends upon the physical factors involved, the instruments available, and the methods which can be used. Frequently, dollars and cents are factors in determining how accurately a measurement should be made. It might be

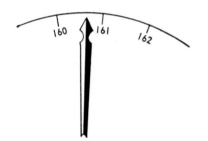

FIG. 6.1. Enlarged diagrammatic representation of an ordinary scale registering a weight of 161 lb.

said that in general the greater the accuracy of a measurement, the greater is the cost of making it. And yet, the advent of mass production in our country and many other factors including scientific and engineering research have demanded more accurate measurements despite increased costs. Engineers have responded by using their imagination and ingenuity together with almost every conceivable physical resource. For example, more accurate measurement and control in the fabricating industries have been made possible not only by more precision in machine tools and in manufacturing processes but also by the adaptation of electrical and optical means and the development of other ingenious methods (Fig. 6.2).

Measurements are made in terms of certain units such as feet or pounds. These units are generally arbitrary and have come to us down through the centuries. The use of the foot for measuring small distances must have led to disputes in bygone days when there were significant differences between the lengths of the feet of two persons. Someone's

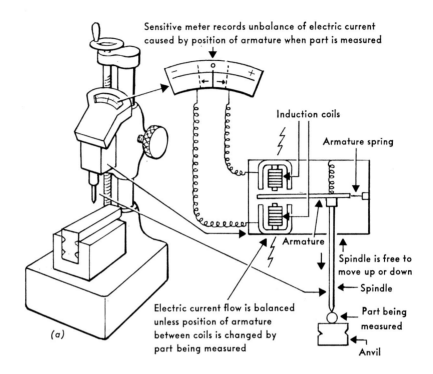

Sensitive meter records unbalance of electric current
caused by position of armature when part is measured

Induction coils

Armature spring

Armature

Spindle is free to
move up or down

Spindle

Part being
measured

Anvil

Electric current flow is balanced
unless position of armature
between coils is changed by
part being measured

(a)

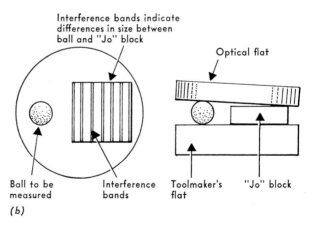

Interference bands indicate
differences in size between
ball and "Jo" block

Optical flat

Ball to be
measured

Interference
bands

Toolmaker's
flat

"Jo" block

(b)

FIG. 6.2. (a) Electromagnetic device which measures to within 0.0000001 in.
(b) Optical measuring device. The "Jo" block is one of a set of extremely precise
standards nicknamed after their Swedish maker, Carl Johansson. (Courtesy of the
General Motors Corporation.)

foot had to be chosen as standard. The standards used today in the United States are duplicates of those in the International Bureau of Weights and Measures in Sèvres, France (Fig. 6.3).

We might say that there are two types of measurements, direct and indirect. Direct measurements of physical quantities are made by direct comparison with the standard unit or its duplicates. Lengths are measured in feet or meters by direct comparisons using foot rulers or meter sticks. Masses are determined by direct comparison with standard masses using balances. Time is measured by watches and clocks which have been standardized by comparison with more accurate timepieces called chronometers. A second is defined to be the 1/86,400 part of a

FIG. 6.3. United States standards of mass and length at the National Bureau of Standards. They are composed of a very stable alloy of 90 per cent platinum and 10 per cent iridium, and are precise duplicates of the international standards at the International Bureau of Weights and Measures at Sèvres, France. The standard of mass is 39 mm in diameter and 39 mm high. The standard meter is the distance between two parallel lines engraved on the meter bar 1 cm from each end. [*Courtesy of the National Bureau of Standards (U.S.).*]

mean solar day based upon a yearly average which is found to be constant.

However, the measurement of many other physical quantities must be made indirectly. For example, velocity is determined indirectly through the measurement of its dimensional components, length and time. We measure the velocity of a moving object by measuring the time which it takes for the object to traverse a given measured distance. These quantities, time and distance, may be extremely small so that the velocity which is measured approaches an instantaneous velocity. However, regardless of how small the time and distance may be, the velocity measured is an average velocity for that particular time interval.

The measurement of the magnitude of small electric currents by a galvanometer is another example of indirect measurement. The magnitude of the current is indicated by the movement of a beam of light on a scale. The beam is reflected from a small mirror attached to a fine wire suspending a coil in the magnetic field of a permanent, horseshoe-type magnet. The electric current to be measured is passed through this coil, creating a magnetic field around it which causes it to rotate an amount proportional to the magnitude of the current. The mirror rotates with the coil and the amount of rotation is measured by the movement of the beam of light.

There are literally hundreds of types of indirect measurements, far too many to enumerate here. Many of these depend upon direct measurements to obtain data which can be used to determine the desired quantity. For example, velocity is measured indirectly by measuring time and distance, both of which are determined by direct measurement. It is interesting to note, however, that quantities which can be measured directly may also be measured indirectly. For example, the altitude of an airplane, or its distance from the ground, may be measured by changes in barometric pressure. The age of fossils less than 30,000 years old can be determined from the per cent of radioactive carbon 14 which they contain. The age of some rocks has been determined to be as much as 2,800,000 years from the ratio of lead 206 to uranium which the rocks contain.

Significant figures

The extent to which a measurement is made determines the number of *significant figures* in it. If a length is measured to be 25 in., the

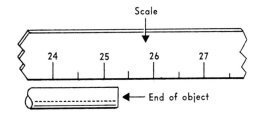

FIG. 6.4. Measurement of length to two significant figures.

measurement is said to have two significant figures and is determined to be closer to 25 in. than to 24 or 26 in. (Fig. 6.4). If the measurement is made more accurately as 25.3 in., then it contains three significant figures. Extending the measurement one more place to 25.32 in. gives a measurement with four significant figures, one which is closer to 25.32 in. than to 25.31 or 25.33 in. (Fig. 6.5).

Some confusion is apt to arise about whether or not zeros are significant figures when one first approaches this subject. If a measurement is made as 25.0 in., this means that the measurement is closer to that value than to 24.9 or 25.1 in. (Fig. 6.6). Accordingly, the zero is a significant figure meaning just that instead of 9 or 1. Similarly, a meas-

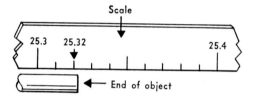

FIG. 6.5. Measurement of length to four significant figures.

urement such as 25.00 in. would contain four significant figures as would a measurement of 2,503 in.

On the other hand, the zeros would not be significant figures in such a measurement as 0.0025 in. In this measurement the zeros are simply used to locate the decimal point, or stated another way, to indicate the size of the unit which was used in making the measurement. This measurement is made in terms of units of 1/10,000 in. instead of units of 1 in. The measurement consists in determining 25 such units of

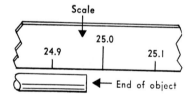

FIG. 6.6. Zero as a significant figure.

1/10,000 in. each (Fig. 6.7). Accordingly, the measurement contains only two significant figures and can be written in several ways, the more common being 0.0025 in., and other ways being the fraction 25/10,000 in., and the expression 2.5×10^{-3} in. Whenever the zero is used, as in this case, to locate the decimal point or determine the size of the unit, it is not significant. Whenever it represents a measurement of zero units instead of nine units or one unit, it is significant.

An ambiguous case occurs in such a measurement as 25,000 in. In this form the measurement could have been made to the nearest 1,000 in., in which case it would have contained only two significant figures, or it could have been made to the nearest inch and have contained five significant figures. In the former case the zeros are used only to locate the decimal point, or indicate the size of the unit, and in the latter case they are significant figures meaning that the measurement is 25,000 in. to the nearest inch rather than 24,999 or 25,001 in.

This dilemma can be resolved if we adopt the convention of writing a number in terms of powers of 10. Reduce the measurement to a number between 1 and 10 which includes the significant figures and

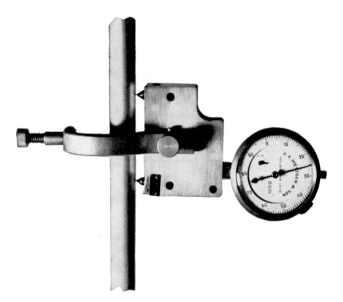

FIG. 6.7.   Ames dial used on a mechanical strain gauge to measure units of 1/10,000 in.

indicate the decimal point by a power of 10. Using this convention, the less accurate measurement would be 2.5×10^4 in. and the more accurate measurement would be 2.5000×10^4 in. If the first zero to the right of the 5 is significant but the other two are not, the measurement could be written then as 2.50×10^4 in.

Therefore, the device of expressing large numbers in terms of powers of 10, which was mentioned in the previous chapter, is useful not only for making them easier to handle but also for indicating the correct number of significant figures in the measurement.

Error and accuracy

Since the accuracy of the measurement depends on both the magnitude of the measurement and the number of significant figures in it, it is necessary to distinguish between the *absolute error* and the *relative error* or *relative accuracy*. Since a measurement cannot be made exactly, the absolute error is that portion of the measurement which could be in error and which amounts at most to as much as one-half of a unit in the last significant figure. For example, if a measurement of 11.2 in. is made to the nearest tenth of an inch, the end of the object falls closer to the mark on the rule for 11.2 in. than it does for 11.1 or 11.3 in. This means that the measurement falls between 11.15 and 11.25 and that the maximum absolute error is 5/100 in. This is shown in Fig. 6.8, where the

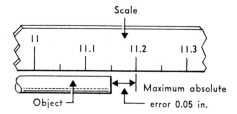

FIG. 6.8. Maximum absolute error.

end of the object falls very close to the center of the interval between 11.1 and 11.2, i.e., very close to the mark for 11.15. The maximum absolute error, then, is always one-half of the unit of the last significant figure.

The relative error or relative accuracy is the ratio of the maximum absolute error to the number itself. The magnitude of the relative error depends only on the number of significant figures in the measurement. It does not depend upon the magnitude of the measurement, whether large or small, or upon the units of the measurement. In other words, it is independent of the location of the decimal point. In the preceding measurement of 11.2 in. the absolute error is 5/100 in. and the measurement is 11.2 in. so that the relative error or relative accuracy is given by the fraction 0.05/11.2 or 1/224. The relative accuracy is said to be 1 in 224. The per cent error in this case is approximately 0.5 per cent. The relative error or relative accuracy can more easily be determined if the decimal point is disregarded. It is the ratio of one-half of the unit in the last significant figure to the total number of such units, or the fraction 1/2 over 112. Since the maximum absolute error will always be one-half of the unit in the last significant figure and the number will contain a total number of such units as indicated by the significant figures, we have the simple rule of thumb: *multiply the significant figures by 2 in order to obtain the relative accuracy.*

For example:

Measurement	Relative accuracy
11.2 in.	1 in 224
312°F	1 in 624
11.76 volts	1 in 2,352
0.14 cu yd	1 in 28
0.006 amp	1 in 12

Again it should be emphasized that although the absolute error depends on the location of the decimal point, the relative error is independent of the decimal point and is a function only of the number of significant figures. Relative accuracy is a ratio and has no dimensions and is expressed in no units.

Many students are apt to think of very accurate measurements as being measurements which are very small in magnitude, say where the absolute error is a very small quantity. Such measurements are not necessarily relatively accurate and as a matter of fact may be relatively inaccurate. Let us take an example to illustrate this distinction.

The diameter of a fine wire is measured to be 0.003 in. with micrometer calipers. The absolute error in this measurement is ½ of 0.001 in., or 0.0005 in., a very small amount. On the other hand, the relative error or relative accuracy is the ratio of one-half of a unit to three units, or a ratio of 1:6. This is relatively a rather inaccurate measurement. Consider now the distance between two points on a highway which is measured to be 327.5 miles. This is a relatively accurate measurement as compared with the measurement of the diameter of the fine wire since its relative accuracy is ½ in 3,275 or 1 in 6,550. The relative accuracy of this measurement is approximately 1,000 times greater than the relative accuracy of the diameter of the fine wire. On the other hand the absolute error in this measurement is ½ of 0.1 mile or 0.05 mile. Expressed in feet the absolute error is 264 ft as compared with an absolute error in measuring the diameter of the wire of 0.0005 in. Although the highway measurement is relatively speaking 1,000 times more accurate than the wire measurement, the absolute error in the highway measurement is not 1,000 times smaller but surprisingly enough is approximately 6,300,000 times greater. Thus, we see the desirability of distinguishing between absolute error and relative accuracy.

Approximate answers

Since there can be such wide variations in absolute error and relative accuracy, one is tempted to ask what accuracy is justified in solving problems. To how many places should answers be carried? Is the slide rule sufficiently accurate or should one use a desk calculating machine? The answers to these questions depend upon the nature of the specific problem and the number of significant figures in the data which are used. The matter is primarily one of relative accuracy. The following rules are generally used to determine the largest number of significant figures that it is reasonable to keep in an answer.

Addition and subtraction.   For the last significant figure in the result, keep the figure in the last full column. The absolute accuracy of the result is determined by the least absolutely accurate number. For example, for the sum

```
4.61
1.235
0.0612
―――――
5.9062
```

the answer should properly be written as 5.91.

One exception to this might be the estimate of the cost of a construction job on which a contractor is bidding. In such cases, the costs of the various items are carried out to dollars and cents and the bid totals are frequently carried out to the same extent (Fig. 6.9). This is because bids are competitive and on public works the law usually requires the contract to be awarded to the "lowest responsible bidder." Occasionally, the bids are very close and only a few dollars make the difference between getting and losing the contract. The two lowest bids in a true case were found to be $71,577.42 and $71,832.41, a difference of only $254.99, or less than 0.4 per cent. Very few contractors, if any, would not be willing to lower their bid by this per cent if it meant getting the job.

Abstract of bids—construction

Invitation no. CIVENG-16-047-58-334
Office: U.S. Army Engineer District, New Orleans Corps of Engineers, New Orleans, La.

Issued: Opened:
25 June 1958   11:00 A.M., CST, 24 July 1958

For: Item D, Dredging, Outflow Channel, Old River, Concordia Parish, La.	Dredging 10,333,000 cu yd	Price Unit	Total
Government Estimate—Reasonable contract without profit		$0.148	$1,529,284.00
McWilliams Dredging Co., 903 S. Jefferson Davis Pkwy., New Orleans 7, La.		0.174	1,797,942.00
Atlantic, Gulf & Pacific Co., 15 Park Row, New York 38, N.Y.		0.1762	1,820,674.60
Bauer-Smith Dredging Co., Inc. P. O. Box BB, Port Lavaca, Tex.		0.1799	1,858,906.70
Standard Dredging Corporation 80 Broad St., New York 4, N.Y.		0.1819	1,879,572.70

FIG. 6.9. Abstract of bids for dredging in the outflow channel of the Old River in Concordia Parish, Louisiana. *(Courtesy of Corps of Engineers, U.S. Army Engineer District, New Orleans, Louisiana.)*

Multiplication and division. The number of significant figures in the result should be no more than the fewest in any number involved. The relative accuracy of the result should be comparable to that of the least relatively accurate number. For example,

$$2.43 \times 36.32 = 88.3 \text{ (not 88.2576)}$$
$$6.3 \times 3.471 \times 2.371 = 52$$
$$62 \times 417 = 26,000, \text{ or } 2.6 \times 10^4$$
$$\frac{12.2}{6,352} = 0.00192, \text{ or } 1.92 \times 10^{-3}$$

Note that the integral numbers in the above examples, such as 62 and 417, are taken to be measurements and are not the counts of numbers of objects. If we had 62 machines in a can factory each processing 417 sheets of steel plate per minute to make cylindrical can bodies, we would be justified in writing $62 \times 417 = 25,854$ can bodies per minute.

FIG. 6.10. Aerial view of the Grand Coulee Dam on the Columbia River in Washington. This concrete gravity dam is 550 ft high and 4,173 ft long. *(Courtesy of the U.S. Bureau of Reclamation.)*

Powers and roots.   These are generally the same as for multiplication and division. For example,

$$(21.3)^2 = 454$$

$$(4.2)^3 = 74$$

$$\sqrt{12.4} = 3.52$$

$$\sqrt[3]{145} = 5.25$$

Series of computations.   In problems which involve a series of computations leading to the final answer, one more significant figure can be carried through in the intermediate answers than will be used in the final answer. If there is much difference in the number of significant figures in the measurements involved, i.e., if there is much difference in

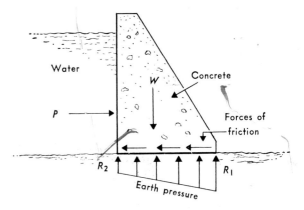

FIG. 6.11. Simplified diagram of the major forces acting on a gravity dam.

the relative accuracy, the numbers may be rounded off to one more significant figure than in the least relatively accurate number. There may be a small error in the last figure kept in the result. Note that a three-digit number beginning with 8 or 9 has about the same relative accuracy as a four-digit number beginning with 1. For example, the relative accuracy of 975 is 1 in 1,950 and the relative accuracy of 1,025 is 1 in 2,050.

The following examples are given to show the student some specific instances in solving problems where a large number of significant figures is not justified in the answers.

This problem involves the calculation of the resulting earth pressures at the base of a concrete gravity dam from the weight of the dam and the lateral thrust of water (Fig. 6.10). The resultant force of the water pressure is represented by the arrow P and is determined from the approximate density of water, 62.4 pcf (Fig. 6.11).

The length of this arrow represents the magnitude of the force. The direction and position of the arrow indicate the direction and position of the line of action of the force. We call this arrow a *vector* and say that a vector quantity has both magnitude and direction in contrast to a scalar quantity, which has only magnitude. A vector is completely specified by three elements, (1) magnitude, (2) direction, and (3) point of application.

The resultant weight of the concrete is also represented by a vector W and is calculated from the approximate density of concrete of 144 pcf. The forces of the water and concrete combine to produce reactive earth pressures on the base of the dam which are not uniform but which vary from one side of the base to the other. The earth pressure is frequently assumed to vary uniformly from a maximum value R_1 to a minimum value R_2. The use of a calculating machine to obtain a

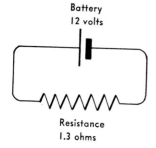

Battery
12 volts

Resistance
1.3 ohms

FIG. 6.12. Simple electric circuit in which the total external resistance is represented by the zigzag symbol.

maximum earth pressure R_1, say of 8,241.7 psf, could not be justified. Such a result should be properly specified as 8,240 psf. This would customarily be written as 8,240 rather than as 8.24×10^3 even though the zero is not significant.

A battery is in a circuit in series with a resistor, as shown in Fig. 6.12. The internal resistance in the battery is, say, 0.5 ohm. The current flowing is calculated as

$$I = \frac{12}{1.3 + 0.5} = 6.67 \text{ amp}$$

Such an answer is not justified if the data in the problem are accurate only to the number of significant figures given. It should rather be $I = 6.7$ amp.

The value of the thermal coefficient of expansion or contraction of steel is usually given as 0.0000065 per °F (remember as five zeros, six five). This could be in terms of inches per inch per degree Fahrenheit, feet per foot per degree Fahrenheit, or other units. If the diameter of the piston in an automobile engine is 3.765 in., how much does it expand owing to a change in temperature from 55 to 188°F? The rise in temperature is 133°F and the expansion is given by

$$d = 6.5 \times 10^{-6} \times 3.765 \times 133$$

$$= 0.003255 \text{ in.}$$

Again this accuracy is not justified. On the basis of the significant figures in the data, it should rather be 0.0033 in. Even this might be too accurate to be of practical significance. If an expansion of 0.003 in. were excessive and might lead to trouble, the second significant figure would be of little interest to the engineers.

On the other hand, instructors in many college courses may give such data as 0.5 ohm, 9 sec, or 15 ft and expect the student to calculate answers to more than one or two significant figures. One reason for this is to develop the student's capacity to make reasonably accurate calculations. In such instances the student may assume that the data are given as more precise measurements such as 0.500 ohm, 9.00 sec, or 15.00 ft for the purposes of the problem but with the zeros omitted.

Precision in measurement

Greater precision of measurements is frequently obtained by repeating the measurement a large number of times and averaging the values which are obtained. In general, there will probably be small variations in the measurements which are called *random errors*. These random errors are usually as often negative as positive and will have little effect on the arithmetic mean. All other errors are classed as *systematic errors*. If they are due to the same cause, they affect the arithmetic mean in the same way and will introduce a definite error.

For example, a systematic error could be an error in the length of a steel tape used in surveying due to temperature. If the tape were precisely 100 ft long at 65°F, it would be longer than this at 105°F.

Accordingly a distance which is marked off to be 100 ft in length when the temperature is 105°F will actually be greater than 100 ft by 0.026 ft, or 0.312 in. (Fig. 6.13). This error will be cumulative, as the tape is used many times in succession in measuring a long distance and a correction would have to be made for it.

If there are no systematic errors, a more precise measurement can be obtained by measuring the same quantity a large number of times and taking the arithmetic mean, i.e., adding all the measurements and dividing by their total number.

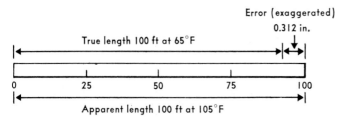

FIG. 6.13.

There are other ways of averaging a number of measurements which depend upon the theory of statistics and probability.

Scale readings

Arithmetic and logarithmic scales which engineers use daily in measuring, plotting, or calculating (slide rule) present some very interesting contrasts when we consider the absolute error and the relative accuracy of scale readings. Take, for example, the two scales shown in Fig. 6.14,

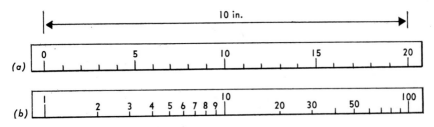

FIG. 6.14. Typical scales: *(a)* arithmetic scale, *(b)* logarithmic scale.

one a 10-in. arithmetic scale subdivided into 20 major parts (again subdivided into tenths in Fig. 6.15), and the other a 10-in. logarithmic scale of values from 1 to 100.

Suppose that the person reading the scales is so careless or is so handicapped by poor vision that his eye is "off" by an actual amount of 0.1 in. In other words, he is actually this far away from the correct

reading on either scale and this represents a true absolute error. However, when we examine this error with reference to its magnitude as
measured by the particular scales, we find some differences.

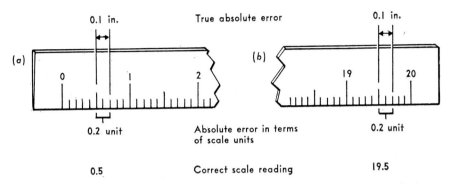

FIG. 6.15. Effect of absolute error on arithmetic scale readings: *(a)* low reading, *(b)* high reading.

The absolute error as measured by the arithmetic scale is 0.2 of a
unit as measured on this particular scale (Fig. 6.15) regardless of where
the reading is being made. On the other hand, the same absolute error
when measured on the logarithmic scale is not constant but increases

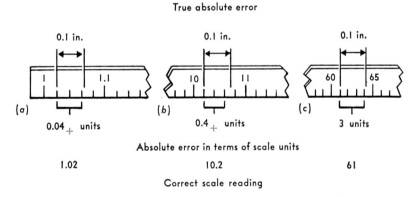

FIG. 6.16. Effect of absolute error on logarithmic scale readings: *(a)* low reading,
(b) middle reading, *(c)* high reading.

in magnitude as the readings become higher (Fig. 6.16). Thus we see
that on an arithmetic scale the effect of the absolute error is constant
and is independent of the position on the scale, whereas on a logarithmic
scale the effect is not constant but increases with the scale reading.

When we consider the relative accuracies which result from this absolute error, we find surprisingly enough that somewhat the reverse is true. The relative error in terms of the scale units on the arithmetic scale is not constant but diminishes as the scale readings increase (Fig. 6.17). The relative accuracy is low for small measurements and

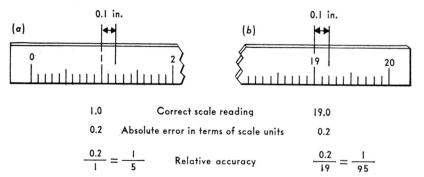

1.0	Correct scale reading	19.0
0.2	Absolute error in terms of scale units	0.2
$\dfrac{0.2}{1} = \dfrac{1}{5}$	Relative accuracy	$\dfrac{0.2}{19} = \dfrac{1}{95}$

FIG. 6.17. Relative accuracy of low and high readings on arithmetic scales: *(a)* low reading, *(b)* high reading.

high for large measurements. However, on the logarithmic scale the relative accuracy in terms of the scale units remains constant for all readings for a particular absolute error. Suppose the absolute error is taken to be a little less than 0.1 in. so that it extends over just four

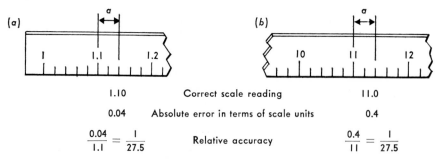

1.10	Correct scale reading	11.0
0.04	Absolute error in terms of scale units	0.4
$\dfrac{0.04}{1.1} = \dfrac{1}{27.5}$	Relative accuracy	$\dfrac{0.4}{11} = \dfrac{1}{27.5}$

FIG. 6.18. Relative accuracy of low and high readings on logarithmic scales: *(a)* low reading, *(b)* high reading.

subdivisions of the log scale as shown in Fig. 6.18. We see the relative accuracy is the same for both readings. This is true of readings anywhere as shown by the two logarithmic scales in Fig. 6.19. Suppose it is desired to line up the B scale with the A scale but it is set in error with the end of the A scale opposite 1.1 on the B scale. The relative accuracy

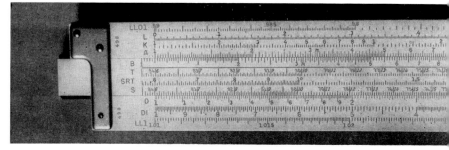

FIG. 6.19. Slide-rule scales set to show same relative accuracy of 1 to 10 at all parts of the scales.

is 0.1/1, or 1/10. Note that 2 on the A scale is opposite 2.2 on the B scale, a relative accuracy again of 0.2/2, or 1/10; and we also have 3 opposite 3.3, 5 opposite 5.5, and 8 opposite 8.8, for example.

Thus it is seen that the *relative accuracy* of the *logarithmic* scale is constant and is *independent of the reading*, but the relative accuracy of the arithmetic scale is *less for small readings than for large ones.*

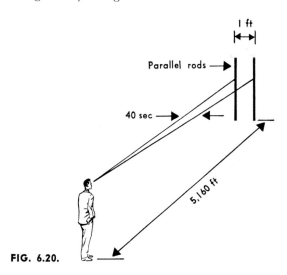

Parallel rods →

1 ft

40 sec →

5,160 ft

FIG. 6.20.

The ability to read a scale accurately depends upon accurate estimates of a fraction of a subdivision and also upon the resolving power of the human eye. This particular property of the eye can be described by its ability to distinguish parallel lines which are very close together. Measurements have indicated that the eye can resolve parallel lines down to an angle of about 40 seconds, below which the lines merge together and are indistinguishable (Fig. 6.20). The student may test the resolving power of his own eyes by using the chart in Fig. 6.21. The parallel lines in this chart are drawn 0.05 in. apart. If they can be distinguished by the human eye from 21.5 ft away from the chart, the angle of resolution is 40 seconds. Not everyone has this high a degree

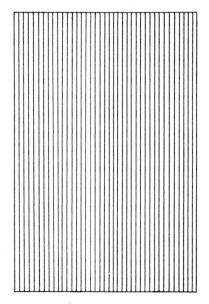

FIG. 6.21. Chart for determining the resolving power of the human eye.

Distance at which lines can be resolved, feet	Angle of resolution, seconds
21.5	40
19.1	45
17.2	50
14.3	60
12.3	70

of resolving power. A table of distances and corresponding angles of resolution is included in Fig. 6.21.

One interesting application of the angle of resolution can be made to reading the scales on the engineer's 10-in. slide rule. Some students

0.0427 in.

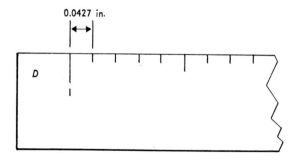

FIG. 6.22.

attempt to read values on the scales to an accuracy which far exceeds the resolving power of the eye. If we assume that the slide rule is held about 12 in. from the eyes, an angle of 40 seconds subtends an arc of about 0.0023 in. at that distance. The first division on the D scale of the 10-in. slide rule (Fig. 6.22) is 0.0427 in. wide so that reading the tenths of this division falls well within the realm of possibility. The student must estimate between imaginary lines approximately 0.004 in. apart with an eye that could distinguish them if they were closer together than that.

However, to read to four significant figures in the middle or right-hand portion of the scale is not possible. For example, suppose a student should attempt to read the position shown in Fig. 6.23 as 40.83, and this sometimes happens. Between 40.50 and 41.00, if we consider four significant figures, there are 50 imaginary subdivisions, and each of these is approximately 0.001 in. apart. Thus our student has picked out the 33d imaginary subdivision among a group of 50 which are only one-thousandth of an inch apart. This is obviously impossible, and students

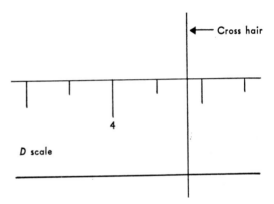

FIG. 6.23.

should not expect in general to obtain more than three-place accuracy with the slide rule. Exceptions would be for readings close to the left end of the scales and on certain of the log log scales.

Suggested references

Fred H. Rhodes and Herbert F. Johnson, "Technical Report Writing," McGraw-Hill Book Company, Inc., New York, 1941, chapter VIII, Mathematical Analysis of Experimental Errors, p. 51. A brief discussion of random errors, least squares, standard deviation, maximum probable error, and weighted averages.

M. Rossweiler and J. M. Harris, "Mathematics and Measurement," Row, Peterson, & Company, Evanston, Ill., 1955.

"Precision, a Measure of Progress," General Motors Corporation, Detroit, 1952. A colorful pamphlet depicting the historical development of measurement techniques and their importance.

Oliver J. Lee, "Measuring Our Universe from the Inner Atom to Outer Space," The Ronald Press, New York, 1950. The development of ingenious and precise instruments and techniques for measuring very small and very large distances.

Ronald J. Sweeney, "Measurement Techniques in Mechanical Engineering," John Wiley & Sons, Inc., New York, 1953. Techniques and instruments for measuring mechanical, thermal, and electrical quantities. There is a brief chapter on the chemical analysis of gas, water, and coal and one on automatic controls.

Problems

6.1 Determine the maximum absolute error, the number of significant figures, and the relative accuracy for each of the following quantities:

17.6 lb	$-273.16°C$
10.06 cu ft	0.1 amp
4,261 miles	0.046 ohm
9.8×10^8 fps	115 books
7.8×10^{-5} ft per °F	12,200 ft

6.2 Round off the answers to the following computations to the number of significant figures justified by the data:

a. $41.5 \times 0.7 \times 13.20 = 383.5$

b. $\dfrac{17.63 \times 4.1}{122.8} = 0.5886$

c. $0.0000065 \times 2,463 \times 35 = 0.56033$

d.
$$
\begin{array}{r}
216 \\
1.872 \\
65.3 \\
0.989 \\
+426.1 \\
\hline
710.261
\end{array}
$$

e.   437.0
      649
    + 76.5
    ─────
    1,162.5
  ─ 130.36
    ─────
    1,032.14

Determine the answers to Probs. 6.3 to 6.7 to the number of significant figures which is justified by the given data.

✗ 6.3 The heating value of a southern coal is given by

$$HV = 16,080 - 21.2V - 81.4A$$

where HV is the heating value in Btu per lb, V is the per cent of volatile matter, and A is the per cent of ash content. V and A are used in the equation in per cent form. What is the heating value if V is 27 per cent and A is 8 per cent?

✗ 6.4 The coefficient of heat transfer C of a surface condenser is given in Btu per sq ft per °F as

$$C = \frac{952Q_1}{S\theta}$$

What is the value of C for a condensate flow Q_1 of 275,000 lb per hr, a condenser heating surface S of 2,645 sq ft, and a mean temperature difference θ of 67°F?

✗ 6.5 The head loss h_F in a rough pipe flowing full is given in feet by

$$h_F = \frac{fLV^2}{64.4D}$$

Calculate the head loss in a pipe 382 ft in length L and 32 in. in diameter D if the friction factor f is 0.03 and the average velocity is 15 fps. This is an empirical relationship in which the various quantities are used in the units which are specified. The lack of homogeneity of the units is taken into account in determining the values of the friction factor.

✗ 6.6 The load P on a helical compression spring is given in pounds as

$$P = \frac{0.194d^3f}{r}$$

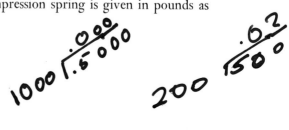

Calculate the load to produce a deflection d of 1.2 in. if the radius r of the spring is 6.75 in. and the shearing stress f is 18,500 psi.

6.7   The equivalent resistance R in ohms of three wires in parallel is given by

$$\frac{1}{R} = \frac{1}{R_1} + \frac{1}{R_2} + \frac{1}{R_3}$$

What is the equivalent resistance of three wires in parallel, R_1, R_2, and R_3, if their respective resistances are 82, 143, and 2,165 ohms?

6.8   A 100-ft steel tape is calibrated to read precisely 100.00 ft at 65°F. The coefficient of thermal expansion or contraction is 0.0000065 ft per ft per °F.

a. If a distance is measured to be 750.00 ft when the temperature is 38°F, what is the true distance measured? What is the relative accuracy of this measurement?

b. If the temperature is 97°F, what apparent distance must be measured in order to lay out a true distance of 1,200.00 ft? What would be the absolute error in measuring 12 full tape lengths at 97°F?

6.9   Suppose that a draftsman makes an absolute error of x in. in reading values on the 40 scale of an engineer's scale. This scale is so subdivided as to have 40 major divisions in a true length of 10 in. Each division is again subdivided into 10 parts.

a. Derive an expression for the relative accuracy of a reading on this scale as a function of the absolute error x and the scale reading R.

b. Suppose that the length of a line is measured to be R_4 using the 40 scale and R_3 using the 30 scale. If the absolute error x is the same in each reading, what is the relationship between the relative accuracies for the two readings?

6.10   The area of a rectangular plot of ground is to be determined from the product of its length a units and width b units. The maximum absolute error in each measurement is, of course, one-half of a unit.

a. Derive an expression for the relative accuracy of the area, assuming a positive maximum absolute error in each measurement. Note that one term in the resulting expression may be neglected.

b. Using the approximate expression of (*a*), what is the relative accuracy of the area of a rectangle measuring about 12 by 403 ft?

c. Under what circumstances might the relative error be very small or zero, i.e., might the relative accuracy be very high?

6.11   *a.* Derive an expression for the relative accuracy of the product of three quantities, *a*, *b*, and *c*, for the maximum positive absolute error of ½ unit.

b. Rewrite the expression in (*a*), neglecting the terms of relatively small magnitude.

c. Choose three quantities, one relatively inaccurate and two relatively accurate, and show that the relative accuracy of their product depends primarily upon the relative accuracy of the least accurate quantity.

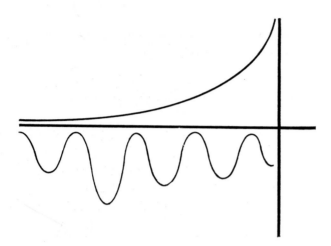

An approach to theory

The preceding chapters have introduced the student to methods and problems which relate to the practice of engineering and have also given him some basic factual knowledge and techniques. It is time now to learn something of the theory used in engineering and to apply it to a number of simple illustrative problems.

There are many ways in which one can approach this phase of an engineer's education. The author has chosen to do this from the standpoint of mass and energy because he believes that this approach probably provides the best common basis for analysis in all fields of engineering. However, the student must realize that this is but one approach and that he will encounter others in more advanced subjects.

Theory

Theory may be broadly defined as a group of fundamental principles which underlie a science. Engineers make varied use of the principles of mathematics and science, depending upon their field of interest and the nature of their activity within the field such as design, research, or teaching. We might say that the theory used by engineers is found primarily in mathematics, physics, and chemistry, and to a lesser extent in the earth sciences such as geology and meteorology and the life sciences such as bacteriology and zoology.

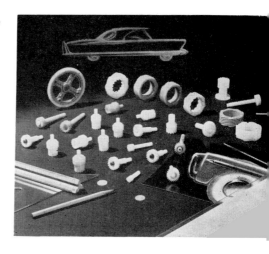

FIG. 7.1. Gears for speedometers, windshield wipers, radio antennas, and other parts are a major automotive use of nylon resin. Almost 250 different parts of Zytel nylon resin including dome lamp lenses, door-latch wedges, carburetor parts, tubing for air-suspension systems, gears, and bushings are used in automobiles. *(Courtesy of E. I. du Pont de Nemours & Company.)*

Since science and mathematics are not static, engineers are continually making use of new knowledge and principles as well as adapting old principles to new applications. For example, new principles have been set forth in physics of the solid state which point the way to new approaches to the study of materials used in engineering. The transistor, which replaces the electron tube in low-power electric circuits, is an outgrowth of solid-state physics. Startling discoveries and developments in the chemistry of plastics (Fig. 7.1) have also given the engineer a host of new materials to use in many ways. Potential uses of plastics extend all the way from tiny machine parts to major structural members. On the other hand, there are periodically new applications to be made of well-known principles. For example, the theories of finite mathematics including probability, sets, and Boolean algebra have been known for many years but have only recently assumed great importance to engineers in solving very complex problems on electronic computers. It is interesting to note that finite mathematics and problem solving on computers can be widely extended to problems in many fields other than engineering such as business and industry, medicine, and even the study of literature.

Theory may be developed either by deduction or by induction. Deduction is a process of reasoning from the general to the more specific as contrasted with induction, which goes from the specific to the more general. Deduction may be described as a process of analysis in which one begins with a general relationship and finds which lesser or more specific relations are implied or contained in the original relationship. Deduction is a matter of strict proof, of the manipulation of symbols to demonstrate that the conclusion is inherent in the premises.

Reasoning based upon observation and experiment is primarily inductive. Here the process leads from specific data to generalization. Frequently, this calls for an "inductive jump" and may be a matter of creative imagination. On the other hand, experiments may be set up to verify deductions rather than to lead to generalizations.

Thus we see that both deductive thinking and the experimental method have contributed to the establishment of our present-day theory. Which is more important, if either, is difficult to say. For instance, among the physicists in the world there are those who call themselves experimental physicists and those who say that they are theoretical physicists. Here the word "theoretical" is used in a specific sense and refers primarily to the deductive process.

The famous electrical wizard Charles P. Steinmetz is credited with the statement, "If the theory and the tests do not agree, then the tests are wrong." However, he was overstating the case for the deductive process at a time when electrical engineers made little use of this approach. Albert Einstein on the other hand concluded that theory was wrong when the results of the Michelson-Morley experiment on the relative velocity of light failed to agree with it. This conclusion was a link in the chain of events that led to nuclear fission and its importance is quite apparent.

However, if the result of an experiment which is based on well-established principles does not agree with these principles, an engineer would do well to question first the conditions of the experiment rather than the principles. For example, students are familiar with the fact that the force of gravity acting on a body falling freely in a vacuum produces a certain acceleration in accordance with the law of gravity. Yet observations on a body falling from a great height through the atmosphere would not agree precisely with results predicted by this simple classical law.

This does not mean that the basic theory is wrong but rather that the physical situation, or "model," to introduce a word which is coming to be used in a general sense in engineering, does not match the theory or the mathematical model. This mathematical model and the theory on which it is based may be modified to include additional variables without invalidating the basic theory in any way. Air resistance is not included in the simple statement of the basic law of gravity. Neither is the variation of the force of gravity with distance from the center of mass of the earth. The physical situation can be further complicated by disturbing high-velocity air currents or by variations in moisture content or temperature within the air mass.

As another example, we may state that the volume of a mixture of two liquids is equal to the sum of the volumes of each liquid.

$$v = v_1 + v_2$$

Although this is generally true for most "models," if we choose a model of water and alcohol, we find that the total volume of a mixture of these liquids is less than the sum of the individual volumes. We may say that water and alcohol do not form ideal solutions.

More than one engineering professor has pointed out that perhaps engineering students meet with more difficulties because of poor choice of model or the lack of any such explicit choice at all than because of any other thing. Our theoretical equations describe precisely some mathematical model unless there is some error in the mathematics. *Rarely ever* do the mathematical models conform precisely with the physical models. There are many instances in which the mathematical or analytical model is defined with full knowledge that it may only roughly approximate the physical phenomenon. However, the equations which are derived may be useful in providing an adequate description of the physical model. In all cases one must precisely define a model in order to use the principles of science and mathematics to derive an equation.

One final word about theory. Time and time again, theories have been accepted universally for decades only to fall before some unconvinced thinkers who had some idea or some data which led them to question their validity. This has not been true of all theories because some are still standing the test of time. But others have been proved either by logic or by experiment to be completely false or to be merely special cases of much broader theory. Such was the fate of Newton's second law of motion, which stood for over two hundred years until Einstein's theory of relativity proved that it did not hold for velocities that approached the velocity of light. Today the velocity of light is generally regarded to be the maximum attainable velocity in the universe. But is it? Perhaps one of these days someone will find something that travels faster than this velocity and another theory will fall. And again, perhaps not. The eager young student of today faces prospects no less exciting than his predecessors, for the universe still holds many secrets which are yet to be unlocked.

FIG. 7.2. Mechanical energy of water thundering from the spillway tube of the Fontana Dam in North Carolina after falling from a height of more than 400 ft. (*Courtesy of the Tennessee Valley Authority.*)

Approach to theory

The approach to theory which is used in this book introduces the student to several quantities, mass, force, acceleration, energy, and power, quantities with which the engineer works to a greater or lesser extent in all areas of engineering. Although the principles and laws which are stated may already be known in their elementary form to most students in physics. Its broad purpose is to give the student more insight into electrical energy and in turn transmits this and reconverts it into the relationships between mass and energy. The more specific purpose is to impart a clearer understanding of the concepts of energy in its mechanical, thermal, and electrical forms (Figs. 7.2 to 7.4), and of the conversion of energy from one form to another.

As Dr. S. J. Kline * has stated, "Energy and mass considerations form an important unifying portion of engineering analysis; since energy transformations and mass flows occur as crucial parts of almost all engineering processes, these considerations provide a common basis for a very large fraction of all engineering studies." It is intended that this approach to basic theory through mass and energy will serve as a

* Department of Mechanical Engineering, Stanford University.

foundation for the more specific knowledge to be gained in later courses in all branches of engineering, and will also give the student a better grasp of the relation of one branch to another. He may also expect to find his understanding grow as he meets additional concepts in these later courses. However, it is not possible to introduce adequately in this book any one of the major areas of the engineering sciences, such as mechanics of solids, mechanics of fluids, electrical theory, thermodynamics, or properties of materials.

Lest the student misunderstand, engineering cannot be defined simply as the "economical conversion and transfer of mass and energy." But these two quantities play a highly significant role in the use of theory by the engineer. We find him converting the raw materials of nature into finished products in every branch of engineering. We observe him transferring and transporting materials in a variety of forms from one place to another in a variety of ways. The masses of these materials are significant in these operations. He also harnesses nature's energy and transfers it to places where he wishes to use it; he converts the mechanical energy of falling water or the thermal energy of burning coal into

FIG. 7.3. Thermal energy of the radiant heat from the sun, which has been indirectly the major source of energy on earth. *(Courtesy of the U.S. Department of Agriculture.)*

FIG. 7.4. Discharge of lightning framed by the George Washington Bridge. *(Courtesy of the General Electric Company.)*

electrical energy and in turn, transmits this and reconverts it into mechanical or thermal energy, or perhaps uses it in the form of electrical energy.

What principles does the engineer use to do these things? We find two laws which continually appear: (1) the law of conservation of matter, which states simply that matter can neither be created nor destroyed, and (2) the law of conservation of energy, which similarly states that energy can neither be created nor destroyed.

Mass and energy were formerly regarded as being distinct and unrelated quantities in general. It was not until the twentieth century that Albert Einstein developed a theory which proved that mass and energy were directly related in a way which few had ever suspected. He derived an equation which is now classical:

$$E = mc^2$$

where E represents energy, m mass, and c the velocity of light. This equation implies the conversion of mass to energy, and vice versa. As we all know, mass has been converted to energy by means of nuclear fission. The matter of converting energy to mass might still be called an open question. But there is nothing mysterious about this equation. The velocity of light, c, is approximately 3×10^{10} cm per sec, or 9.8×10^8 fps. The amount of energy available in a body is obtained simply by multiplying its mass by c^2. How to release this energy is another matter, quite difficult and expensive. This has been done in atomic bombs (Fig. 7.5) and nuclear reactors. It is significant to note that man has been able to release only a small fraction of the total available energy in the masses involved in these achievements.

The reader must recognize, however, that the conversion of mass to energy is a phenomenon which occurs within the atom and that this does not apply to phenomena involving only the conservation and conversion of matter such as the burning of a solid rocket propellant and its conversion to the gaseous state. Neither does it apply to phenomena involving only the conservation and conversion of energy such as the conversion of the internal energy of the solid rocket propellant into kinetic energy and heat. Of course there are many more principles used by engineers than the conservation laws. Some of these will be men-

FIG. 7.5. Underwater explosion of atomic bomb at Bikini, showing the slick due to the shock wave and the cloud-chamber effect produced by water vapor condensing on particles. (Courtesy of the Atomic Energy Commission.)

tioned in this chapter and in later chapters in order to bring out more clearly a number of relationships between energy and mass and among the various forms of energy. However, emphasis is placed upon the conversion of mechanical, thermal, and electrical energy from one form to another. It is perhaps through this approach that one best gains an understanding of the relationships among the principles which are used in each of the various branches of engineering.

The student may think at this point that we are talking in terms of abstract quantities, mass and energy. He may be impatient to work on a real engineering problem such as the design of an automobile engine,

FIG. 7.6. An automobile engine, a common sight, and yet an engineering marvel of endurance and efficiency.

rather than working with these basic quantities. But these quantities are far from abstract and their consideration is important in designing an automobile engine (Fig. 7.6). Matter in the form of gasoline is converted from the liquid to the gaseous state with an increase in temperature and pressure through the explosive burning of gasoline. This is a molecular phenomenon rather than nuclear, and would not be represented by $E = mc^2$. Thus the internal energy of molecular nature in liquid gasoline is converted to internal energy of hot gas in compression and to heat. This internal energy is converted to kinetic energy of rotation of the crankshaft, and transmitted by the drive shaft and differential to the wheels.

Heat which is transferred to the engine parts as a result of the material conversion must be transferred away from the engine or it will become too hot. There must be a cooling system which transfers heat to the air through which the automobile is moving. And why cannot the engine get hotter and hotter? Using the word "conversion" in its broadest sense, the transfer of heat produces changes in temperature which convert materials in size and properties. Metal expands with increased temperature. Physical properties change somewhat for small changes in temperature and change drastically at critical temperatures. The steel in an automobile engine would lose about 50 per cent of its ultimate strength at 600°C and the changes in size could well impair engine performance, if not ruin the engine.

Again, another material is involved, the lubricating oil. Excessive increases in temperature would change or convert the properties of this oil, ruining its usefulness as a lubricant. A temperature of about 250°C might set the oil on fire.

What about the parts of the engine, the block, pistons, rings, crankshaft, and valves? Matter must be converted from iron ore to steels of various kinds—these must be forged, machined, shaped to perform specific functions under specific conditions of stress, strain, temperature, and corrosion. This conversion certainly involves both mass and energy.

The gasoline itself is a product of the conversion of crude oil. Its chemical composition must be developed to produce the greatest energy release with least corrosive by-products and to meet other conditions.

Little wonder that it has taken decades to produce the modern automobile engine. Its design to meet certain standards of performance has certainly involved energy and mass conversion and transmission. This simple example should dispel any doubts which the student may have that mass and energy are abstract and theoretical. They definitely enter into the everyday life of the professional engineer.

Mass

Matter as it is defined in physics is something which occupies space. It has the basic physical property of *inertia*, of "staying put" unless something comes along to move it. This is formally expressed in Newton's first law of motion, which states: *A body remains in a state of rest,* *or of uniform motion in a straight line, unless acted upon by outside forces.* *

Everyone has experienced this property of the inertia of matter in many ways in his lifetime, beginning in childhood. Who has not pulled another child in a wagon, or coasted on bicycles or skates? Many times a child learning to roller skate has wanted to stop to avoid hitting some object and has experienced a feeling of helplessness because he continued to coast in spite of his desires. Of course, he would not coast forever, as small friction forces in the bearings, between the wheels and the surface on which they roll, and between his moving body and the air would ultimately stop him. The inertia of a gas such as air is appreciable and can be observed by sticking one's hand or head out of the window of a fast-moving car. The inertia of air becomes a serious matter in ejecting pilots from jet aircraft flying at supersonic speeds. A diver at a swimming pool can testify to the inertia of water, especially if he makes a poor dive and hits flat.

This property of matter which is described qualitatively by the term "inertia" is also described quantitatively by the term "mass." We might say that mass is the measure of inertia for a particular body of matter. The term "body" is used here in a general sense and refers to a macroscopic object such as a bullet, to a microscopic object such as an electron, or to a system of objects. For example, the bullet in its ultimate form is a system of subatomic particles.

Students must recognize the subtle distinction between mass as a *property* of matter and mass as being *synonymous* with matter. Both meanings are used by engineers. They speak on the one hand of the mass of a projectile, meaning the measure of its property of inertia, and on the other hand of a "large mass" of concrete, meaning simply a body of matter.

Force

The concept of energy is not so simple to grasp as one might think. What we call energy exists in many forms. Authors of physics and engineering books differ markedly in their approach to this concept.

---

* Sir Isaac Newton, *Philosophiae naturalis principia mathematica*, 1686. Translation: "Every body continues in its state of rest, or of uniform motion in a straight line, unless it is compelled to change that state by forces impressed upon it."

The author believes that an introduction to energy in mechanical form is perhaps the approach which will be most readily understood by students. The concept of *force* is essential to this approach and accordingly this section will be devoted to a brief discussion of force.

A force may be defined simply but adequately as that which can be replaced by an equivalent muscular push or pull. This brings the concept of force within the grasp of everyone, as who has not pushed or pulled something in his lifetime? A more formal definition may be given in Newton's second law of motion, which gives a relationship between force and mass. Stated broadly, it is: *If a resultant force acts on a body, the acceleration which it produces is proportional to the force and is in the same direction as the force.** For a body with a given

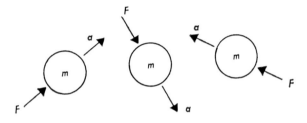

FIG. 7.7. Forces and masses in space. Force F is the only force acting on each mass m and produces the acceleration a.

mass, the greater the force, the correspondingly greater is the acceleration produced. The symbolic expression of this law is generally written as

$$F = ma$$

which states that force is equal to the product of mass and acceleration. This is more than a quantity relationship because there is also a directional or vector relationship. Both the force F and the acceleration a are quantities which have direction, and a must be in the same direction as F (Fig. 7.7). Every person has had the experience of pushing objects and knows this law intuitively. The object moves in the direction in which he pushes and with increasing speed if he continues to push just as hard.

The law in the form $F = ma$ may be regarded as defining force in terms of mass and the acceleration produced by the force. It is interesting to note that the relationship may be approached in another way

---

* *Ibid.* Translation: "The change of motion is proportional to the motive force impressed and is made in the direction of the straight line in which that force is impressed."

more in accord with Newton's statement of proportionality between force and acceleration. In this form the law may be stated as

$$\frac{F}{a} = \text{constant (for a given body)}$$

and this constant is what we call mass for the given body. Thus we write

$$\frac{F}{a} = m$$

The ratio would of course be different for different bodies. When approached in this way, we see that the constant ratio for a particular body may be considered to determine its mass in terms of force and the acceleration which that force produces.

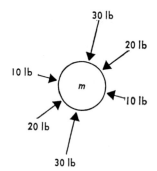

$a=0$ **FIG. 7.8.** Mass acted on by forces which are in equilibrium.

The dimensions of the quantity force can be determined from $F = ma$. These have already been determined in Chap. 5 but will be repeated here.

$$a = [L][T]^{-2}$$

$$m = [M]$$

Therefore the dimensions of force F are given by

$$F = [M][L][T]^{-2}$$

Force then can be considered to be a compound made up of mass and acceleration or of mass, length, and time. If there is no resultant force acting, there is no change in the motion of a body and no acceleration. This does not imply that there are no forces acting, but only that there is no resultant force acting. For example, a body may be subjected to a number of forces, but if these forces are in equilibrium, i.e., they counterbalance each other so that the resultant or net force is zero (Fig. 7.8), there will be no change in motion.

One of a person's earliest experiences in life is with the force of gravity acting on the mass of his body. Many are the falls which all of us have suffered. This is a manifestation of the fundamental law of universal gravitation, which states that there is a force of attraction between any two masses, in this case the earth and the person. The force of gravity is what causes a person to press against the earth or against the platform of scales on which he measures his weight. This weight, accordingly, is not directly a measure of his mass but is rather a direct measure of a force acting on his mass, the force of gravity (Fig. 7.9).

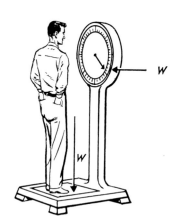

FIG. 7.9. Weight *W* is the force of gravity, not a direct measure of mass.

Accordingly, it is an *indirect* measure of his mass. This distinction between *weight* and *mass* is quite important in engineering and should be clearly understood at the outset.

The acceleration which is produced by the force of gravity on a freely falling object is 32.2 fps² * and is represented by the letter *g*. If *W* is weight or the force of gravity, then by Newton's second law,

$$W = mg$$

Or we have

$$m = \frac{W}{g} = \frac{W}{32.2}$$

* More precise values of 32.1739 fps² or 980.665 cm per sec² have been chosen by international agreement as the standard acceleration of gravity. However, it should be noted that these values have been determined by experiment and that they may be revised as experimentation continues.

which is the measure of mass m in terms of the force of attraction of the earth and the resulting acceleration of gravity. This means in effect that force of 1 lb and a mass of 1 lb are defined such that the 1-lb force gives a 1-lb mass an acceleration of 32.2 fps². The poundal is a smaller unit of force and is defined to be the force which gives a 1-lb mass an acceleration of 1 fps². The poundal is seldom used in engineering. In the cgs system a force of 1 g gives a mass of 1 g an acceleration of about 981 cm per sec².*

The *mass* of a person on the moon would still be the *same* although he would weigh less,

$$m = \frac{W_m}{g_m} = \frac{W}{g}$$

where W_m is the weight of the person on the moon which would be less than on earth, and g_m is the acceleration of gravity of the moon which is proportionately less than that of the earth. It has been determined that the moon's gravity is about one-sixth that of the earth so that a person who weighs 180 lb on earth would weigh only 30 lb on the moon. Accordingly the muscles of his legs and back would be able to support many pounds of equipment including space suit and air tanks. It is interesting to note that he could walk with a load of 900 "earth-pounds" of equipment on the moon with almost the same ease as walking unloaded on the earth.

It is customary in engineering practice to use the weight of a body W instead of its mass m since weight is the measure of mass which is most easily and directly obtained. Since we have determined the relationship between m and W to be $m = W/g$, we can use this in Newton's second law $F = ma$ to express it in a more practical or useful form in engineering as

$$F = \frac{W}{g} a$$

or

$$F = \frac{Wa}{g}$$

For example, suppose that the resultant force acting horizontally on an automobile over and above frictional resistance is 800 lb and that the car weighs 2,400 lb. What is the resulting acceleration? Substitute the

* *Ibid.*

known quantities into the relationship between force and acceleration:

$$800 = \frac{2,400a}{32.2}$$

$$a = \frac{800}{2,400} \, 32.2$$

$$= 10.7 \text{ fps}^2$$

Note that the acceleration a can be expressed generally by the equation

$$a = \frac{F}{W} \, g$$

This is a convenient form to use in calculating quick approximate answers by simple mental arithmetic. If the force is equal to the weight of a mass, it imparts the acceleration of gravity. If the force is one-fourth the weight, the acceleration is one-fourth the acceleration of gravity. If the force is three times the weight, the acceleration is three times the acceleration of gravity. This refers of course to the resultant force, which is the unbalanced force or the net force acting above and beyond other resisting forces. If a missile is being propelled vertically upward with an acceleration a, this will be determined by the amount of the force which *exceeds the weight* of the missile (Fig. 7.10).

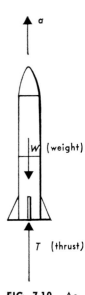

FIG. 7.10. Acceleration $a = [(T - W)/W]g$.

Suggested references

Edward A. Burtt, "Principles and Problems of Right Thinking," Harper & Brothers, New York, 1928. A philosopher's analysis of thought, including an initial chapter on types of thinking and a long chapter on correct reasoning, with interesting examples.

Percy W. Bridgman, "The Nature of Physical Theory," Dover Publications, New York, 1936. A physicist's rather philosophical discussion of such topics as thought, language, logic, and mathematics.

Editors of *Fortune*, "The Mighty Force of Research," McGraw-Hill Book Company, Inc., New York, 1956. A set of 15 articles on various aspects and fields of research in science and engineering.

F. T. Bonner and M. Phillips, "Principles of Physical Science," Addison-Wesley Publishing Company, Reading, Mass., 1957.

J. G. Brennan, "A Handbook of Logic," Harper & Brothers, New York, 1957.

Max Black, "Critical Thinking," 2d ed., Prentice-Hall, Inc., Englewood Cliffs, N.J., 1952.

Problems

7.1   *a.* A person weighing 173 lb is subjected to a deceleration of 8 *g* in a rocket-propelled test sled running on a horizontal track. What force is acting upon his body?

   b. If a rocket weighing 27 tons is being propelled vertically upward by a thrust of 84,000 lb, what is its upward acceleration in terms of *g*?

7.2   *a.* A jet plane weighing 26,500 lb is flying vertically upward at an acceleration of 12.5 fps². What thrust is its jet engine producing? Neglect air resistance.

   b. What would be the acceleration of this plane in feet per second per second in horizontal flight due to this same thrust?

7.3   Newton's law of gravitational attraction is stated in the form

$$F \propto \frac{m_1 m_2}{R^2}$$

where F is the force of attraction between two masses m_1 and m_2 whose centers of mass are a distance R apart. On earth the force of attraction between the mass of the earth and the mass of a human being is called his weight.

   a. If the density of Earth is 5.52 (density of water $= 1$) and that of Mars is 3.97, and the mean diameter of Earth is 7,920 miles and that of Mars is 4,215 miles, how much would a person weigh on Mars who weighs 186 lb on Earth?

   b. What is the acceleration of gravity on Mars in feet per second per second?

   c. How much would this person weigh on Jupiter if the density of this planet is 1.34 compared with water and its mean diameter is 86,700 miles?

7.4   How far above mean sea level would a person on earth have to be to find his weight reduced (*a*) by 1 per cent, (*b*) by 10 per cent?

7.5   If an elevator starts to descend at an initial acceleration of 3.6 fps², what per cent of the normal weight of a person would be registered on scales if he were standing on them in the elevator?

7.6   A rifle bullet weighing 175 grains is accelerated from rest to a muzzle velocity of 2,900 fps in a 31-in. barrel. What is the magnitude of the force in pounds which acts upon this bullet? Assume the force to be constant throughout its action.

7.7 A steel cable with a breaking strength of 14,000 lb supports a steel beam which weighs 5.2 tons.

What is the maximum upward acceleration with which the beam can be lifted without breaking the cable?

7.8 The weight of an automobile exclusive of the wheels is 100 times the weight of a single wheel and is distributed equally among the four wheels.

If the car comes to a sharp break in the road surface so that support of a wheel by the road is very suddenly withdrawn, what is the initial downward acceleration of the wheel in feet per second per second?

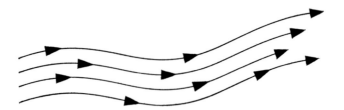

EIGHT

Energy in general

This chapter continues the discussion of an approach to theory which began in Chap. 7 and also calls upon the discussion of dimensions in Chap. 5. The four topics which are presented are the nature of energy, the various forms of energy, power or the rate of transfer of energy, and the units of energy and power.

Nature of energy

We find that many terms are used to express energy in its various forms. We also observe that very few writers of science and engineering textbooks approach the concept of energy by means of a dictionary type of definition, especially in thermodynamics and electricity. Thus it is important for the student to learn at the outset that although the terms are different and although the approaches to the concept of energy vary considerably, energy in any form is basically the same quantity.

What is the nature of energy? The author believes that the best way to answer this question is in terms of the dimensions of this quantity which we call energy, for energy in every form has the same basic dimensions. The origin of the word is found in the Greek words *en ergos* which mean literally *in work*. And probably the form of energy which is most readily understood is mechanical work, work done by a steam engine in lifting steel beams and columns for the skeleton of a skyscraper, work done by the force of gravity in driving piles into the ground with a heavy drop hammer, or work done by a diesel locomotive in pulling a heavy train against the forces of friction.

Mechanical work is defined to be the product of a *force* times the *distance* through which it acts in the *direction* of its *line* of action (Fig. 8.1). Mechanical work is a form in which energy is transferred; it is a particular form of energy. Thus the dimensions of mechanical work are the dimensions of energy in general. We may derive the dimensions of work from those of its elements, force and distance, which we have already learned. The dimensions of force are

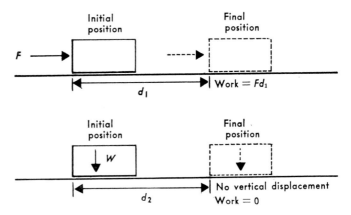

FIG. 8.1. Work done by force $F = F \times d_1$; work done by force $W = W \times 0 = 0$.

$[M][L][T]^{-2}$ and thus we have for mechanical work and also energy in general

$$[E] = [W]$$

$$= [F][L]$$

$$= [M][L][T]^{-2}[L]$$

$$= [M][L]^2[T]^{-2}$$

Although we have determined the dimensions of energy in terms of the dimensions of force and distance, it is interesting to note that these dimensions can be rearranged in terms of other physical quantities. The dimensions of velocity are $[L][T]^{-1}$ and accordingly $[L]^2[T]^{-2}$ represents the square of velocity, $[v]^2 = ([L][T]^{-1})^2$. Thus energy can also be considered to have the dimensions of the product of mass $[M]$

and the square of velocity $[v]^2$. Energy in this form is called kinetic energy. For example, an automobile engine does work on an automobile by applying a force which acts through a distance to move the car from a state of rest to a certain speed. The work of the engine may be said to be converted into kinetic energy of the speeding mass.

Thus we see that it is not always necessary or even desirable to express energy in terms of force. Many problems in engineering can be solved more directly and more easily by relating the energies which are involved to velocities or to other forms of energy rather than to forces which may be acting. Forces which exist in the mechanical concept of equivalent muscular exertion are not present in the same sense in thermal and electrical phenomena although they might be represented by analogies in some instances. The nature of energy and its dimensions are the same, however, regardless of its form. Whenever energy is used

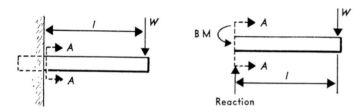

FIG. 8.2. Simple cantilever beam; bending moment BM = WI.

in any form in solving any problem, it is a quantity which has the dimensions $[M][L]^2[T]^{-2}$.

It should be emphasized again that mechanical work is the product of a force times the distance in which it acts *in the direction of the force*. The force of gravity acts vertically downward. If a mass is in motion horizontally, the force of gravity then does no work on the mass because there is no motion in the direction in which the force of gravity is acting, i.e., vertically downward. The force of gravity does no work upon an ice skater who is coasting on the surface of a frozen pond.

It should also be pointed out that the force need not act in a straight line to do work. An automobile engine supplies forces to turn a crankshaft which in turn exerts rotary force to turn the wheels of the car through the clutch, drive shaft, and differential. In this case the force traverses distance along a circular path and the direction of the line of action of the force is constantly changing as it follows this path.

It is important to understand that although energy in any form has the dimensions $[M][L]^2[T]^{-2}$, the converse is not true. There are physical quantities which have the dimensions $[M][L]^2[T]^{-2}$ which *are not energy*. The simplest example is the bending moment on a simple cantilever beam (Fig. 8.2) which is the product of a force and a distance, but in this case a distance which is perpendicular to the line of action of the force and in a system in which there is no motion. The dimensions of the bending moment are the same as those for energy.

$$[BM] = [W][L]$$
$$= [M][L][T]^{-2}[L]$$
$$= [M][L]^2[T]^{-2}$$

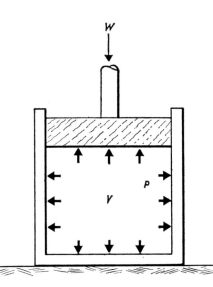

FIG. 8.3. Gas of volume V and at pressure p under load W.

Also the product of pressure and volume gives a quantity which is not energy but which has the same dimensions (Fig. 8.3). Pressure has the dimensions of force per unit area so that we have

$$[PV] = \left(\frac{[M][L][T]^{-2}}{[L]^2}\right)[L]^3$$
$$= [M][L]^2[T]^{-2}$$

However, the student should not become discouraged at this state of affairs. Man's attempts to discover, understand, and explain the nature of the universe in which he lives are constantly hampered by the limitations of language. He has had to invent words to express new ideas which have come from his observations and reasonings. He has also had to do this in the face of incomplete or inaccurate knowledge, for the secrets of the universe have yet to be unlocked. For example, we speak of the mass of the electron and most people immediately think of a very small sphere which has mass like a steel ball bearing. However, the theory of relativity tells us that the mass of an electron is not constant but increases with velocity and even approaches infinite magnitude as the velocity of the electron approaches the velocity of light.* It was first assumed that the mass is made up of two parts, one the mechanical or Newtonian mass and the other an electromagnetic property associated with the electric charge of the electron and the energy of the magnetic field produced by the motion of the electron. The mechanical mass does not vary with velocity but the "energy" property does vary.

A second theory throws away the concept of mechanical mass and relates the inertial properties of the electron entirely to the energy associated with the electron. This theory replaces mass by energy. Yet what are mass and energy but two terms invented by man to symbolize certain phenomena which he has observed and certain concepts which he wishes to express to other men? Future discoveries may completely change the present concepts, for science and engineering are on the move with almost fantastic speed.

Forms of energy

There are a number of ways in which one might classify the terms and concepts which are used to describe energy in its various forms. The author has selected one which is relatively simple.

Forms in which energy is stored
 Potential energy
 Kinetic energy
 Internal energy

---

* The effective mass of the electron has been determined experimentally to be

$$m = \frac{m_0}{\sqrt{1 - (v/c)^2}}$$

where m = effective mass at velocity v
   m_0 = "rest" mass (9.1066×10^{-31} kg)
   v = velocity of electron
   c = velocity of light (3×10^8 m per sec)

Forms in which energy is transferred
  Mechanical work
  Heat
  Electric and magnetic work

Various aspects of this classification will be brought out in subsequent chapters which are devoted to more detailed discussions of these forms of energy. It is important to note the two broad categories, (1) energy which is stored and (2) energy which is transferred.

Power

The preceding section mentioned energy which is transferred but said nothing about how fast or how slow it might be transferred or transmitted. The *rate* of *transfer* of energy with respect to *time* is called *power*. For example, suppose that we have two automobiles of equal mass but one has an engine rated at 125 hp and the other has an engine rated at 250 hp. Both engines will do the same amount of work in accelerating the cars from rest to a speed of, say, 60 miles per hour. Each car has acquired the same kinetic energy. However, the more powerful engine can accelerate its car to this speed in less time than the other engine, i.e., it does the same work faster.

As another example, a man can carry a 50-lb load up the steps of a building to a certain height and do the same work as a powerful hoisting engine would do in performing the same task. The engine, however, can yank the weight up much faster than the man can carry it.

The dimensions of power, then, are the dimensions of energy per unit of time. We can derive these dimensions in terms of elementary physical quantities.

$$\text{Power} = \frac{\text{energy}}{\text{time}}$$

$$[P] = \frac{[M][L]^2[T]^{-2}}{[T]}$$

$$= [M][L]^2[T]^{-3}$$

These are the dimensions of power regardless of the form in which energy is transferred, whether it be mechanical, thermal, or electromagnetic.

Units of energy and power

Energy and power are characteristically expressed in different physical units for different forms. It will be sufficient for the purposes of this book to give the units in the systems that are most commonly used in this country.

Mechanical energy is usually expressed in *foot-pounds* or horse-power-hours, thermal energy in *British thermal units* (Btu), and electric energy in *watthours* or *kilowatthours*. A kilowatthour is equal to 1,000 watthours.

Mechanical power may be expressed in foot-pounds per second or per minute but is more commonly used in terms of *horsepower*. Thermal or heat power may be expressed in *Btu per unit of time*, and electric power is expressed in *watts* or *kilowatts*. The adjective electric is used in the same sense as electromagnetic.

One Btu may be defined as the quantity of heat required to raise the temperature of one pound of water through one degree Fahrenheit.

The watt and watthour require more explanation. A *watt* is the electrical unit of *power* and is defined to be the product of the electric current and voltage expressed, respectively, in terms of amperes and volts. One watt is the power produced by a current of one ampere flowing in a conductor between two points whose potential difference is one volt. We have by definition

$$1 \text{ watt} = 1 \text{ volt} \times 1 \text{ ampere}$$

or electric power in general is

$$\text{Power} = \text{volts} \times \text{amperes}$$

This relationship is used for both direct and alternating current circuits, but the current and voltage are average or effective quantities for alternating currents. However, this expression is always true for instantaneous power.

Note that mechanical and thermal power are expressed as the expenditure of energy *per unit of time*, i.e., as foot-pounds per minute or Btu per second. Horsepower implies a rate since 1 hp is defined to be 550 ft-lb per sec or 33,000 ft-lb per min.

No time unit appears to enter the electrical unit of power, the watt. This is because the electric current in amperes is not a quantity of electricity as such, but is a rate of flow or quantity per unit of time. Accordingly, the product of current and voltage equals power or the rate of flow of energy. The amount of electric energy transferred or stored in a given time is equal to the product of electric power (in watts or kilowatts) and the given time (usually in hours). Electric energy is therefore usually expressed in watthours or kilowatthours.

We have now for comparison the following units which are commonly used in the United States:

Mechanical energy, stated in foot-pounds or horsepower-hours
Thermal energy, stated in Btu
Electric energy, stated in watthours or kilowatthours
Mechanical power, stated in foot-pounds per sec (min, hr) or horsepower
Thermal power, stated in Btu per sec (min, hr)
Electric power, stated in watts or kilowatts

The relationships among these units are shown below (see Appendix E for relationships with units in other systems):

1 Btu = 778 ft-lb (mechanical equivalent of heat)

1 kwhr = 3,413 Btu

= 1.341 hp-hr

1 hp = 550 ft-lb per sec

= 33,000 ft-lb per min

= 2,545 Btu per hr

= 0.7457 kw

1 kw = 3,413 Btu per hr

= 1.341 hp

It should also be pointed out that there is nothing inherent about the various units for energy and power which are commonly used. For examples, one could rate incandescent lamps in terms of horsepower or of Btu per hour as well as in watts. One could also speak of an automobile, not as having a motor rated at 250 hp, but a motor rated at 177 Btu per sec or at 187 kw. Also if the course of history had been different, the unit of electric power might have been named for someone other than James Watt. Instead of British thermal units and horsepower, we might just as well have had French thermal units and mulepower.

Suggested references

William F. Cottrell, "Energy and Society," McGraw-Hill Book Company, Inc., New York, 1955. Man's use of energy, from draft animals to nuclear fuel, and its impact upon the development of our civilization.

Eugene Ayres and Charles A. Scarlott, "Energy Sources: The Wealth of the World," McGraw-Hill Book Company, Inc., New York, 1952. Estimates of energy reserves of all kinds, including solar and nuclear energy, vegetation, rain, wind, and tides. Interesting chapters on waste and the energy balance sheet.

Palmer C. Putnam, "Energy in the Future," D. Van Nostrand Company, Inc., Princeton, N.J., 1953. A study of the potential world demands for energy over the next 50 to 100 years, sponsored by the Atomic Energy Commission.

William M. White, "Power, Production, Prosperity," Newcomen Society of England, American Branch, New York, 1946. A short lecture on the influence of mechanical horsepower on the production of goods in the twentieth century.

Woodrow C. Jacobs, Energy Exchange between Sea and Atmosphere and Some of Its Consequences, *Bull. Scripps Inst. Oceanog. Univ. Calif.*, vol. 6, no. 2, pp. 27–122. A scientific study with emphasis on the North Atlantic and North Pacific Oceans.

Abraham Marcus and Rebecca B. Marcus, "Power Unlimited," Prentice-Hall, Inc., Englewood Cliffs, N.J., 1959. The story of power, from windmills to nuclear power and magnetic-pinch plasma propulsion, in layman's language.

Centennial of Engineering, 1852–1952, Centennial of Engineering, 1952, Museum of Science and Industry, Chicago, 1953, book II, sec. X, p. 833, Energy.

"Estimated Future Power Requirements of the United States by Regions, 1955–1980," U.S. Federal Power Commission, Washington, D.C., 1956.

Problems

8.1 What is the origin of the word energy, and how is energy related to work?

8.2   Derive the dimensions of energy from force and work and show that these are the same as for the product of mass and the square of velocity.

8.3   Give and explain examples of physical quantities which have the same dimensions as energy but which do not represent energy.

8.4   Assuming that the rest mass of an electron is the mechanical or Newtonian mass, what per cent of the effective mass of the electron at a velocity of 2.5×10^8 m per sec may be attributed to the energy of the magnetic field produced by its motion?

8.5   A hydroelectric power plant is rated at 25,000 kw. What are its equivalent ratings in horsepower and in Btu per minute?

8.6   What would be the rating of a 200-watt incandescent light bulb in terms of horsepower and Btu per hour?

8.7   If a man can do 24,500 ft-lb of work per minute in lifting loads, what power in kilowatts must be supplied to a machine to do this work in one-sixth the time required by the man? Neglect any losses of energy in the operation of the machine.

8.8   If solar energy is measured to be 5.8 Btu per sq ft per min at a certain place on the earth's surface at a certain time, what power does this represent in kilowatts and in horsepower for a rectangular area which measures 3 by 5 ft?

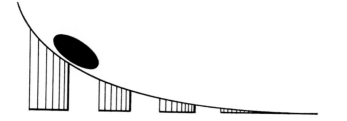

Potential and kinetic energy

This is the first of four chapters which are devoted to discussions of energy in its various forms and conversion of energy from one form to another. Potential energy and its conversion to or from mechanical work are presented first with typical examples. Then follows a discussion of kinetic energy with a derivation of this form of energy from mechanical work. Examples of the conversions among potential energy, kinetic energy, and mechanical work are included.

Potential energy

Potential energy is sometimes called the energy of position and is best approached by explaining mechanical potential energy. In engineering practice on earth, mechanical potential energy is stored in a body by virtue of its vertical distance above a horizontal plane of reference (Fig. 9.1). It is energy which is released when the force of *gravity* is permitted to act and to produce motion. The idea is implicit in this form of energy that mechanical work has been done against the force of gravity in raising the mass to its position relative to the surface of the earth and that the amount of work done will be equal to the amount of potential energy which is stored assuming no losses of energy in the process.

$$PE = Wh$$

where PE is the mechanical potential energy, W is the weight, and h is the height above a plane of reference. The potential energy in foot-pounds would be equal to the weight of the mass in pounds times the height above a horizontal reference plane (which need not necessarily be the surface of the earth) in feet. If an object weighing 160 lb is lifted a distance of 10 ft to a position of rest, its mechanical potential energy with respect to its original position will be 1,600 ft-lb.

Mechanical potential energy, then, comes from the force of attraction between two masses as stated in Newton's law of universal gravitation. We may think of a gravitational field as composed of lines of force in much the same manner as we speak of lines of force in a magnetic field. Thus we see that we can also have potential energy stored in a magnetic sense in a magnetic mass such as a steel bar which is held at a certain distance away from a magnet, either a natural magnet or an

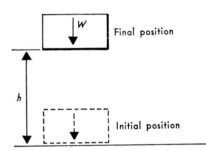

FIG. 9.1. Mechanical potential energy $= W \times h$.

electromagnet. Another example is the case of two charged particles, one positive and one negative, which attract each other but which are held apart forming an electric field. Thus we may speak broadly of potential energy as energy of position with respect to fields of force, gravitational, electric, or magnetic (Fig. 9.2). However, the illustrations and problems in this chapter will be limited to mechanical potential energy because the theory and the calculations are not so difficult as for electric and magnetic potential energies.

One further point should be made with respect to mechanical potential energy in order to give the student the proper perspective. When an object is pried loose from the earth, the earth is also pried loose from the object. In other words, as one lifts an object from the floor and raises it above his head, he also pushes the earth down and away from the object. However, the earth moves only an imperceptible amount because its mass is so great with respect to the object. Suppose that a man is drifting in space with, say, two large spherical satellites of equal mass and density. If he stood on one and pushed against the other, he would find that each would move the same distance away from him in opposite directions.

A student weighing 165 lb walks up two floors in a building to attend class. If the floors are 10 ft 6 in. apart, how much has he increased his potential energy?

The amount of work which is done against the force of gravity is equal to the increase in potential energy.

$$\text{Work} = \text{PE} = 165 \times 2 \times 10.5$$

$$= 3,460 \text{ ft-lb}$$

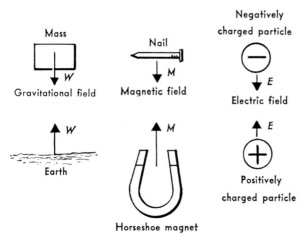

FIG. 9.2.   Potential energy of fields.

What is the potential energy of a 1,400-lb elevator in the Chrysler Building at the nineteenth floor, which is, say, 220 ft above street level? Assume zero potential energy at street level.

$$\text{PE} = 1,400 \times 220 = 308,000 \text{ ft-lb}$$

What average horsepower would be required to raise the elevator from street level to this floor in 15 sec? Power is the rate of doing work or expending energy.

$$\text{Rate of doing work} = \frac{308,000}{15}$$

$$= 20,600 \text{ ft-lb per sec}$$

$$\text{Horsepower required} = \frac{20{,}600}{550}$$

$$= 37.5 \text{ hp}$$

In an actual installation this much horsepower would not be required because elevators of this kind have counterweights which balance the weight of the elevator with an average number of passengers.

A shallow lake 10 ft deep and 22 acres in area is on a mountain top. The bed of the lake is 235 ft above the valley floor. What is the potential energy of the water in the lake with respect to the valley floor? The average height of the water above the floor is

$$h = 235 + \frac{10}{2} = 240 \text{ ft}$$

1 acre = 43,560 sq ft

The volume of the water is

$$V = 22 \times 43{,}560 \times 10$$

$$= 9.59 \times 10^6 \text{ cu ft}$$

Water weighs 62.4 pcf.

$$\text{PE} = (62.4 \times 9.59 \times 10^6)240$$

$$= 1.43 \times 10^{11} \text{ ft-lb}$$

This problem could be related to the use of falling water to generate electricity in hydroelectric plants. However, it is not feasible to empty a lake completely as is done in this case where the water surface is drawn down from a depth of 10 ft to the bottom. Normally the rate of withdrawal of water would be comparable to the rate of inflow so that there would be very little drawdown (lowering of the surface) except during long dry spells. The available potential energy would be estimated on the basis of (1) the elevation of the water surface of the lake which might be taken at an average constant value for a period of time (weeks or months) and (2) the average inflow of water during that period.

The student may question the computation of the mechanical potential energy of the water from the surface elevation. He may ask, "What if the water is drawn off at a depth of so many feet below the surface of the lake?" This water is not so high as the water at the surface. However, the water beneath the surface is under pressure from water above which increases directly with depth. We say that water at a certain depth is under a certain "pressure head" and designate this pressure head usually in terms of feet of water above the elevation in question (Fig. 9.3). The sum of the elevation of water z_1 at a particular depth and the pressure head h_1 at that depth equals the elevation z of the water surface.

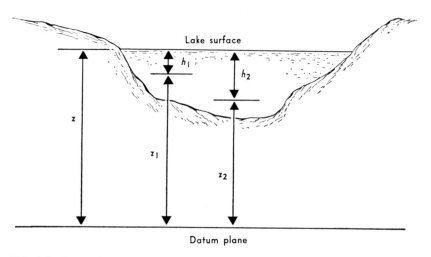

FIG. 9.3. Potential energy of surface waters; $z_1 + h_1 = z,\ z_2 + h_2 = z.$

Kinetic energy

This is a form of energy which is stored in a body in motion with respect to a frame of reference. The idea is implicit in this form of energy that work has been done on the body to give it motion with a certain velocity v. In other words the body has been accelerated to this velocity by some force acting through a distance according to the law $F = ma$. The work which has been done is then stored in the form of kinetic energy which is released when work is done in stopping or slowing the body.

The derivation of the expression for kinetic energy is quite simple. We shall do this for the special case of a constant force and also for the general case of a nonconstant force. First, consider a constant force F acting upon a body of mass m which is initially at rest. Suppose the force acts through a certain distance s. This force F is the net force over and above any force required to overcome frictional resistances and as such is the effective force in producing motion with a constant acceleration a. Thus we have

$F = ma$

Now acceleration is the rate of change of velocity, and if we start from rest

$$a = \frac{v}{t}$$

where v is the velocity gained in time t, and we now have

$$F = \frac{mv}{t}$$

The kinetic energy stored in the mass is equal to the mechanical work done in increasing the velocity from 0 to v.

$KE = Fs$

The distance s can also be expressed in terms of v and t. Since the velocity increases uniformly from 0 to v, the average velocity is $v/2$, and we have

$$s = \frac{v}{2} t$$

Substituting for s and F in the relationship for kinetic energy and mechanical work, we obtain

$$KE = \frac{mv}{t} \times \frac{v}{2} t$$

$$= \frac{1}{2} mv^2$$

If the force F is not constant, the acceleration will also vary and we have

$$a = \frac{dv}{dt}$$

The force can be expressed in general as

$$F = m \frac{dv}{dt}$$

The mechanical work done in a differential distance ds is

$dW = F \, ds$

Since $ds = v\,dt$, we may write

$$dW = Fv\,dt$$

The kinetic energy gained from an initial velocity of zero to a final velocity v is

$$\begin{aligned}
KE &= \int dW \\
&= \int Fv\,dt \\
&= \int mv\,\frac{dv}{dt}\,dt \\
&= \int_0^v mv\,dv \\
&= \frac{mv^2}{2}
\end{aligned}$$

This is an expression for the kinetic energy of an object in terms of its mass m and velocity v with respect to a frame of reference. The quantity of mass is not usually used in engineering, but rather weight. We note that mechanical potential energy is expressed in terms of weight and height, $PE = Wh$. It is more useful to express kinetic energy in the same form. Since we measure mass indirectly in terms of weight by $m = W/g$, we substitute this in the expression for kinetic energy to obtain the commonly used equation

$$KE = \frac{Wv^2}{2g}$$

What is the kinetic energy of an automobile weighing 2,100 lb when it is moving at a speed of 35 mph? It is assumed of course that the earth is the frame of reference. Note that in the expression for kinetic energy, $Wv^2/2g$, the acceleration of gravity g is expressed in English units as approximately 32.2 ft per sec². Accordingly, the velocity v must be in feet per second to avoid mixed units.

For converting miles per hour to feet per second, and vice versa, it is convenient to know that 60 mph equals 88 fps (see Appendix E). Accordingly,

$$35 \text{ mph} = 35\left(\frac{88}{60}\right) = 51.3 \text{ fps}$$

$$KE = \frac{2,100(51.3)^2}{2 \times 32.2}$$

$$= 85,800 \text{ ft-lb}$$

What constant force would be required to stop this automobile in a distance of 50 ft on level ground?

The work required to stop the car would be equal to the kinetic energy which would have to be overcome. We equate the work to the kinetic energy.

$$F \times 50 = 85{,}800$$

$$F = \frac{85{,}800}{50}$$

$$= 1{,}720 \text{ lb}$$

An object is dropped from a height of 44 ft above the ground and falls freely. Neglecting air resistance, what is the velocity when it strikes the ground?

The potential energy of height is converted to kinetic energy of motion. Let W = weight, and equate the two energies.

$$W \times 44 = \frac{Wv^2}{2g}$$

$$v^2 = 2g \times 44$$

$$v = \sqrt{64.4 \times 44}$$

$$= 53.3 \text{ fps}$$

Note that we have derived an expression for the velocity of a falling object in terms of the height by the "energy method." In general,

$$Wh = \frac{Wv^2}{2g}$$

$$v^2 = 2gh$$

or

$$v = \sqrt{2gh}$$

A body weighing 75 lb slides down a smooth frictionless surface in the shape of the arc of a circle of radius 20 ft (Fig. 9.4). What is its horizontal velocity at the bottom?

$$PE = KE$$

$$75 \times 20 = \frac{75v^2}{2g}$$

$$v^2 = 2g \times 20$$

$$v = \sqrt{64.4 \times 20}$$

$$= 36.0 \text{ fps}$$

It is interesting to note that this horizontal velocity is the same as would be the vertical velocity if the body had fallen freely for 20 ft. Why is this?

A baseball player throws a baseball 161 ft in the air above the point of release from his hand. What initial velocity did he impart to the ball in miles per hour? Assume that air resistance absorbs 3 per cent of the kinetic energy.

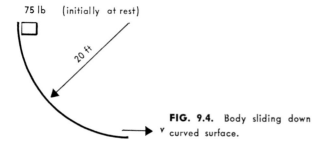

75 lb   (initially at rest)

20 ft

FIG. 9.4. Body sliding down curved surface.

In this problem kinetic energy is transformed into potential energy with a slight loss in the process. Note that the change in potential energy is with respect to the point of release above the ground rather than the ground surface.

Effective KE = 97 per cent of initial KE

$$= 0.97 \frac{Wv^2}{2g}$$

where W = weight of baseball.

PE at maximum height = $161W$

$$\frac{0.97\,Wv^2}{2g} = 161W$$

$$v^2 = \frac{2g \times 161}{0.97}$$

$$v = \sqrt{\frac{64.4 \times 161}{0.97}}$$

$$= 103.4 \text{ fps}$$

However, the answer is requested in miles per hour; therefore we have

$$v = 103.4 \left(\frac{60}{88}\right)$$

$$= 71 \text{ mph}$$

Note that the calculations in this example were carried to one more significant figure in the intermediate steps than is justified, and that the final answer is rounded off properly.

What average horsepower is required to accelerate a car weighing 3,200 lb to a speed of 55 mph from a standing start in 8 sec?

$$\text{Speed} = 55 \left(\frac{88}{60}\right)$$

$$= 80.6 \text{ fps}$$

$$\text{KE} = \frac{3,200 \times (80.6)^2}{2 \times 32.2}$$

$$= 323,000 \text{ ft-lb}$$

$$\text{Average power} = \frac{323,000}{8 \times 550}$$

$$= 73.5 \text{ hp}$$

How much mechanical work is done in slowing this car from a speed of 60 mph to 30 mph?

The mechanical work is the difference in the kinetic energies at the two speeds. Since 60 mph is 88 fps and 30 mph is 44 fps, we have

$$W = \frac{3,200(88)^2}{2 \times 32.2} - \frac{3,200(44)^2}{2 \times 32.2}$$

$$= \frac{3,200[(88)^2 - (44)^2]}{2 \times 32.2}$$

$$= 288,000 \text{ ft-lb}$$

Note that we must take the difference in the *squares* of the velocities rather than the difference in velocities and then square this, i.e., $v_1^2 - v_2^2 \neq (v_1 - v_2)^2$.

Suggested references

George Barrow, "Your World in Motion," Harcourt, Brace and Company, Inc., New York, 1956. A popular account of "motion, motion, everywhere" which leaves the reader with a sweeping sense of living in a world in which nothing is still.

Harvey F. Girvin, "A Historical Appraisal of Mechanics," International Textbook Company, Scranton, Pa., 1948. A review of mechanics from the Greeks to the present, with particularly interesting chapters on Dynamics, the Science of Motion, Period between Galileo and Newton, Isaac Newton: 1642–1727, and Works of Newton's Contemporaries and Followers.

Problems

9.1 The large power shovel in Fig. 9.5 is used to strip overburden from coal seams in the strip mining of coal. The dipper has a capacity of 60 cu yd. Assume that the weight of the overburden scooped up by the dipper is 104 pcf in the loose, fragmented state. Assume that the weight of the dipper and that portion of the dipper handle supported by the hoist cables is 82,000 lb.

a. What is the total load on the hoist cables in tons when the dipper is filled to capacity?

b. The maximum dumping height is 101 ft. If the dipper picks up a full load at a height of 18 ft 6 in. above the ground, how much work is done in raising the load to the maximum dumping height?

c. If the load is raised from minimum to maximum position in part (*b*) in 16 sec, what average horsepower is being exerted by the hoisting motors?

9.2 A four-story warehouse has an effective storage area of 140 by 280 ft on each floor. The floors are 12 ft apart with the first floor being

FIG. 9.5. Stripping shovel with a 60-cu-yd dipper on a 150-ft boom. It can be operated by one man who reaches his third-floor operating cab by means of an electric elevator which goes up through the hollow center pin on which the upper frame rotates. The shovel can fill its dipper up a bank as high as a 12-story building and dump it on top of a 10-story building a city block away. (*Courtesy of the Marion Power Shovel Company.*)

at the level of the beds of the trucks which deliver boxes and crates to be stored. The floors are designed for a maximum load of 150 psf and the average height of the loading is 2 ft above the floor levels. How much work must be done in loading the warehouse to capacity, i.e., by how much is the potential energy of the stored materials increased in the process of being stored?

9.3 A mountain lake is supplied by rainfall on a watershed area of 45 sq miles which drains into the lake. Assume that 30 per cent of the rainfall is absorbed or retained by the ground and forests and that 2 per cent is lost by evaporation. The surface of the lake throughout the year remains fairly constant in elevation and is 240 ft on the average above the floor of a nearby valley. Suppose that a power company contemplates building a hydroelectric plant in the valley and using water from the lake as the source of energy.

a. How many foot-pounds of potential energy would be available on an average daily basis if the average rainfall is 60 in. per year?

b. If the hydroelectric plant operated at an efficiency of 78 per cent, how many kilowatts of electricity could it generate on the average?

9.4 a. Estimate the total work in foot-pounds which you do daily in increasing your mechanical potential energy. Be specific in making this estimate and include and identify all your work as well as your assumptions.

b. How many stories high would the energy you have expended in part (a) raise an elevator carrying 10 persons in an office building?

c. Estimate how much work you could do in increasing your potential energy if you gave your full time and effort to walking up stairs or mountains for four continuous hours.

d. What is your average horsepower in part (c)?

9.5 Make an estimate of how much potential energy is stored daily in the Empire State Building in New York City (Fig. 9.6) among the people who work in the offices and visit the building on business or sightseeing. What happens to this energy when these people leave?

9.6 a. If a body of weight W is raised to a height h above its original position with respect to the earth, its mechanical potential energy is

FIG. 9.6. The Empire State Building at night. Offices extend up to the 85th floor. Observation platforms are located on the 86th and 102d floors. About one million sightseers visit the building every year. It has 75 elevators and can house about 25,000 tenants. *(Courtesy of the Empire State Building Corporation.)*

increased by an amount Wh. This is true regardless of whether it is elevated slowly or rapidly. Why?

b. Although we use the expression $PE = Wh$ for most engineering problems, this is not precisely true. Why not?

9.7   An automobile is moving at a speed of 58 mph on a level road. It weighs 3,340 lb.

a. If the brakes exert a constant retarding force equal to 55 per cent of the weight of the car, how far will it travel from the time the brakes are applied until it comes to a stop?

b. How much horsepower are the brakes exerting in stopping the car? Since the retarding force is taken to be constant, the average speed during the period of coming to a stop is one-half of the maximum speed.

c. If the kinetic energy of the automobile at a speed of 65 mph is converted completely into work which lifts just yourself above the ground, how high would you go?

9.8 A car mounted on ball-bearing rollers coasts down a loop-the-loop track as shown in Fig. 9.7 starting at point *A*. Neglect friction.

a. What is the speed of the car as it passes point *B?*

b. What is the speed of the car at the top of the loop at point *C?*

9.9 *a.* What is the kinetic energy of an ocean liner which displaces 47,000 tons when it is cruising at a speed of 32 knots? The displacement is the weight of water which the liner displaces as it floats which in turn is equal to the weight of the vessel.

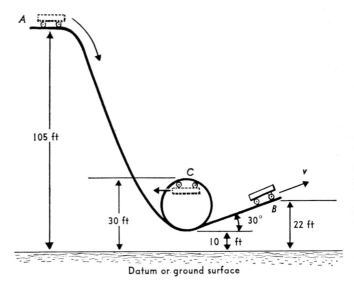

FIG. 9.7.

b. What horsepower would be required to bring the liner to a halt in a distance of 1 statute mile at a uniform rate of deceleration? Neglect frictional resistance and assume that all the work is done by the engines running in reverse.

9.10 A diesel truck is going at a speed of 52 mph on a level highway when it comes to a hill which has a uniform 8 per cent grade. The grade is the ratio of rise to horizontal distance expressed as a per cent (Fig. 9.8).

If the truck is allowed to coast up the hill and if 7 per cent of its kinetic energy is lost in frictional and air resistance, how far up the hill along the roadway will it coast?

9.11   A jet plane which is moving at a speed of 700 mph fires a projectile at a propeller plane which is flying at a speed of 380 mph directly in front of it and going in the same direction. If the projectile weighs 28 lb and is fired at a speed of 1,200 fps, what is the kinetic energy of the projectile with respect to (*a*) the earth and (*b*) the propeller plane?

9.12   A diver weighing 180 lb does a swan dive from a 10-ft board but hits flat.

   a. If his body goes no deeper than 2 ft into the water, estimate the average force of the water against him.

   b. With what velocity in miles per hour does he strike the water?

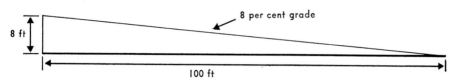

F!G. 9.8.   Determination of grade: grade = rise/horizontal length = 0.08 = 8 per cent.

9.13   A rocket is fired upward to a peak altitude of 700 miles. What will be the vertical velocity component of the rocket when it has fallen to 150 miles? Neglect atmospheric resistance. Use Newton's law of universal gravitation to determine a value of g at mid-height of the fall as compared with g at the earth's surface, and use this value in your calculations.

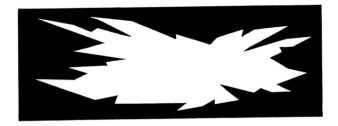

TEN

Internal energy

Internal energy is a form of stored energy which is difficult to define, especially in dictionary fashion. The concept of internal energy is not so specific as the concepts of mechanical potential energy, kinetic energy, and work. For example, internal energy appears in various phenomena, mechanical, thermal, electrical, and chemical. This chapter presents a simple approach to the determination of internal energy and a corresponding definition, followed by a brief discussion of internal energy and systems. Several examples of internal energy of a mechanical nature are given.

Internal energy and energy transfer

Let us consider in this section the internal energy of some simple devices such as a steel spring, a storage battery, an electrical capacitor, or a hot-water storage tank. Each of these may be considered to have energy stored in the form of internal energy when the spring has been compressed, the battery and the capacitor charged, and the water heated.

How should we think of this energy? Is it to be classified as mechanical, chemical, electrical, and thermal, respectively? And does internal energy actually exist in these distinct forms or is there a fundamental mechanism which is common to all forms? We might say that the answer to the last question is still being sought. For practical purposes we do speak of the internal energy of a compressed spring as being mechanical because the spring is compressed by mechanical work and also functions mechanically. Yet we are told that the forces which bind atoms and molecules together and which must have something to do with what goes on inside the spring may be electrical in character.

And we may speak of the internal energy of the hot water in a storage tank as thermal energy, but what is thermal energy? We are told that when the temperature of matter is increased, whether the matter is in the solid, liquid, or gaseous state, there is a corresponding increase in molecular activity. In gases particularly the velocities of molecules moving to and fro in the body of the gas are increased with an increase in temperature. Thus we see here an increase in the mechanical kinetic energy of the molecular masses in what we call for practical purposes a thermal phenomenon. There are many questions yet to be answered concerning the basic nature of matter in its various forms.

How, then, can we define internal energy? More than that, how can we measure it especially since it exists in such complex states within matter? The answer is that we do not measure internal energy directly and absolutely. But we can determine and also define internal energy in one breath by saying that the internal energy of a body or a device is the *difference between the amount of energy transferred into it and that transferred out of it with reference to some assumed zero state.* For example, consider a steel spring with no load as being in the zero state. If the spring is compressed a certain distance, the internal energy which is stored in it and which is known as elastic potential energy is equal to the work done on the spring or transferred into it by the forces which produced the compression.

The internal energy of a storage battery might be determined with respect to a zero state of being completely discharged. Its internal energy at any time would equal the amount of energy transferred into it minus that transferred out of it. The energy transferred in would be determined from the amount of electrical energy expended by the charging device. The energy transferred out would be determined by measuring the electrical work done by the battery itself. Although chemical reactions and what we might call chemical energy are involved in the process, the internal energy would be determined from electrical measurements and time.

Not all authors may agree with this very simple concept of internal energy as the difference between energy in and energy out. Some may define it broadly as the energy possessed by matter due to a state of molecular activity. Others use much more sophisticated concepts and mathematical relationships, especially in thermodynamics. However, the author believes that the approach which has been presented is sound and can be used without difficulty as a foundation for more advanced concepts to come in later courses.

Internal energy and systems

The term internal energy implies that the energy to which it refers must be inside of something, or more explicitly, inside the boundaries

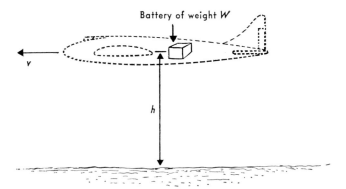

FIG. 10.1. Internal energy = electrical work which battery can do; mechanical potential energy = Wh; kinetic energy = $Wv^2/2g$.

of something. But this something need not be a simple device or a single body. It could be a group of bodies or a portion of space, or in a word a system. For example, consider a fully charged battery being delivered from factory to distributor by air express. The battery has a certain amount of stored internal energy. It also has a certain amount of stored potential energy and kinetic energy with reference to the earth while in flight (Fig. 10.1). Here the system is bounded by the battery case and the potential and kinetic energies are external to the system.

However, if we extend our boundaries to enclose the earth and everything within a thousand miles of its surface, all three forms of energy associated with the battery in flight become part of the internal energy of the new system. Thus we see that internal energy is relative not only to some arbitrary zero level but also to the system which is selected, and we note that internal energy can include potential and kinetic energies.

The greatest system is the entire universe, for which boundaries have yet to be determined. The engineer works with much smaller systems, for which he selects boundaries which are suited to the problems at hand. In Chap. 7 the importance of selecting an accurate model was stressed, and the same reasoning applies to the choice of a system in solving a problem.

A system may be set up in two ways, either as a quantity of matter or as a region in space. Professor Edward F. Obert has proposed the following definition of a system based upon a study of definitions which were advanced by a number of writers in the field of thermodynamics:* "The *system* is *either* a restricted region of *space* or else a finite portion of *matter*. The system is surrounded by an *envelope*, called the *boundary*. Outside of the boundary are the surroundings which are one or more other systems and these systems, too, must be evaluated."

A simple basic system is the hydrogen atom consisting of a positively charged proton and a negatively charged electron. The internal energy of this system consists primarily of the electrical potential energy of the electric field and the kinetic energy of the mass of the electron in orbit around the proton. The physical configuration of this system would be roughly similar to one basketball orbiting around another at a radial distance of approximately two miles.

The boundaries of a system need not be constant or fixed in position. The many phenomena which involve the internal energy of expanding gases are examples where boundary conditions are not constant. However, the same definition of internal energy may be used for a system, whether or not the boundaries are constant, as was stated in the preceding section for a device or a body. The internal energy of the system is the difference between the amount of energy transferred into the system and that transferred out of the system referred to some arbitrarily chosen zero level.

---

* Edward F. Obert, Teaching the Concepts of State Properties, Boundaries, Systems, etc., *Proc., 1951 Summer School for Thermodynamics Teachers*, Michigan State University, July, 1951, p. 10.

Elastic potential energy

The remainder of this chapter will be devoted to a more detailed consideration of one particular example of internal energy, elastic potential energy. Discussions of other examples of internal energy and corresponding problems are given in Chap. 11, Heat, and Chap. 12, Electric and Magnetic Energy. Materials are said to be elastic if they regain their original shape after being deformed and released. A spring is a simple example of an elastic material formed in a particular way to permit relatively large deformations. Mechanical work is done to deform an elastic material and to store in it internal energy which is called elastic potential energy. When the material is released, this energy is transferred in one form or another as the material regains its original shape.

Elastic coil spring

Consider an elastic coil spring in which the elongation or compression of the spring is directly proportional to the force applied. For example, the spring may stretch 1 in. when a force of 2 lb is applied gradually and stretch 3 in. when three times as much force, or 6 lb, is applied gradually. By applying a force gradually we mean building it up from zero to its maximum value slowly. The 6-lb force when applied gradually begins at zero, and when it reaches 1 lb it has deformed the spring $\frac{1}{2}$ in. As we continue to increase the force, when it reaches 2 lb the spring has stretched 1 in. At 4 lb the stretch is 2 in., and at 6 lb the stretch has reached 3 in. Thus we see that the work done is *not* the full 6 lb acting through a distance of 3 in. but is less than this.

This proportionality between force (or stress) and deformation (or strain) for any elastic body is known as Hooke's law and was first stated by Robert Hooke in 1678. It applies only within a certain limited range of deformations or strains which varies from one elastic material to another. For instance, if a spring is stretched too much, it does not regain its original shape when the force is removed.

The *spring constant* k is the force required to deform the spring one unit of distance, and in the preceding case, $k = 2$ lb per in. Note that this is not a dimensionless constant but has the dimensions of force per unit distance. The dimensions of k are determined by the following equations:

$$F = kl$$

$$k = \frac{F}{l}$$

$$[k] = \frac{[F]}{[L]}$$

$$= [F][L]^{-1}$$

How much work is required to compress a spring of spring constant k a distance l from its normal position of no stress or strain? In other words, how much elastic potential energy is stored in the spring in compressing it a distance l? The force exerted is not constant but is

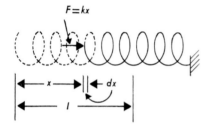

$F = kx$

FIG. 10.2. Compression of a linear spring.

gradually increased to overcome the increasing resistance of the spring. If the spring is compressed a distance x, the force exerted on the spring in this position is kx (Fig. 10.2). The increment of work done in compressing this spring an infinitesimal distance dx is

$$dW = (kx)\, dx$$

The total work done in compressing (or stretching) this spring a distance l is the sum of these increments, or

$$W = \int_0^l kx\, dx$$

$$= \frac{kx^2}{2}\Big]_0^l$$

$$= \frac{kl^2}{2}$$

This is equivalent to the average force exerted, $kl/2$, times the distance moved, l.

A spring of this type is said to be a linear spring or to have linear characteristics. The deformation of the spring is directly proportional to the force or load applied, as shown in Fig. 10.3. If the deformation-load curve is not a straight line, the spring is nonlinear.

If a horizontal elastic spring with a spring constant k equal to 4.80 lb per in. is compressed a distance of 6 in., how much internal energy in the form of elastic potential energy is stored in it?

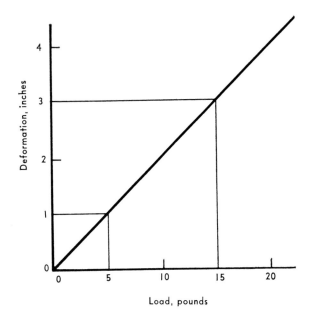

FIG. 10.3. Graph of the relationship between load and deformation for a linear spring.

Elastic PE stored = work done

$$= \frac{4.80(6)^2}{2}$$

$$= 86.4 \text{ in.-lb}$$

$$= 7.20 \text{ ft-lb}$$

If a mass weighing 2.15 lb is placed against the spring and the spring is released, what horizontal velocity will the mass be given? Neglect friction and the mass of the spring itself.

KE = stored PE

$$\frac{Wv^2}{2g} = 7.20$$

$$\frac{2.15v^2}{64.4} = 7.20$$

$$v = \sqrt{\frac{7.20 \times 64.4}{2.15}}$$

$$= 14.7 \text{ fps}$$

The units are determined from the dimensional equation:

$$v^2 = \frac{(PE) \times 2g}{W}$$

$$v^2 = (\text{ft})(\cancel{lb}) \times \frac{\text{ft}}{(\text{sec})^2} \times \frac{1}{\cancel{lb}}$$

$$= \left(\frac{\text{ft}}{\text{sec}}\right)^2$$

$$v = \text{fps}$$

The number 2 is a dimensionless constant, or pure number.

If the spring were placed vertically and released, how high would it throw the weight in the air above the end of the spring at rest? Again neglect the mass of the spring and resistance to motion through air.

$$2.15h = 7.20$$

$$h = \frac{7.20}{2.15}$$

$$= 3.35 \text{ ft}$$

However, this is the height above the initial position of the spring when compressed. Since the end of the spring at rest will be 6 in. higher, the height above it will be

$$\text{Net height} = 3.35 - 0.50$$

$$= 2.85 \text{ ft}$$

It is obvious that the velocity and the height would be less in an actual experiment because of the mass inertia of the spring, which would absorb some of the stored potential energy as kinetic energy of motion of the spring. This kinetic energy would be converted to internal energy as indicated by an increase in temperature in the metal of the spring as it vibrated to its position of rest. This internal energy would be dissipated in a flow of heat to the surrounding atmosphere.

There would also be a very small amount of energy dissipated in over-coming air resistance consisting of mass inertia of the air which is dis-placed and frictional resistance between the air and the weight and spring. Such air resistance would be negligible in this case.

Elastic beam

A steel beam subjected to bending behaves in the same way as does a coil spring, since steel is an elastic material within a limited range of strains or deformations (Fig. 10.4). If a certain load P produces a certain deflection d downward at the center of the beam, then a load twice as great applied at the same point will produce twice the deflection.

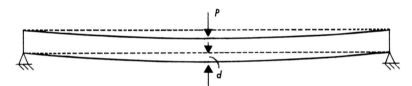

FIG. 10.4. Loading of an elastic beam; d is the deflection under load P.

For a certain steel beam, a load of 30 lb at the center produces a deflection at that point of 0.01 in.

How much internal energy in the form of elastic potential energy is stored in the beam by a load of 840 lb? By direct ratio, the deflection d produced is

$$\frac{d}{840} = \frac{0.01}{30}$$

$$d = \left(\frac{840}{30}\right) 0.01$$

$$= 0.28 \text{ in.}$$

Stored internal energy = average force $\times$ distance

$$= \frac{840}{2} \times 0.28$$

$$= 117 \text{ in.-lb}$$

This problem could also be solved by the same method as used for the spring, although the term "spring constant" is not customarily used in structural engineering.

$$k = \frac{30}{0.01}$$

$$= 3,000 \text{ lb per in.}$$

$$\text{Stored internal energy} = \frac{kl^2}{2}$$

$$= \frac{3,000(0.28)^2}{2}$$

$$= 117 \text{ in.-lb}$$

It is important to note that although the so-called spring constant is 3,000 lb per in., this does not necessarily mean that the beam might successfully carry a load of 3,000 lb. It is possible that this load, which would deflect the beam 1 in., might overload the beam in the sense of deforming it so much that the internal forces exceed the elastic limit of the beam. This is the limit beyond which it no longer springs back to its original shape, but retains a *permanent deformation* or *set*. Most students have had the experience of playing with springs and stretching them too far so that they do not regain their original length. The spring has been stretched or deformed beyond its elastic limit.

Note also that if the 30-lb load were placed elsewhere on the beam than at the center, the deflection would be different. As the load is moved closer to either of the supports, the deflection becomes smaller. This is one reason why the term spring constant is not used, because it is not actually a constant for a particular beam, but varies with the position of the load.

Elastic rod

Steel is an elastic material, as are many other materials, although it behaves in this way only for very small deformations. It stretches or compresses when subjected to direct stresses. Tension and compression are forms of direct stress with which the student is familiar. When a steel rod is pulled by equal and opposite forces as shown in Fig. 10.5, it is in tension. The external 40,000-lb forces are acting directly to produce internal forces which are called *stresses* to distinguish them from forces acting outside the rod (Fig. 10.6).

The forces must be equal and opposite at each end; otherwise the rod would move. Thus there is a direct stress of 40,000 lb acting in the steel of the rod. *Unit stress* is the stress per unit area. In this case the

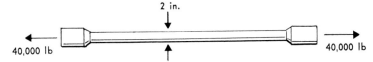

FIG. 10.5. Round steel rod, with upset ends for clamping in testing machine, subjected to tensile forces.

cross-sectional area of the rod is $\pi(2)^2/4 = \pi$ sq in. and the unit stress in pounds per square inch is given by

$$f = \frac{40,000}{\pi}$$

$$= 12,700 \text{ psi}$$

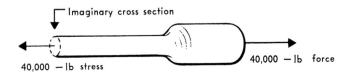

FIG. 10.6. External and internal forces.

Compression and compressive stresses occur when a steel block, for example, is squeezed by forces as shown in Fig. 10.7. Tension and compression are opposite in direction and in sign, tensile stress usually being considered as positive and compressive stress as negative.

FIG. 10.7. Steel block subjected to compressive forces.

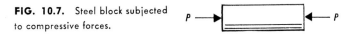

Steel is equally elastic in tension or compression within the elastic limit. The elastic property of steel is an inherent property of the material which is independent of cross section or length. We speak of the *modulus of elasticity E* of steel or any other elastic material as we speak of the spring constant k for a spring. But there is one major difference in the nature of these quantities. The spring constant k is determined individually for each particular spring and varies considerably from one spring to another. The modulus of elasticity E of steel, for example, does not vary with the shape or size of a steel member but represents an inherent property of the material itself.

The spring constant is defined in terms of external forces and deformations as the force required to deform a particular spring a unit distance. The modulus of elasticity on the other hand is defined in terms of internal forces and deformations as the ratio of the unit stress to the unit strain for any and all portions of the material

$$E = \frac{f}{\delta}$$

where E is the modulus of elasticity, f is the unit stress or stress per unit area, and δ is the unit strain or deformation per unit length.

Let us calculate the modulus of elasticity for steel, using a typical set of laboratory data. A steel bar 2 in. wide and ¾ in. thick is placed in the jaws of a universal testing machine for a tensile test. Before any load is applied, a distance of 8 in. is marked off on the bar as the gage distance to be measured as the bar is elongated. A tension of 54,000 lb is applied to the bar and the elongation of the 8-in. gage length is measured to be 0.0096 in. (Fig. 10.8). The unit stress is found from

$$f = \frac{54,000}{2 \times ¾}$$
$$= 36,000 \text{ psi}$$

The unit strain is calculated similarly:

$$\delta = \frac{0.0096}{8}$$
$$= 0.0012 \text{ in. per in.}$$

The value of the modulus of elasticity for steel is then

$$E = \frac{36,000}{0.0012}$$
$$= 30,000,000 \text{ psi}$$

or

$$= 3 \times 10^7 \text{ psi}$$

This value of course varies to a small degree for various kinds of steel but is the commonly accepted value for structural steel. It is frequently used as 30×10^6 psi, which is easy to compare with the values for concrete, which vary from 2×10^6 to 3.75×10^6 psi. The moduli of elasticity of both of these materials must be considered when they are used together in reinforced concrete.

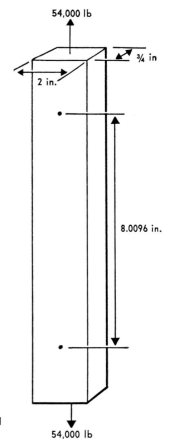

54,000 lb

¾ in

2 in.

8.0096 in.

54,000 lb

FIG. 10.8. Elongation of a steel bar in tension.

Let us make one calculation of the elastic potential energy stored in a steel rod, for example, in tension. The rod will be assumed to be 1.5 in. square and 5 ft long and is stretched 0.048 in. by an applied tensile force. What force is required to produce this elongation?

$$\text{Unit strain} = \frac{0.048}{5 \times 12}$$

$$= 0.0008 \text{ in. per in.}$$

From the definition of the modulus of elasticity we have

$$3 \times 10^7 = \frac{f}{0.0008}$$

$$f = 0.0008 \times 3 \times 10^7$$

$$= 8 \times 10^{-4} \times 3 \times 10^7$$

$$= 24{,}000 \text{ psi}$$

If F is the tensile force we have

$$F = \text{unit stress} \times \text{cross-sectional area}$$

$$= 24{,}000(1.5)^2$$

$$= 54{,}000 \text{ lb}$$

The elastic potential energy may be calculated using the average force which is applied:

$$\text{Elastic PE} = \frac{54{,}000}{2} \times 0.048$$

$$= 1{,}300 \text{ in.-lb}$$

Suggested references

Henry Margenau, William W. Watson, and C. G. Montgomery, "Physics, Principles and Applications," 2d ed., McGraw-Hill Book Company, Inc., New York, 1953. A one-page discussion of the basic nature of internal energy (p. 251) and the first law of thermodynamics (pp. 279, 305).

Francis W. Sears and Mark W. Zemansky, "University Physics," 2d ed., Addison-Wesley Publishing Company, Reading, Mass., 1955, pp. 272, 303. More on the distinction between heat and internal energy.

Ovid W. Eshbach (ed.), "Handbook of Engineering Fundamentals," 2d ed., John Wiley and Sons, Inc., New York, 1952, p. 8-02. A definition of internal energy.

Problems

10.1 A spring is hung vertically and loaded with a weight of 12 lb. When the load is increased to 18 lb, the spring is stretched 7 in. Neglect the weight of the spring.

a. What is the spring constant?

b. How far has the spring been stretched from its no-load position?

c. How much internal potential energy is stored in the spring under the 18-lb load?

10.2 The runway ejection system for a jet plane has four compressed springs attached under the seat at the corners to eject the pilot and seat upward to a height of 65 ft. A parachute opens at that point and the pilot lands on earth with minor injuries if any. Assume that the pilot weighs 175 lb and the seat 30 lb. Assume that the four springs are identical and are each compressed a distance of 3 ft from the "no-load" position to the "ready" position.

a. What must be the spring constant of these springs in pounds per foot? Neglect the weight of the springs.

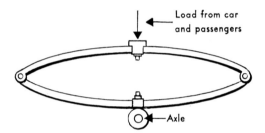

FIG. 10.9. Diagrammatic representation of a carriage-type spring.

b. The initial acceleration of the pilot and seat is how many times the acceleration of gravity?

c. Do you think this system is feasible? State reasons.

10.3 A diving board has a "spring constant" of 65 lb per in. for loads applied at a point close to the end where divers hit the board on take-off.

a. If a diver weighing 160 lb leaps a foot and a half into the air above the board at the end, how far would he depress the end of the board when he comes down on it?

b. How many foot-pounds of elastic potential energy are stored in the board when it is depressed the full amount in (*a*)?

10.4 Suppose you are designing a simple automobile spring of the type shown in Fig. 10.9 which may be assumed to have linear characteristics. The spring is to carry one-fourth of the total combined weight of car and passengers and has a spring constant of 373 lb per in.

Now suppose that this spring is on a car which has a total combined weight of 4,480 lb. As the car travels along the highway at high speed, it comes to a sharp break in the road surface which "drops" the axle to which the spring is attached a distance of 2 in. very suddenly.

a. As the car falls back on the spring, calculate how much it will fall beyond the point at which it normally rides above the axle.

b. On the basis of your answer would you say this is or is not a good design and why?

c. What would you do to improve it?

d. As the car comes to the break in the road, the wheels appear to drop very suddenly, much more rapidly than does the car. Explain this phenomenon.

10.5   A steel wire 0.05 in. in diameter is hung vertically in a skyscraper elevator shaft to support a 60-lb weight. It acts as a plumb bob to determine the movements of the top of the skyscraper caused by steady wind forces and by temperature differences between the shady and sunny sides of the structure.

a. If the wire is 900 ft in length, how much is it elongated under the 60-lb weight? Neglect the effect of the weight of the wire itself.

b. How much elastic potential energy is stored in the wire?

10.6   A wooden pile 70 ft long with an average diameter of 10 in. is to be driven by a drop hammer which weighs 240 lb. The modulus of elasticity of the wood is 1.2×10^6 psi. Suppose that the pile is placed upright on an unyielding surface of concrete and that the hammer is dropped from a height of 40 ft above the top of the pile.

a. What is the maximum amount of compression or shortening of the wooden pile under this blow?

Assume that the force exerted by the drop hammer increases uniformly throughout the compression. Also assume that the pile remains straight and does not deflect laterally.

b. Drop hammers have been largely replaced by steam hammers in which steam under pressure drives the hammer down on the pile with a relatively short stroke and also lifts the hammer in position for the next stroke. What single factor is most significant in making the steam hammer more economical to use?

10.7   a. Derive an expression for the total elongation Δh of the steel casing for an oil well under its own weight, assuming that it is swinging free of the sides of the hole. Let ρ be the density of steel, h the depth of the casing, and E the modulus of elasticity.

b. What is the total elongation of the casing in a well 12,000 ft deep? Steel may be assumed to have a density of 490 pcf and a modulus of elasticity of 3×10^7 psi.

FIG. 10.10.   Cauliflower after-cloud from the Bikini explosion rising after dumping two million tons of water sucked up by the underwater explosion. *(Courtesy of the Atomic Energy Commission.)*

10.8 *a.* Suppose an atomic bomb has 35 lb of plutonium and in an explosion as in Fig. 10.10 one twelve-thousandth of the mass is converted to energy. If this occurs in 2 microseconds (μsec),* what horsepower is produced by the explosion? The conversion of mass to energy is determined from $E = mc^2$.

b. How high in the air would this energy raise a fleet of 50 warships averaging a displacement of 25,000 tons apiece?

* A microsecond is one-millionth of a second and a millisecond is one-thousandth of a second.

ELEVEN

Heat

The subject of this chapter, heat, is one of several forms in which energy is transferred. Mechanical work, another such form, has been discussed in Chap. 8, and electrical and magnetic work will be considered in the following chapter. This chapter treats briefly of the distinction between heat and internal energy, of ways in which the transfer of energy in the form of heat occurs, of specific heat and heats of transformation, and of friction and heat.

Heat versus internal energy

Any discussion of heat and its relationship to internal energy involves the concept of temperature. A simple definition of the temperature of a body or a system is that it is a measure of the relative hotness or coldness of that body or system.* This is a subjective definition based upon the sense of touch of human beings. And temperature is correctly designated as a measure of a *relative* quantity because melting ice is colder than steam but hotter than liquid air. For example, scales for measuring temperature are chosen arbitrarily. The temperatures of ice at the point of melting and steam at the point of condensing have been chosen for standard fixed points to which to refer some temperature scales.

* See F. W. Sears and M. W. Zemansky, "University Physics," 2d ed., p. 255, Addison-Wesley Publishing Company, Reading, Mass., 1955.

More precisely, the temperature at which ice is in equilibrium with air-saturated water under atmospheric pressure is taken to be 0° on one scale, the centigrade scale, and to be 32° on another, the Fahrenheit scale. The temperature at which steam is in equilibrium with pure water under atmospheric pressure is taken to be 100° on the centigrade scale and 212° on the Fahrenheit scale under atmospheric pressure. Both of these standard points depend upon what value is assigned for standard atmospheric pressure.

More objective approaches to defining temperature are found in texts on thermodynamics. For example, Zemansky defines temperature as follows:* "The temperature of a system is a property that determines whether or not a system is in thermal equilibrium with other systems." This definition is developed through a careful and extensive discussion of the internal states and thermal equilibria of systems. It is interesting to note that the words "hot" and "cold" are not mentioned in this discussion.

There is a distinction between heat and internal energy. The term heat has sometimes been used loosely to indicate internal energy, but this is no longer regarded as correct. Internal energy is used only to designate stored energy, and heat is used only to designate energy which is being transferred. Temperature and internal energy are related in that in general an increase in temperature of a system signifies an increase in internal energy, i.e., stored energy, and vice versa. We do not speak of the heat stored in a system, but rather of the heat being transferred from one system to another. We may say that we have heat, or for that matter work, only when energy is being transferred across the boundary of a system. Obert defines heat as follows: † "*Heat is the transfer of energy, without mass transfer, across the boundary of a system because of a temperature difference between system and surroundings.*" The transfer is *from* the system to its surroundings if the system is at a *higher* temperature than the surroundings. The transfer is *to* the system if it is at a *lower* temperature than the surroundings.

The distinction between internal energy and heat assumes more significance when we realize that the internal energy and correspondingly the *temperature* of a system can be increased by a transfer of energy into the system in the form of *work* as well as in the form of heat. For

* M. W. Zemansky, "Heat and Thermodynamics," 4th ed., p. 7, McGraw-Hill Book Company, Inc., New York, 1957.

† E. F. Obert, Teaching the Concepts of State Properties, Boundaries, Systems, etc., *Proc., 1951 Summer School for Thermodynamics Teachers*, Michigan State University, July, 1951, p. 16.

example, the internal energy and the temperature of the body of air in a bicycle pump can be increased by doing mechanical work in compressing it in the pump as well as by a transfer of heat when the pump is placed in the noonday sun.

Ways in which heat is transferred

Energy in the form of heat may be transferred from a hotter system to a colder system in one of two ways, by *conduction* or by *radiation*. Conduction is a transfer of energy by actual contact of systems and may be regarded as the transfer of some of the internal molecular kinetic energy of the hotter system to the more slowly moving molecules of the colder system by collision. Radiation is the transmission of energy through space from a hotter system to a colder system in the form of electromagnetic waves. It is difficult in most heat-flow processes to determine the precise amounts of energy transmitted by radiation and by conduction, but this is seldom of practical importance because heat includes all the energy transferred between two systems because of a temperature difference.

The heat which reaches us from the sun is transferred by radiation. The heat which boils water in a pot is largely transferred by conduction through the metal of the pot which is in contact with the water, although some heat is radiated, as we say, from the metal of the pot. The student can perform an interesting experiment at home to distinguish the transfer of heat by radiation from that by conduction.

Place the hand very close to the glass bulb of an incandescent lamp at room temperature before it is turned on. Now turn on the current and notice that the hand immediately feels the heat radiated from the filament. Then move the hand and touch the glass bulb, which is found to be cooler than the hand. This shows that the heat has been transferred by radiation which has passed through the glass of the bulb. The glass will continue to absorb heat and soon reach a temperature where it will feel hot to the touch. Now the hand is receiving radiated heat directly from the hot filament and also heat by conduction from the glass bulb. The experiment is more striking if the light bulb is placed in the refrigerator for a few minutes before the experiment is tried. Be sure that the base of the bulb is dry before inserting it into a socket.

Convection is more a form of mass transfer than energy transfer. It is the transfer of a body of liquid or gas with its internal energy from one place to another. We speak of two types of convection, *forced* and *free*. Examples of forced convection are hot-air and hot-water heating systems in which the fluid is forced to move by means of a blower or pump, respectively. Free convection implies motion within a fluid due to differences in density which are caused by differences in temperature. Hot air in a room will rise and cool air will settle, thus producing convection currents. Better circulation of air in a room is obtained by partially raising the lower sashes and partially lowering the upper sashes of the windows than by raising the lower sashes fully. The warmer air goes out at the top and the cooler air comes in at the bottom.

Not all writers necessarily agree that convection is mass transfer. Free convection in which hot fluid rises and cool fluid descends is a phenomenon involving both mass transfer and heat transfer. Masses of fluid are moving but at the same time heat is being transferred by conduction and radiation from the hotter mass to the cooler. In other words, mass and heat transfer frequently occur simultaneously and it is difficult to distinguish between them except by arbitrary definition.

Specific heat and heats of transformation

The capacity to store internal energy varies from one material to another. For instance, a certain amount of heat Q is transferred into 1 lb of material A and the same amount of heat Q is also transferred into 1 lb of material B. We find, however, that there is a different increase in temperature between materials A and B which indicates a different capacity to store internal energy. We designate the ratio of the amount of heat Q transferred into the material to the corresponding increase in temperature Δt as the *heat capacity*.

$$\text{Heat capacity} = \frac{Q}{\Delta t}$$

This represents also the ratio of the increase in internal energy to the increase in temperature. Oddly enough this property of a material is called heat capacity despite the sharp distinction between stored internal energy and heat. The student must avoid the false implication that heat capacity means amount of heat stored. Heat capacities are expressed in terms of Btu per degree Fahrenheit or in calories * per degree centigrade.

The heat capacity of several pounds of material would be greater than that of just one pound. Accordingly the heat capacity is not as useful as a property of a material as is the specific heat capacity, which is abbreviated and used as *specific heat* and is represented by the letter c. Specific heat is the heat capacity per unit weight of a material and is expressed in Btu per pound per degree Fahrenheit or in calories per gram per degree centigrade. These units are so related that they have the same numerical value for any material. If we find that the specific heat of aluminum is 0.224 Btu per lb per °F, it is also 0.224 cal per g per °C.

Specific heats of various materials are determined by experiment. For example, a block of iron weighing 3 lb may be placed in a calorimeter and undergo an increase in temperature caused by a transfer of heat into it. If it is found that 25 Btu transferred into the iron raises the temperature 74°F, the specific heat of iron is then

$$c = \frac{25}{3 \times 74}$$

$$= 0.113 \text{ Btu per lb per °F}$$

$$= 0.113 \text{ cal per g per °C}$$

The specific heat of water is taken to be 1 Btu per lb per °F. Strangely enough, almost no other materials, gases, liquids, or solids, have a specific heat as great as that of water.

It is also interesting to note that the specific heat of most materials is not constant but varies slightly with temperature and sometimes greatly with phase or state, i.e., gaseous, liquid, or solid. Also heat is generally involved just to make a change in phase without a corresponding change in temperature. Generally, heat must be transferred into a material to change it from the solid to the liquid phase or from the liquid to the gaseous phase without corresponding changes in temperature. The reverse is generally true and heat is transferred out of a material without change in temperature when it condenses from the gaseous to the liquid phase or solidifies from the liquid to the solid phase.

* The term calories is used as an abbreviated form of gram-calories.

The heat required to change any material from the solid to the liquid phase without change in temperature is called *heat of fusion*. The heat required to change a liquid to the gaseous phase without change in temperature is called *heat of vaporization*. Conversely, the energy which is given off in the form of heat when a material changes from the gaseous to the liquid phase is called *heat of condensation* and from the liquid to the solid phase *heat of solidification*. The heats of vaporization and condensation for a material are equal and so are the heats of fusion and solidification. All of these can be designated by the general term *heats of transformation*.

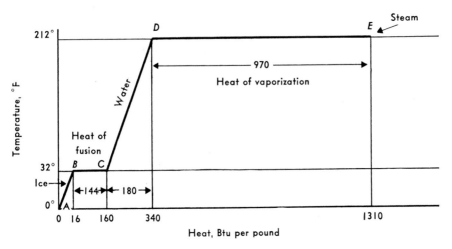

FIG. 11.1.   Graph of heat required to change 1 lb of ice at 0°F to steam at 212°F.

Let us consider the changes in phase of water from ice (solid phase) to water (liquid phase) to steam (gaseous phase). It requires 144 Btu per lb to change ice at 32°F to water at 32°F, and 970 Btu per lb to change water at 212°F to steam at the same temperature. The specific heat of water is 1 Btu per lb per °F and the specific heat of ice is 0.504 Btu per lb per °F. The energy required to change 1 lb of ice at 0°F to steam at 212°F is shown graphically in Fig. 11.1.

A total of 1,310 Btu is required. These are distributed as follows:

A to *B*:   0.504 × 32 = 16+ Btu to increase temperature of ice from 0°F to 32°F

B to *C*:   144 Btu to change phase from solid to liquid (no change in temperature)

C to *D*: $1 \times 180 = 180$ Btu to increase temperature from 32°F to 212°F

D to *E*: 970 Btu to change phase from liquid to gaseous (no change in temperature)

One other heat quantity which is of importance in engineering is the *heat of combustion* of a material. This is defined as the quantity of heat liberated when a unit weight of the material, or a unit volume, is completely burned. Heats of combustion of solids and liquids are usually designated in Btu per pound and of gases in Btu per cubic foot measured at a pressure of 30 in. of mercury, at a temperature of 60°F and saturated with water vapor.

An 8-lb block of iron at a temperature of 40°F is placed in an insulated vessel containing 10 lb of water at a temperature of 75°F. The specific heat of water is 1 Btu per lb per °F and that of iron is 0.113 Btu per lb per °F.

What common temperature is attained by both masses, i.e., what is the equilibrium temperature? Assume that no heat is lost to the container. If *t* is the equilibrium temperature,

Heat transferred from water $= 1 \times 10 \times (75 - t)$

Heat transferred to iron $= 0.113 \times 8 \times (t - 40)$

$$10(75 - t) = 0.113 \times 8(t - 40)$$

$$750 - 10t = 0.904t - 36.2$$

$$10.90t = 786$$

$$t = 72.1°F$$

How many Btu are transferred in the process?

$$Q = (75 - 72.1)10 = 29 \text{ Btu}$$

An aluminum casting weighing 43 lb is taken from a furnace at 422°F and dropped into a tank containing 900 lb of oil ($c = 0.5$ Btu per lb per °F) at 75°F. If the equilibrium temperature is 81.8°F and if 7 per cent of the heat transferred is lost to the atmosphere or taken up by the tank itself, what is the specific heat of aluminum?

The heat transferred to the oil is

$$Q_{oil} = 0.5 \times 900(81.8 - 75)$$

$$= 3,060 \text{ Btu}$$

The heat transferred from the aluminum is

$$Q_{al} = c \times 43(422 - 81.8)$$

$$= 14,600c$$

However, 7 per cent of this is transferred to the tank or the surrounding air so that only 93 per cent of it is transferred to the oil. We have, then,

$$0.93 \times 14,600c = 3,060$$

$$= \frac{3,060}{0.93 \times 14,600}$$

$$= 0.226 \text{ Btu per lb per } °F$$

An insulated aluminum calorimeter for measuring quantities of heat has itself a heat capacity of 0.42 Btu per °F. If it contains 15 lb of water at 63°F and if 2 lb of ice at 24°F is placed in the water, what will be the equilibrium temperature? Assume no heat is lost through the insulation.

The internal energy given up in the form of heat by the water and the aluminum container will be

$$Q_{water} = 1 \times 15(63 - t) = 945 - 15t$$

$$Q_{al} = 0.42(63 - t) = 26.5 - 0.42t$$

$$Q_{water+al} = 971 - 15.42t$$

The heat required to bring the ice up to the equilibrium temperature consists of three parts: (1) heat to raise the temperature from 28 to 32°F, (2) heat to melt the ice, and (3) heat to raise the temperature of the melted ice (water) to equilibrium temperature:

$$Q_{ice} = 0.504 \times 2(32 - 24) + 2 \times 144 + 1 \times 2(t - 32)$$

$$= 8 + 288 + 2t - 64$$

$$= 232 + 2t$$

Equating the heats transferred,

$$971 - 15.42t = 232 + 2t$$

$$17.42t = 739$$

$$t = 42.4°F$$

How many pounds of coal must be burned to heat 75 gal of water from 60 to 150°F, assuming 37 per cent stack loss? The heat of combustion of coal may be taken as 12,000 Btu per lb.

$$\text{Weight of water} = \frac{75 \times 62.4}{7.48}$$

$$= 625 \text{ lb}$$

$$Q = 1 \times 625(150 - 60)$$

$$= 56,200 \text{ Btu}$$

This heat represents $100 - 37$, or 63 per cent of the total heat produced by burning the coal. The weight of coal required then is

$$\text{Weight of coal} = \frac{56,200}{0.63 \times 12,000}$$

$$= 7.44 \text{ lb}$$

If the water is heated in 40 min, how many horsepower could be generated by this coal? Note that 1 hp is equal to 42.4 Btu per min (Appendix E).

$$\text{Power} = \text{rate of heat transfer} = \frac{56,200}{40}$$

$$= 1,405 \text{ Btu per min}$$

In terms of horsepower

$$P = \frac{1,405}{42.4}$$

$$= 33.1 \text{ hp}$$

Some attention has been given to the storing of solar energy for use in heating homes (Fig. 11.2). Compare the respective volumes of water and glauber salt as means of storing such energy from a minimum temperature of 72°F to a maximum of 120°F.

Properties of glauber salt:

Specific heat (solid) = 0.46 Btu per lb per °F

Specific heat (liquid) = 0.68 Btu per lb per °F

Melting point = 90°F

Heat of fusion = 104 Btu per lb

Specific gravity = 1.6

FIG. 11.2. The MIT Solar House IV, in Lexington, Massachusetts. The solar collector has an area of 640 sq ft and is set to be perpendicular to the sun's rays at noon on December 15. The house is equipped with a 1,500-gal solar-heated water storage tank and an alternative 275-gal oil-heated supply. *(Courtesy of the Massachusetts Institute of Technology.)*

A specific gravity of 1.6 means that the glauber salt is 1.6 times as heavy as an equal volume of water.

This problem can be solved in several ways, for example, (1) find the respective volumes to store the same energy or (2) find the respective energies stored by equal volumes. We shall solve it by the latter method, starting with 1 lb of water. The same volume of glauber salt would weigh $1.6 \times 1 = 1.6$ lb.

$$Q_{\text{water}} = 1(120 - 72)$$

$$= 48 \text{ Btu}$$

$$Q_{\text{glauber}} = [0.46 \times 1.6(90 - 72)] + (1.6 \times 104)$$

$$+ [0.68 \times 1.6(120 - 90)]$$

$$= 1.6[(0.46 \times 18) + 104 + (0.68 \times 30)]$$

$$= 1.6 \times 132.7$$

$$= 212 \text{ Btu}$$

The ratio of the volumes to store equal energies is the inverse of the ratio of energies stored in equal volumes. Accordingly we have for the ratio of the volumes

$$\frac{V_{\text{glauber}}}{V_{\text{water}}} = \frac{48}{212}$$

$$= \frac{1}{4.4}$$

The glauber salt will occupy slightly more than one-fifth the volume of the water. However, as yet there does not seem to be an economical method of making the glauber salt perform to its full theoretical capacity in field installations.

Friction and heat

Friction may be defined as the resistance to forces which produce or tend to produce sliding motion between two masses in contact. Fric-

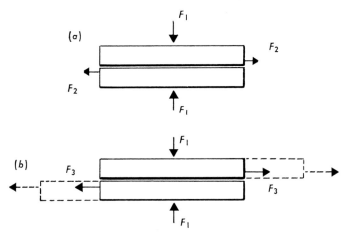

FIG. 11.3. Static and kinetic friction: *(a)* no motion—F_2 is not great enough to overcome the static friction produced by F_1 pushing the masses together; *(b)* relative motion is resisted by the kinetic friction produced by F_1.

tion acts to raise the temperature of the materials in the vicinity of sliding surfaces and increase their internal energy when work is done to produce sliding. In turn, this energy is usually dissipated to the surrounding medium in the form of heat which generally is not recoverable for doing work. Accordingly where there is relative motion between two masses and work is being done, there are usually "friction losses" in the form of heat. The phenomenon of friction can be demonstrated simply by rubbing the palms of the hand together vigorously. Ideally, there would be no frictional resistance for perfectly smooth surfaces. However, in reality there is no such thing as a smooth surface even though the frictional resistance might be so small as to be negligible.

There are two types of friction between solid masses, *static* and *kinetic* friction (Fig. 11.3). Static friction is found in the resistance to a force which tends to produce sliding between two bodies which are at *rest* with respect to one another. Kinetic friction is found in the frictional resistance which opposes the *motion* of one mass sliding along another. In all such cases, there must be some force pushing the two masses together on the sliding surface in order for friction to be developed (Fig. 11.3). Friction between solid masses can occur in various ways such as one mass sliding against the flat surface of another in linear motion or such as circular shafts rotating or pivoting in journals or bearings in rotary motion (Fig. 11.4).

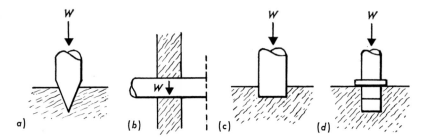

FIG. 11.4. Various types of pivot friction: *(a)* conical pivot, *(b)* shaft in journal, *(c)* flat pivot, *(d)* collar-bracing pivot.

The frictional resistance between masses or materials depends upon the properties of the materials themselves. It is usually expressed as a dimensionless ratio between the sliding force which starts or maintains motion and the normal force which acts perpendicular to the surface of sliding and presses the masses together. This ratio is called the coefficient of friction (Fig. 11.5). For dry surfaces, the coefficient of friction is generally constant for all normal forces or pressures and is independent of the area of contact. The coefficient of kinetic friction is generally constant for all relative velocities. Static friction is generally greater than kinetic friction.

Where lubrication is used to reduce frictional resistance, the sliding surfaces do not come in contact with each other but rather rest on a thin film of lubricant which is deformed internally as motion occurs. This produces frictional resistance internally in the mass of lubricant or, perhaps more properly, a resistance to the relative motions of the molecules of the lubricant. Although the coefficient of friction f is still expressed as a ratio of the forces, it depends upon the properties of the lubricant rather than upon the properties of the materials in the shaft and bearing. The thickness of the film of lubricant must be large compared with the surface irregularities of the materials.

A cast-iron block weighing 40 lb is being pulled horizontally along an oak floor. The coefficient of kinetic friction between the cast iron and oak is 0.41. At what rate is energy being wasted in the form of heat produced by friction if the block is being pulled at the rate of 12 fps?

Force to overcome friction $= 0.41 \times 40 = 16.4$ lb

Mechanical power loss $= 16.4 \times 12 = 197$ ft-lb per sec

$$\text{Heat power loss} = \frac{197}{778} = 0.25 \text{ Btu per sec}$$

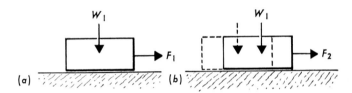

FIG. 11.5. Coefficients of sliding friction: (a) impending motion, coefficient of static friction $= F_1/W_1$; (b) motion with constant velocity, coefficient of kinetic friction $= F_2/W_1$.

The locomotives of a freight train are pulling it at a constant speed of 45 mph on a level track with a constant force of 35.6 tons (Fig. 11.6). How many Btu of heat are developed and dissipated in a distance of 1.5 miles?

Since the train is moving at a constant speed, no work is being done in changing its motion. The force exerted by the locomotives is used completely in overcoming frictional resistances.

Force $= 35.6 \times 2,000 = 71,200$ lb

Distance $= 1.5 \times 5,280 = 7,920$ ft

Work $= 71,200 \times 7,920$

$= 7.12 \times 10^4 \times 7.92 \times 10^3$

$= 5.64 \times 10^8$ ft-lb

$$\text{Heat} = \frac{5,640 \times 10^5}{778}$$

$= 7.25 \times 10^5$ Btu

FIG. 11.6. Heavy freight train being pulled by four diesel units. *(Courtesy of the Southern Railway System.)*

Note that the work 5.64×10^8 ft-lb was restated in the following step as $5{,}640 \times 10^5$ ft-lb. This was done to avoid getting a number less than one when we divided by 778. If we had not done this, the calculation would have been $(5.64/778)10^8 = 0.00725 \times 10^8$. Students are more likely to make a mistake in setting the decimal point for these very small numbers than for numbers greater than one.

What horsepower is exerted by the locomotives?

This could be computed by determining the time required for the train to travel a mile and a half and then converting the total number of foot-pounds of work done in this time to horsepower. However, it is simpler to determine the number of foot-pounds of work done per second from the force exerted and the speed in feet per second.

$$\text{Speed} = 45 \left(\frac{88}{60} \right)$$

$$= 66 \text{ fps}$$

$$\text{Horsepower} = \frac{71{,}200 \times 66}{550}$$

$$= 8{,}550 \text{ hp}$$

An automobile weighing 2,750 lb is moving at a speed of 30 mph. How much heat is generated in bringing the car to a standstill? This heat is developed primarily in the brakes (Fig. 11.7).

The kinetic energy of the car is

$$KE = \frac{2,750 \times \left[30 \left(\frac{88}{60} \right) \right]^2}{2 \times 32.2}$$

$$= \frac{2,750 \times 1,940}{64.4}$$

$$= 82,700 \text{ ft-lb}$$

$$Q = \frac{82,700}{778}$$

$$= 106 \text{ Btu}$$

What horsepower is exerted by the brakes in stopping this car in 5 sec? One horsepower is equal to 42.4/60, or 0.707 Btu per sec.

$$\text{Horsepower} = \frac{106}{5 \times 0.707}$$

$$= 30 \text{ hp}$$

A dummy weighing 160 lb is dropped from an airplane at a height of 2 miles. The dummy attains a terminal (or constant) velocity of 180 mph, at which the force of air resistance is equal to the force of gravity.

FIG. 11.7. Automobile brakes. *(a)* Interior view of a brake drum showing the brake shoes and lining. *(b)* Exterior view of finned brake drum on Chevrolet Corvette. This construction is designed for more rapid transfer of heat from the drum to the air. *(Courtesy of the General Motors Corporation.)*

(a)   *(b)*

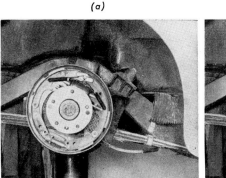

How much heat is generated per second and what horsepower is being exerted by the attraction of gravity?

$$v = 180 \left(\frac{88}{60}\right)$$
$$= 264 \text{ fps}$$

$$\text{Heat per sec} = \frac{264 \times 160}{778}$$
$$= 54.3 \text{ Btu per sec}$$

$$\text{Power} = \frac{54.3}{0.707}$$
$$= 76.8 \text{ hp}$$

The specific heat of air is approximately 0.24 Btu per lb per °F, and the density of air at the prevailing conditions of 60°F and normal atmospheric pressure at or close to the earth's surface is 0.0763 pcf. Assuming that the falling dummy acts on a column of air 6 sq ft in area, how much is the temperature of this air raised close to the earth? Assume 10 per cent of the heat absorbed by the dummy.

The velocity is 264 fps; therefore calculate the rise in temperature for a column of air of this height and 6 sq ft in cross-sectional area.

$$\text{Weight of air in column} = 6 \times 264 \times 0.0763$$
$$= 121 \text{ lb}$$

A total of 54.3 Btu are being generated per second and 90 per cent of this goes into the air mass. Equating heat generated and heat absorbed, and letting Δt = increase in air temperature, we have

$$0.90 \times 54.3 = 0.24 \times 121 \times \Delta t$$
$$\Delta t = \frac{0.9 \times 54.3}{0.24 \times 121}$$
$$= 1.7°F$$

A steel bullet strikes the ground with a velocity of 1,150 fps. The bullet weighs ⅙ oz. The specific heat of steel may be taken as 0.113 Btu per lb per °F. How much is the temperature of the bullet raised by the impact, assuming that none of the heat is absorbed by the earth?

This problem can be solved by computing the kinetic energy of the bullet first, converting this to equivalent Btu, and then determining the increase in temperature from the specific heat and the weight. However, if the general equations are set up first relating the kinetic energy to the increase in temperature, it is observed that the weight of the bullet does not enter the problem. This is because both the kinetic energy and the increase in temperature are directly proportional to the weight W.

$$KE = \frac{Wv^2}{2g} \quad \text{ft-lb}$$

Heat energy to increase temperature $\Delta t(°F) = cW \ \Delta t$ Btu, where $c =$ specific heat of steel in Btu per pound per degree Fahrenheit. Equate and insert conversion factor:

$$\frac{Wv^2}{2g} = 778cW \ \Delta t$$

$$\Delta t = \frac{v^2}{1,556gc}$$

$$= \frac{(1,150)^2}{1,556 \times 32.2 \times 0.113}$$

$$= 234°F \text{ increase in temperature}$$

Lead has a much lower specific heat than steel of approximately 0.03 Btu per lb per °F and lead bullets melt upon impact with hard objects except at low velocities (Fig. 11.8).

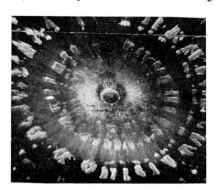

FIG. 11.8. Sequence photographs of a 22-caliber lead bullet striking a steel plate. Note the residual lead button after the melted lead has dispersed in all directions in a sheet. *(Reprinted by permission from Flash by Professor H. E. Edgerton, published by the Charles T. Branford Company.)*

An aluminum canteen weighing 1 lb and containing 1.6 lb of water, all at a temperature of 52°F, is dropped from the top of a sheer cliff to the ground 2,800 ft below. Assuming that 5 per cent of the energy is given to the ground by the impact and that 4 per cent of the energy is dissipated by air resistance in the fall, what is the temperature of the canteen and water just after impact?

Potential energy is converted to kinetic energy and then to internal energy with an increase in temperature. The effective potential energy is only $100 - 4 - 5 = 91$ per cent of the total available potential energy.

$$\text{Effective PE} = 0.91 \times (1 + 1.6)2,800$$

$$= 6,630 \text{ ft-lb}$$

$$Q = \frac{6,630}{778}$$

$$= 8.52 \text{ Btu}$$

Let Δt be the increase in temperature. The specific heat of aluminum is 0.225 Btu per lb per °F.

$$8.52 = (1 \times 0.225\Delta t) + (1.6 \times 1 \times \Delta t)$$

$$= 1.82\Delta t$$

$$\Delta t = \frac{8.52}{1.82}$$

$$= 4.7°F$$

$$\text{Final temperature} = 52 + 4.7$$

$$= 56.7°F$$

Steam is changed back to water in a condenser which is supplied with cooling water which enters at 65°F and is discharged at a temperature of 75°F. If the condenser is designed to condense 40 lb of steam per min under these conditions, how much cooling water must be supplied? The amount of heat to be transferred from the steam per minute is

$$Q \text{ per min} = 40 \times 970$$

$$= 38,800 \text{ Btu per min}$$

The weight of water required per minute for this energy transfer is

$$W = \frac{38,800}{1 \times (75 - 65)}$$
$$= 3,880 \text{ lb per min}$$

$$\text{Volume water} = \frac{3,880}{62.4}$$
$$= 64.3 \text{ cfm}$$

Suggested references

Mark W. Zemansky, "Heat and Thermodynamics," 4th ed., McGraw-Hill Book Company, Inc., New York, 1951.

H. Dean Baker, E. A. Ryder, and N. H. Baker, "Temperature Measurement in Engineering," John Wiley & Sons, Inc., New York, 1953. Methods, techniques, and details of execution for measuring temperatures in a variety of situations.

E. J. Burda (ed.), "Applied Solar Energy Research: A Directory of World Activity and Bibliography of Significant Literature," Stanford Research Institute, Stanford, Calif., 1955.

Farrington Daniels and John A. Duffie (eds.), "Solar Energy Research," University of Wisconsin Press, Madison, Wis., 1955.

Problems

11.1 A bullet weighing ¼ oz is moving at a speed of 1,775 mph when it strikes a wooden block at rest which weighs 2 lb.

a. What per cent of the kinetic energy is lost in the impact and converted to heat if the block and the embedded bullet move with a common resulting speed of 20.2 fps?

b. If the specific heat of the bullet is 0.117 Btu per lb per °F and if the wood is 0.55 Btu per lb per °F, what is the increase in temperature of the combination, assuming the same final temperature for both bullet and block?

11.2 The specific heat of pure liquid sulfuric acid (100 per cent) is 0.344 Btu per lb per °F, and the specific gravity is 1.83, i.e., the density is 1.83 times the density of water at 4°C.

a. If 40 lb of pure sulfuric acid at 72°F is mixed with 95 lb of water at 42°F, what is the resulting temperature of the solution? Neglect any heats of chemical reactions.

b. What is the specific gravity of the solution of (*a*)?

11.3 Natural gas may be assumed to have an average gross heating value of 1,150 Btu per cu ft at standard atmospheric pressure. How many cubic feet of natural gas would be required to convert 40 lb of ice at 12°F into steam at 212°F, assuming an efficiency of 67 per cent in the heating process?

11.4 How many pounds of pulverized coal must be burned per hour to provide an average supply of power for a manufacturing plant of 5,400 kw? Assume the heat of combustion of coal to be 16,500 Btu per lb. In the process of burning coal, there are losses of heat through the stacks, through the heating value of unburned coal which drops through the grates, through radiation, and such. We may assume that 75 per cent of the heat of combustion is effective in producing steam. Again there are losses of energy occurring in the process of generating electricity using steam turbines so that we may assume that 29 per cent of the energy available in the steam is effective in producing electric power.

11.5 An iron casting weighing 245 lb is at a temperature of 1,640°F when it is dropped into a tank of water at 65°F. The tank is 5 ft in inside diameter and the water is 2 ft 6 in. deep. The water, casting, and tank come to an equilibrium temperature of 76°F.

Assume that 10 per cent of the heat is transferred to the tank or lost to the surrounding air. How many pounds of water are converted into steam?

11.6 Assume that a residence requires an average of 25,000 Btu per hr for heating in the winter months.

a. How many pounds of glauber salt are required to store enough energy to keep the house at a temperature of 72°F for 3 days if the maximum temperature of the storage reservoir is 160°F?

b. How many gallons of water would be needed under the same conditions in part (*a*)?

c. Suppose that solar energy falls upon an area at a certain latitude at an average rate of 4.12 Btu per sq ft per min for an average period of

6 hr per day. The area so exposed is perpendicular to the sun's rays at noon on December 15. How many square feet of absorber surface would be required for storing the energy computed in part (*a*) during one day of sunshine on December 15? Assume that the conversion efficiency of the absorber is 60 per cent.

11.7 Assume that the average solar energy in the southern part of the United States is 1,300 Btu per sq ft per day on a yearly basis and that the heat of combustion of wood is 4,800 Btu per lb. If an acre of land produces 180 tons of timber in 15 yr, what is the conversion efficiency in per cent if the timber is used as fuel?

11.8 How much energy in terms of Btu is dissipated in the form of heat by the brakes of an automobile in bringing it down a steep mountain road from an elevation of 6,400 ft to an elevation of 560 ft? The automobile weighs 3,700 lb. Assume that air resistance and motor drag dissipate 7.5 per cent of the energy.

11.9 An automobile which weighs 4,250 lb is moving at a speed of 55 mph on a level road. The gasoline mileage under these conditions is 15.3 miles per gal. The power required to overcome air resistance and friction is indicated by simple measurements on a level road. It is found that when the car is coasting, it takes an average of 6.1 sec for it to drop from 60 to 50 mph.

a. What horsepower is required to maintain this speed of 55 mph?

b. If the heat of combustion of gasoline is 20,200 Btu per lb, what per cent of this energy is being used to maintain a speed of 55 mph on a level road? Gasoline weighs 42 pcf.

11.10 What must be the velocity of a lead bullet striking squarely against a hard granite surface to generate enough heat upon impact to melt the bullet. Assume that only 2 per cent of the heat is transferred to the granite. The specific heat of lead is 0.0297 Btu per lb per °F, the melting point is 327°C, and the heat of fusion is 11.3 Btu per lb. The initial temperature of the bullet before impact is 110°F.

11.11 A steel bullet weighing $\frac{1}{60}$ lb is moving at a speed of 1,600 mph when it strikes a wooden wall. It pierces the wall and leaves it at a speed of 250 mph. The specific heat of steel may be taken to be 0.115 Btu per lb per °F.

Assume that 13 per cent of the energy loss is absorbed by the wood. What is the temperature of the bullet as it leaves the wall if its initial temperature before impact was 86°F?

11.12   An automobile weighing 2.62 tons is speeding on a turnpike at 80 mph when the brakes are suddenly applied and the car is stopped. Assume that 90 per cent of the energy is absorbed by the steel brake drums, which weigh 11.5 lb per set on each wheel. The specific heat of steel may be taken to be 0.117 Btu per lb per °F.

If the initial temperature of the brake drums is 92°F, what is the final temperature when the car has been stopped?

11.13   An ocean liner which weighs 32,000 tons is cruising at a speed of 25 mph. The turbines which drive the vessel are thrown into full reverse to bring it to a stop under emergency conditions. Assume that frictional resistance between the hull and water dissipates 10 per cent of the energy and that the combination of turbines and propellers operates at an efficiency of 34 per cent.

If the heat of combustion of the diesel fuel oil is 16,500 Btu per lb, how many pounds of fuel oil must be burned to stop the vessel under these conditions?

11.14   The rocket exhaust gas in passing through the nozzle cools 1,050°F. The specific heat of the exhaust gas is 0.26 Btu per lb per °F. What is the velocity of the exhaust gas relative to the rocket? Assume a 5 per cent energy loss in the nozzle.

11.15   An aluminum missile weighing 42 lb on earth is shot to the moon, where the acceleration of gravity is one-sixth that of the earth. At a distance of 2.5 miles from the moon's surface, the missile is falling directly toward the moon with a speed of 180 mph. The moon has no atmosphere so that the missile is falling in a vacuum. The specific heat of aluminum is 0.225 Btu per lb per °F. Assume that the moon surface absorbs only 20 per cent of the energy upon impact.

What is the increase in temperature in degrees Fahrenheit of the missile due to the impact?

11.16   As a space satellite reenters the earth's atmosphere, its kinetic energy is dissipated in work required to compress the air behind the shock wave, heat transferred to the atmosphere by mass transfer of hot gas from the boundary layer, radiation from the satellite surface, and heat absorbed by the satellite. Assume that the heat absorbed by the satellite is 52 per cent of the total change in kinetic energy, and that the initial temperature is 100°F.

Properties of aluminum:

Specific heat = 0.225 Btu per lb per °F

Melting point = 1,220°F

Heat of fusion = 168 Btu per lb

Boiling point = 3,730°F

Heat of vaporization = 3,550 Btu per lb

Assume specific heat is constant for all temperatures.

How much would the temperature of an aluminum satellite weighing 78 lb be increased when its speed is reduced from 17,500 to 8,600 mph?

11.17 An automobile weighing 4,200 lb is going downhill at an initial speed of 80 mph. The brakes are applied and slow the automobile to 20 mph in a certain distance. Assume that 80 per cent of the energy which is dissipated goes into heating up the steel brake drums, which weigh 12 lb apiece (four-wheel brakes). The specific heat of steel may be taken as 0.120 Btu per lb per °F.

If the temperature of the brakes is increased by 220°F, what is the difference in elevation (i.e., vertical distance) between the initial and final positions of the auto?

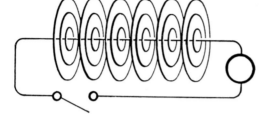

Electric and magnetic energy

This chapter concludes the discussion of energy in its various forms, which in this book are limited to the classification in Chap. 8. The title, electric and magnetic energy, is used to include both energy which is stored and that which is being transferred. We have read in Chap. 9 of the stored potential energy of electric and magnetic fields, and in Chap. 10 of the storage of electric energy in batteries.

Perhaps the best way to approach the subject of this chapter is through a consideration of charges of electricity and their relationship to electric and magnetic fields. This leads to brief discussions of electromagnetic radiation and of electric circuits. The topic of electric and magnetic work is then presented with illustrative examples.

Electric charges

The present state of scientific knowledge postulates the existence of what are called *electric charges*. There are two kinds of electric charges which are arbitrarily designated as *positive* and *negative* and which have definite magnitudes. They are associated with the electron and the proton, two basic particles which constitute the atoms of matter along with other particles. The electron is said to have what we might call a *unit negative charge* and the proton is said to have a *unit positive charge*. These unit charges are equal in magnitude but opposite in sign. All quantities of electricity appear to occur as integral multiples of these unit charges.

It is an experimental fact that *like charges repel* and *unlike charges attract* each other (Fig. 12.1). It is furthermore assumed that there are the same number of negative charges and positive charges in the universe.

The model of an atom visualized by Niels Bohr in 1913 consists of a nucleus composed of protons and neutrons * around which electrons whirl in orbit. The *neutron* is an uncharged or electrically neutral particle of about the same mass as the proton, 1.67×10^{-24} g, as compared with the mass of the electron, 9.11×10^{-28} g. The undisturbed atoms themselves are neutral, having an equal number of electrons and protons. If an atom loses one or more electrons, there is an excess of

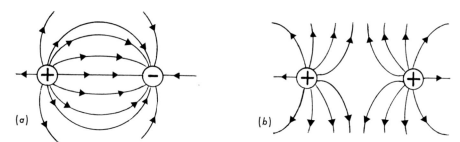

FIG. 12.1. Positive and negative electric charges: *(a)* attraction of unlike charges; *(b)* repulsion of like charges.

positive charge and the remaining portion of the atom is called a *positive ion*. If an atom gains one or more extra electrons, it is called a *negative ion*. Electric charges are always associated with basic particles of matter.

In all substances there exist some electrons which have become detached from the atoms and which move freely in the interatomic spaces. These are called *free electrons*. Some substances have more of these free electrons per unit volume than others. Metals, in general, part more readily with one or more electrons in the outer orbits of their atoms than do nonmetals. It is for this reason that metals are generally good conductors of electricity and nonmetals are not. The best insulators have the least number of free electrons.

---

* Except the hydrogen atom, whose nucleus contains no neutrons but only one proton, and which has only one electron in orbit around this proton.

Fields

Field theory is an area of study of some magnitude and complexity in electrical engineering and it is not possible to do more than present a few of the basic concepts in this book. Electric and magnetic fields are not confined to circuits but exist generally in space. They are related to electric charges in the following three ways:

1. Static electric fields are due to electric charges at rest.

2. Static magnetic fields are produced by electric charges in uniform motion.

3. Time-varying electric and magnetic fields are produced by electric charges in accelerated motion.

These fields, electric and magnetic, static and time-varying, might be visualized as being similar to the gravitational field of attraction existing between two masses. We may consider that energy is stored in the fields and that electric charges in these fields have potential energy according to their position in the fields.

When electric charges are being accelerated, they produce both time-varying electric and magnetic fields which are called an electromagnetic field. This electromagnetic field is not a single field but is a combination of a time-varying electric field and a time-varying magnetic field. Electric and magnetic fields are at right angles to each other in free space but not when confined by boundaries such as the walls of a wave guide.

The student must not get the impression that electric and magnetic fields necessarily exist separately and apart from each other. The statement that a static magnetic field is produced by electric charges in uniform motion does not mean that an electric field is not also present. As a matter of fact it is the presence of a static electric field maintained at constant strength which might be said to produce the uniform flow of electric charges which in turn produces the static magnetic field; and vice versa, if electric charges are moved through a magnetic field, say as free electrons in a wire conductor moved through the field, a flow of these charges could occur in the conductor as a result of the electric field which is set up.

But it is helpful in working with electrical concepts and quantities to dissociate the two kinds of fields even though they are closely interrelated. And it is important to remember that there is energy associated with these fields. Suppose that we have a constant rate of flow of electric charges through a conductor. In order to start this flow, there must be a period during which the flow builds up from zero to the particular rate. This is called a *transient* period. As electric charges begin to flow and continue in increasing quantities, the magnetic field is built up from zero to the strength developed by the final rate of flow. During this stage, part of the energy being transferred into the system is used to build up the magnetic field and is stored in it. So long as the constant flow of electric charges is maintained, no further energy is transferred into or out of the magnetic field. If the flow of charges is suddenly stopped, the magnetic field collapses and its energy is transferred out of the system, sometimes with damaging violence.

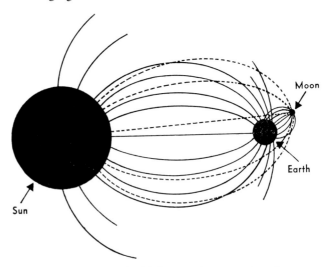

FIG. 12.2. *Gravitational fields between the sun, earth, and moon.*

Electromagnetic radiation

Electric and magnetic fields extend throughout space just as do gravitational fields. However, most of us are more familiar with gravity than with electromagnetic phenomena. The earth is held in orbit around the sun by forces of the gravitational field existing between the sun and the earth. The earth is at a mean distance of about 90 million miles from the sun, showing the tremendous extent of this gravitational field. Other planets in the solar system are much further away. Such gravitational fields are set up between any two masses in accordance with Newton's law of gravitational attraction, which was stated in Chap. 5. Thus gravitational fields also exist between the sun and the far-distant stars, or between the earth and such stars, or the earth and the moon (Fig. 12.2).

In fact, the universe is one great complex of a fantastically large number of gravitational fields. However, as in the case of the earth and the moon, the local gravitational field between them is so much stronger than any of the other fields that it predominates in earth-moon calculations.

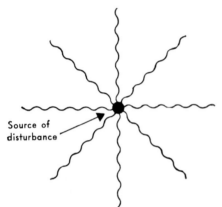

Source of disturbance

FIG. 12.3. Propagation of electromagnetic radiation in all directions.

Just so is the universe a complex of electric and magnetic fields which make possible the propagation or transmission of electromagnetic radiation. The idea of using a model is of assistance in visualizing this phenomenon, the model being a transverse wave being propagated through some medium. The simplest example is a wave which is set up by some disturbance and which travels out in all directions from the source of the disturbance in a manner analogous to the two-dimensional wave which ripples the still surface of a pond when a pebble is dropped into it. The surface of the pond might be said to correspond to electric and magnetic fields and the waves to an electromagnetic wave (Fig. 12.3). Other waves are guided by reflectors or special antennas in one direction only in much the same way a light from a source is focused into a beam by a parabolic reflector (Fig. 12.4).

In brief we might define *electromagnetic radiation as the disturbance of electric and magnetic fields.* The radiation we visualize as a wave phenomenon in these fields.

The question arises now as to what creates these disturbances? We would reason, of course, that they would have to be caused by the acceleration of electric charges and this is correct. However, electric charges are accelerated in different ways, and we find that there are variations in the *frequencies* of the disturbances or waves as a result. Radio waves, for example, are generated by accelerating electrons in electric circuits. They have frequencies of approximately from 10^3 to 10^{12} cycles per second (cps). Other mechanisms for producing radiation of higher frequencies are increasing the temperature of a substance, stopping high-velocity electrons suddenly, or disrupting atoms or atomic nuclei.

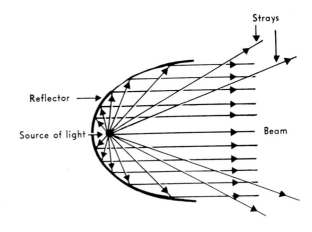

FIG. 12.4. Reflection of light rays into a beam by a parabolic reflector.

A classification of electromagnetic radiation with respect to frequency is given in the following table.

Radiation	Approximate range of frequencies, cps
Long radio waves	10^3-10^5
Radio broadcast waves	10^6-10^7
Short radio waves	10^7-10^{12}
Infrared rays	$10^{12}-5 \times 10^{14}$
Visible light	$5 \times 10^{14}-10^{15}$
Ultraviolet rays	$10^{15}-8 \times 10^{16}$
X rays	$8 \times 10^{15}-8 \times 10^{20}$
Gamma rays	$10^{18}-10^{23}$
Cosmic rays	$10^{23}+$

Electric circuits

The electric circuit might be said to be a "model" which represents certain electrical phenomena. This circuit model was conceived before it was known that there were electric charges in motion, but it has continued to be useful in solving electrical problems as the knowledge of electricity and magnetism has grown.

We have previously spoken of conductors which are usually in the form of metallic wires. The simplest circuit consists of a *conductor* and a source of *electromotive force* which is expressed in units of volts. The electromotive force is not a force in the mechanical sense of the term. Its true nature is perhaps better expressed by the *potential difference* which it produces and which indicates a certain difference in potential energy in an electric field.

FIG. 12.5. Source of emf with conductor of zero resistance.

The primary sources of electromotive force (emf) are (1) electromagnetic induction and (2) contact of two dissimilar bodies. In simplest terms electromagnetic induction has to do with the generation of potential difference and the accompanying motion of electric charges either by moving a conductor through a magnetic field or by moving a magnetic field with respect to a conductor; the effect is the same in either case.

Potential difference arising from the contact of two dissimilar bodies occurs in storage batteries and primary cells as well as in a number of special effects.*

The simplest circuit is shown diagrammatically in Fig. 12.5. The source of emf is shown by the two cross lines, which also represent the magnitude of emf. The long thin line represents the positive terminal and the short heavy line the negative terminal. The loop joining the terminals represents the conductor. If the potential difference is maintained, i.e., if the electric field is maintained, there will be a flow of electric charges in the conductor. The rate of flow of these charges is the magnitude of the electric *current*, which is measured in units of

* Volta effect, thermoelectric effects, pyroelectric effect, piezoelectric effect.

amperes. If the current in a circuit is in one direction only, we call this *direct current.* If there is no variation in the rate of flow, we say that the current is *constant*, but if the current increases and decreases although still flowing in the same direction we call this *pulsating* current. The term direct current includes both cases. If the current reverses flow, first in one direction, then in the opposite direction, we call this *alternating current.* An alternating current would be produced by a source of alternating emf.

The emf produces a potential difference which is measured in volts and which, in turn, produces a flow of electric charges. If the potential difference between two ends of a conductor is a certain number of volts, it follows that there must be a voltage drop or change in the potential difference between any two points along the conductor. For example if a uniform conductor 10 ft long is connected across the terminals of a battery whose potential difference is 12 volts, the voltage drop is $12/10 = 1.2$ volts per ft. Why this is so is explained in the next paragraph.

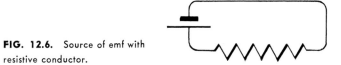

FIG. 12.6. Source of emf with resistive conductor.

No conducting material permits a completely free flow of electrons under most conditions. There is a resistance to the flow of electric charges or to current which is analogous to frictional resistance to the flow of fluids through pipes. This characteristic property varies from one material to another and depends also upon the geometry of the material among other factors. We call this property *resistance* and express it in units of *ohms.* We find that the resistance of cylindrical metallic conductors varies directly with the length and inversely with the cross-sectional area. Resistance also varies with temperature for metallic conductors, increasing with an increase in temperature and decreasing with a decrease in temperature. For example, an increase in temperature of from 32 to 86°F will produce an increase in resistance of a copper conductor of about 11 per cent. The symbol for the resistance of a conductor in a circuit is a zigzag line as shown in Fig. 12.6.

The resistance to the flow of electric charges increases the temperature of a conductor and usually results in a loss of energy through heat which flows from the conductor to the surroundings.

Another element of the electric circuit is the *capacitance* which is associated with the electric field. When two uncharged or neutral conductors are connected to a source of emf, one to the positive terminal and the other to the negative terminal, there is a transfer of charge between conductors, one acquiring an excess of positive charges and

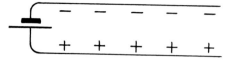

FIG. 12.7. Storage of electric charges in unconnected conductors.

the other an excess of negative charges (Fig. 12.7). The closer together the conductors, the greater the transfer of charges. Such an arrangement is called a *capacitor* and is usually constructed with parallel plates rather than parallel wires to give much greater capacity for storing electric charges. The closer together the conductor plates which

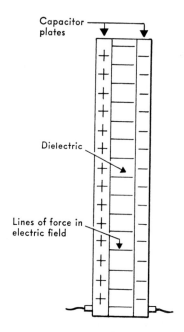

FIG. 12.8. Diagrammatic sketch of a capacitor.

are separated by a *dielectric* (insulating material) (Fig. 12.8), the stronger is the electric field intensity between plates for a given charge.

The capacitor is a means of storing electric energy and might be compared with the elastic spring for storing mechanical energy.

Elastic spring:

Stored energy $= \frac{1}{2}kl^2$

where $k =$ spring constant

$l =$ deformation or difference in length

Capacitor:

Stored energy $= \frac{1}{2}CV^2$

where $C =$ capacitance

$V =$ potential difference across the capacitor

Both the spring and the capacitor store potential energy, one mechanical and the other electrical. We may write $W = CV^2/2$, where W is the electrical work done in changing a capacitor. The *capacitance C* is expressed in farads, V in volts, and W in joules. Thus we have

$$\text{Joules} = \frac{\text{farads} \times (\text{volts})^2}{2}$$

Since the farad is a rather large unit, a more convenient size is a microfarad (μf), which is one-millionth of a farad (10^{-6} farad), or a micromicrofarad ($\mu\mu$f), which is 10^{-12} farad. One joule is equivalent to 1 watt-sec, or 0.7376 ft-lb.

The electrical energy stored in a 5-μf capacitor in charging it to 150 volts is

$$W = \frac{1}{2} \times 5 \times 10^{-6} \times (150)^2$$

$$= 0.0562 \text{ joule}$$

or

$$= 0.0562 \text{ watt-sec}$$

or

$$= 0.0415 \text{ ft-lb}$$

The circuit pictured in Fig. 12.7 is called an *open* circuit. If the conductors were placed in contact or joined, we would have a *closed* circuit and a flow of electric charges would take place. All circuits, open or closed, have capacitance, although this may be small in many circuits unless a capacitor itself is inserted. The symbols for capacitors are shown in Fig. 12.9.

Current does *not flow through* a capacitor. If we have a capacitor and a resistor in *parallel* with a constant source of emf (Fig. 12.10), current will flow through branch B of the circuit but not branch A.

Energy will be stored in the capacitor to an amount determined by the potential difference existing between points m and n.

What about a simple circuit with a capacitor and a resistor in series (Fig. 12.11)? If we assume that the source of emf is constant, say a bat-

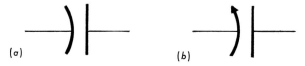

(a)   (b)

FIG. 12.9. Symbols for capacitors: *(a)* fixed capacitor;
(b) variable capacitor.

tery, then no current will flow and the potential difference across the capacitor plates will be equal to that of the source but opposite in sign. Or we might say that the *back emf* of the capacitor is equal to the *emf* of the battery. But, one may ask, if there is no flow of current,

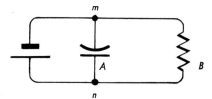

FIG. 12.10. Capacitor and
resistor in parallel.

how does the capacitor acquire its charge and its potential difference? We know that electric charges must *flow* to the plates of the capacitor for it to become charged.

The answer is, of course, that we must first assemble the circuit and

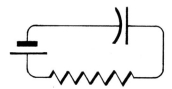

FIG. 12.11. Capacitor and
resistor in series.

then close it, say with a switch (Fig. 12.12). Before the switch is closed, there is no charge on the capacitor. When it is closed, there will be a very brief period of time during which current will flow, i.e., positive charges in one direction to one plate of the capacitor and negative charges in the other direction to the other plate. This flow will continue until the potential difference across the capacitor equals that of the battery. Thus we see that there can be a flow of current in a series circuit with a capacitor even though there is no current flowing through the capacitor, i.e., no electric charges moving across the dielectric from one plate to the other.

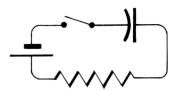

FIG. 12.12. Capacitor and resistor in series with switch.

In the preceding case, the capacitor was charged by a transient current produced by a battery when a switch was closed. The constant source of emf could just as well be a generator, whose symbol is shown in Fig. 12.13. The capacitor could also be charged by a transient cur-

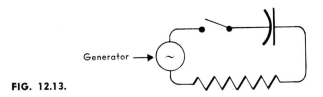

Generator →

FIG. 12.13.

rent from a nonconstant source such as another capacitor (Fig. 12.14). In this case the charge would be distributed between capacitors A and B, flowing from A to B when the switch is closed until the potential differences are equal.

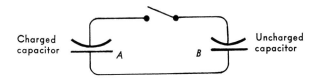

Charged capacitor A B Uncharged capacitor

FIG. 12.14.   Two capacitors in series.

Current would also flow in a series circuit containing a capacitor if there is a source of alternating emf (Fig. 12.15). There would be four stages in the process as the voltage across the capacitor varies and changes direction. Consider one plate of the capacitor. In stage 1, say positive charges build up on the plate as the voltage increases (0 to A, Fig. 12.15). In stage 2 (A to B), the positive charges are discharged.

In stage 3 (*B* to *C*) negative charges build up on the plate, and in stage 4 (*C* to *D*) the negative charges are discharged. The other plate of the capacitor would follow the same cycle, first with negative charges, then with positive charges. However, there would be no flow of charges across the dielectric which separates the plates of the capacitor.

Variable capacitors are used extensively in radio circuits for tuning to various frequencies. Capacitors find many other uses, one of which is to eliminate sparking at switches or break points when circuits containing inductances are suddenly opened.

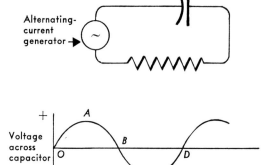

FIG. 12.15. Capacitor in alternating-current circuit.

Another element of the electric circuit is *inductance*, which is associated with a varying magnetic field. This electrical property is analogous to the mechanical mass inertia of a body which tends to oppose a change in motion. Suppose that we have a source of increasing emf which in turn produces an accelerated flow of electric charges or an increasing electric current. The increasing current produces a time-varying magnetic field. This in turn induces a *back emf* which is analogous to the reactive force against one's hand when pushing against an object to accelerate it. Likewise, if an electric current decreases, it is accompanied by a decreasing magnetic field which induces a back emf which tends to oppose the decrease in current. This is analogous to the force exerted, say, by a coasting automobile against any attempt to stop it.

The inductance of a straight conductor is very small compared with that of a conductor which is wound in the shape of a coil, and especially so if a ferromagnetic core is placed inside the coil. The symbol for an *inductor* is a coil of wire (Fig. 12.16).

To explain the action of an inductor, let us take two simple circuits, one with just a resistor and the other with a resistor and an inductor.

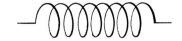

FIG. 12.16. Symbol for inductor.

When the switch is closed in the circuit with a resistor only (Fig. 12.17), the current increases from zero to its maximum value, $I = E/R$, almost instantaneously. The symbol E is used to signify electromotive

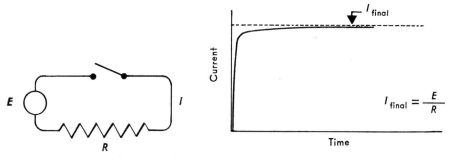

FIG. 12.17. Circuit with resistor only.

force at a source as contrasted with the symbol V to signify potential difference between any two points in a circuit. Both E and V are expressed in volts.

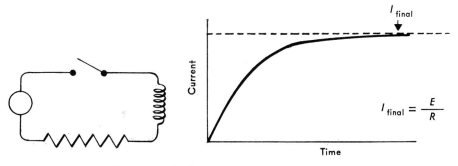

FIG. 12.18. Circuit with resistor and inductor.

In the circuit with both a resistor and an inductor (Fig. 12.18), the back emf produced by the inductor acts to retard appreciably the rise of the current to its maximum value. We might think of this phenomenon as electrical work being done against the back emf, which thereby stores potential energy in the magnetic field being built up in the inductor. This is analogous to mechanical work done by a force which is accelerating a body and thereby storing kinetic energy in the body as its velocity increases. The forms of the expressions for these two kinds of stored energy are similar. Let W be the mechanical or electrical work done in storing an equal amount of energy as kinetic or magnetic energy, respectively.

Kinetic energy:

$$W = \tfrac{1}{2}mv^2$$

Magnetic energy:

$$W = \tfrac{1}{2}LI^2$$

where W is work or energy customarily expressed in joules, L is *inductance* in *henrys*, and I is current in amperes. We have then

$$\text{Joules} = \frac{\text{henrys} \times (\text{amperes})^2}{2}$$

For example, if we have a circuit with a battery that supplies an emf of 12 volts, an inductor with an inductance of 14 henrys, and a resistance of 0.5 ohm including that of the inductor, the final constant current will be

$$I = \frac{12}{0.5} = 24 \text{ amp}$$

The magnetic energy stored in the inductor will be

$$E = \tfrac{1}{2} \times 14 \times (24)^2$$

$$= 4{,}030 \text{ joules}$$

$$= 4{,}030 \text{ watt-sec}$$

$$= 2{,}980 \text{ ft-lb}$$

$$= 3.82 \text{ Btu}$$

It should be emphasized again that an inductor produces back emf only when the current is changing. When the current is increasing, energy is accumulated in the magnetic field of the inductor; when the current remains constant, energy remains stored in the inductor, which produces no back emf under this condition; when the current is decreasing, energy is released from the magnetic field of the inductor. If a circuit with an inductor and a constant current is suddenly opened, the magnetic field will collapse and discharge the stored energy back into the circuit. This release of energy is responsible for the arc that often flashes when a switch is opened in an inductive circuit. It also results in heating of the circuit elements due to their resistance. The induction coil is used in automotive ignition systems to provide the sudden release of electric energy which produces the spark in a spark plug. The circuit is so designed that a spark discharge with a potential difference of about 5,000 volts is obtained from energy delivered by a 6-volt battery. Electric power is given by $P = VI$ and electric energy by $E = VIt$. If the current and time are very small, as in the case of a spark, the potential difference is relatively large.

It should be pointed out that all circuits are inductive in the sense of producing magnetic fields when current flows, but that many circuits without inductors as such in the circuit have relatively negligible inductance.

At the beginning of this section, we referred to the electric circuit as a "model" of an electrical system. Certain elements of this model have been discussed, a "source" of emf, a resistor, a capacitor, and an inductor. We may now assign a circuit model to such electrical devices as batteries, motors, and generators. Batteries have internal resistance and so may be modeled as a source of emf and a resistor. The circuit model for a d-c generator likewise would be a source of emf and a resistor. The circuit model for an a-c generator would be a source of emf, a resistor, and an inductor. Although the conventional symbol for a battery is ⊣⊢ , for a d-c generator ─○─ , and for an a-c generator ─⊛─ , if we wish to represent fully the internal resistances and inductances, we would use ⊣⊢WW─ , ─○─WW─ , and ─ƳƳƳ─⊛─WW─ as the respective symbols.

Electric motors are devices for converting electrical work to mechanical work as contrasted with generators, which convert mechanical to electrical work. Motors are also sources of emf in one sense of the word; they produce a back emf as they work against mechanical forces. This back emf is a very real source of emf which opposes that supplied by generators. Accordingly a circuit model of a d-c motor consists of a source of back emf and a resistor, and of an a-c motor a source of back emf, a resistor, and an inductor.

Electric and magnetic work

We have seen that electric and magnetic energy, either stored or being transferred, is inseparably related to electric and magnetic fields. Whether we say that the energy is in the fields or in the electric charges which produce them depends upon the frame of reference which is selected. We see a possible ambiguity here. Also, we have spoken of an electric current with its flow of electrons, ions, or other charged particles as being a transfer of electric energy. Yet electrons and other particles have mass so that there is also mass transfer involved if we choose to consider it. Again, for example, some writers characterize convection as energy transfer or a combination of energy and mass transfer rather than as simply mass transfer.

The conclusion that we reach when we are confronted with these ideas is that scientists and engineers have invented terms to try to describe natural phenomena which they have observed or ideas about these phenomena which they have conceived. As Dr. Willis Harman [*] has stated: "It seems to me important that the beginning student have some understanding of the fact that energy is a concept which we use because it is convenient to do so, and not because we 'understand' it in any deep philosophical sense. There is a certain amount of arbitrariness involved, particularly in the classification of different forms of energy, and the student should not be too disturbed when he encounters ambiguities of the sort pointed out above."

It is easier for beginning students to study problems involving electrical work and power from the standpoint of circuits rather than fields. Accordingly in this section we shall consider a number of simple examples of the transfer or conversion of electric and magnetic energy using the quantities in the practical dimension system mentioned in Chap. 5 (also Appendix C). The basic elements of this system are current I, resistance R, and time T. Voltage, or potential difference, is defined as

$$V = IR$$

which is one of the basic relationships. Capacitance C has the dimensions of $[R]^{-1}[T]$ and inductance L the dimensions $[R][T]$.

---

[*] Electronics Research Laboratory, Stanford University.

Electric energy is expressed by *

$$E = VIt$$

and electric power by

$$P = VI$$

These expressions are always valid for constant direct current but are valid only for instantaneous values for transients and alternating currents. Their use in the examples which follow will be confined only to constant direct currents. In such d-c circuits, there are energy and power losses due to the resistance of the conductors. These are deter-

FIG. 12.19. Early electric-light bulb with transparent glass through which the filament is clearly visible.

mined by substituting for V from $V = IR$ in the energy and power equations. We thus have

Energy loss $= I^2Rt$

Power loss $= I^2R$

These losses occur as heat which is transferred from the conductors.

The primary uses of electric energy are to produce mechanical energy, heat, light, and electromagnetic radiations. Electric motors are the primary means of converting electric to mechanical work. Incandescent and fluorescent bulbs are used to convert electric work to light. High-resistance wires provide sources of heat. Various electrical devices which were mentioned previously in this chapter generate electromagnetic radiations.

* The symbol E is used to signify both energy and electromotive force. To avoid confusion, some writers use E for energy and ε for electromotive force.

The incandescent light bulb is an interesting example of the use of electric current to raise the temperature in a high-resistance metallic filament sufficiently to make it "white hot," thus radiating both light and heat (Fig. 12.19). In this instance, the heat usually represents a loss of energy, although incandescent bulbs have been used industrially as sources of heat in drying ovens.

How much heat is generated per minute by a 75-watt incandescent light bulb?

1 watt = 3.413 Btu per hr

$$P = \frac{3.413 \times 75}{60}$$

$$= 4.3 \text{ Btu per min}$$

What is the resistance of the filament of this bulb if it is designed to operate at 110 volts?

$$I = \frac{P}{V} = \frac{75}{110}$$

$$= 0.682 \text{ amp}$$

$$R = \frac{V}{I} = \frac{110}{0.682}$$

$$= 161 \text{ ohms}$$

Suppose that this bulb is used to heat water in a pot which contains 2.52 lb of water at 68°F. Assume that 70 per cent of its surface area is beneath the surface of the water. If the temperature of the water is raised to 125°F in 2 hr, compute the efficiency of the heating process.

The total heat transferred from the bulb is

$$Q_{bulb} = 3.413 \times 75 \times 2$$

$$= 512 \text{ Btu}$$

The heat required to raise the temperature of the water is

$$Q_{water} = 1 \times 2.52(125 - 68)$$

$$= 144 \text{ Btu}$$

$$\text{Efficiency} = \frac{144}{512}$$

$$= 28 \text{ per cent}$$

If electrical energy is being supplied to a house at $0.04 per kwhr, how much would it cost to cook a meal on an electric stove? Assume that two 1,500-watt eyes are turned on for full power for 20 min and at one-third power for 40 min, a 500-watt eye is used at full power for 30 min, and the 2,000-watt oven is used at an average of three-fourths full power for an hour and a half.

1,500-watt units:

$$E_1 = 2 \times 1,500 \times \frac{1}{3} = 1,000 \text{ whr}$$

$$E_2 = 2 \times \frac{1,500}{3} \times \frac{2}{3} = 667 \text{ whr}$$

500-watt unit:

$$E_3 = 500 \times \frac{1}{2} = 250 \text{ whr}$$

Oven:

$$E_4 = 2,000 \times \frac{3}{4} \times 1.5 = 2,250 \text{ whr}$$

$$\text{Total energy} = 4,167 \text{ whr, or } 4.17 \text{ kwhr}$$

$$\text{Cost of cooking meal} = 4.17 \times 0.04$$
$$= \$0.17$$

How many Btu are liberated in the kitchen, assuming that only 30 per cent of the energy released is retained by the food and the stove?

$$1 \text{ whr} = 3.413 \text{ Btu}$$

$$\text{Heat liberated} = 0.70 \times 4,167 \times 3.413$$
$$= 9,950 \text{ Btu}$$

If the energy were used to accelerate a loaded truck weighing 16 tons, what speed in miles per hour would it give this vehicle, assuming that 25 per cent of the energy is used up in overcoming friction and air resistance?

$$\frac{16 \times 2,000v^2}{2g} = 0.75 \times 9,950 \times 778$$

$$v^2 = \frac{0.75 \times 9,950 \times 778 \times 64.4}{32,000}$$

$$= 11,700$$

$$v = 108 \text{ fps}$$

$$= 74 \text{ mph}$$

A special cooking unit is to be designed to heat the equivalent of 15 lb of water in a specially insulated vessel by means of an electrical heating coil operating on 110 volts. The water is to be heated from 65 to 212°F in 40 min. Assume the cooking unit to be 80 per cent efficient. What must be the resistance of the wire coil?

$$\text{Rate of heat flow to water} = \frac{1 \times 15(212 - 65)}{40}$$

$$= 55.1 \text{ Btu per min}$$

Since this represents 80 per cent of the power required, we have

$$\text{Power required} = \frac{55.1 \times 17.58}{0.80}$$

$$= 1{,}210 \text{ watts}$$

$$\text{Current} = \frac{1{,}210}{110} = 11 \text{ amp}$$

From the equation $V = IR$, we have

$$R = \frac{V}{I}$$

$$= \frac{110}{11}$$

$$= 10 \text{ ohms}$$

A hydraulic turbine (Fig. 12.20) drives a d-c electric generator which produces at its terminals a maximum current of 2,430 amp at a potential difference of 13,800 volts. Assuming that there is a loss in energy of 8 per cent in transmission from the turbine and generation in the generator, what horsepower must the turbine supply?

$$\text{Power output} = \frac{2{,}430 \times 13{,}800}{1{,}000}$$

$$= 33{,}500 \text{ kw}$$

This represents 92 per cent of the total energy input from the turbine.

$$\text{Power input} = \frac{33{,}500 \times 1.341}{0.92}$$

$$= 48{,}900 \text{ hp}$$

An electric motor runs at full load when supplied with a current of 55 amp at 110 volts. If the equivalent internal resistance of the motor is

FIG. 12.20. Cast-steel runner for a hydraulic turbine in the Kerr Dam on the Roanoke River in Virginia. The turbine has a 201-in.-diameter discharge and operates at 85.7 rpm under a 90-ft head of water. *(Courtesy of the Newport News Shipbuilding and Dry Dock Company and the Corps of Engineers, U.S. Army.)*

0.30 ohm, how much horsepower does it deliver in mechanical work and what is its efficiency?

Power loss in the form of heat is

$$P = (55)^2(0.3)$$

$$= 908 \text{ watts}$$

$$\text{Power input} = 55 \times 110$$

$$= 6{,}050 \text{ watts}$$

$$\text{Power output} = 6{,}050 - 908$$

$$= 5{,}142 \text{ watts, or } 6.89 \text{ hp}$$

$$\text{Efficiency} = \frac{5{,}142}{6{,}050} \times 100$$

$$= 85 \text{ per cent}$$

The flow of water over Niagara Falls is about 465,000 tons per min. The average drop is about 160 ft. If all this energy could be successfully harnessed, how many kilowatts of electric power would it produce?

The energy available per minute, or the power, is

$$P = 4.65 \times 10^5 \times 2,000 \times 160$$

$$= 1.49 \times 10^{11} \text{ ft-lb per min}$$

$$= \frac{1.49 \times 10^{11} \times 0.746}{33,000}$$

$$= 3,370,000 \text{ kw}$$

Solar energy falls upon the surface of the earth in the vicinity of the equator at an average rate of about 7 Btu per sq ft per min on clear days. This is energy which comes from directly overhead, i.e., which falls upon an area perpendicular to the rays of the sun.

If this energy should be converted at 5 per cent efficiency to electrical energy which was sold for 3 cents per kilowatthour, what would be the gross income on 40 acres of land near the equator, assuming an equivalent average time for sunshine directly overhead of 5 hr per day and 300 days of sunshine per year? Let E_{in} be the energy input per day on 40 acres and E_{out} be the output of useful energy for electrical purposes.

$$E_{in} = 40 \times 43,560 \times 7 \times 60 \times 5$$

$$= 3.66 \times 10^9 \text{ Btu per day}$$

$$E_{out} = 0.05 \times 3.66 \times 10^9$$

$$= 1.83 \times 10^8 \text{ Btu per day}$$

$$= \frac{1.83 \times 10^8}{3,413}$$

$$= 5.37 \times 10^4 \text{ kwhr per day}$$

$$\text{Total } E_{out} = 5.37 \times 10^4 \times 300$$

$$= 16.1 \times 10^6 \text{ kwhr per year}$$

$$\text{Income} = 16.1 \times 10^6 \times 0.03$$

$$= \$483,000 \text{ per year}$$

Assuming that the heat of combustion of coal is 12,000 Btu per lb, how many tons of coal would be required to produce the same total heat which falls on the surface of the earth from the sun in 1 sec?

The rays of the sun would not fall perpendicularly upon all of the surface (Fig. 12.21). The equivalent or effective area would be the horizontal projection of any area; therefore the total equivalent area would be equal to the area of a great circle of the earth.

Effective area $= \pi(3,980)^2$

$$= 4.98 \times 10^7 \text{ sq miles}$$

$$= 1.39 \times 10^{15} \text{ sq ft}$$

$$Q = \frac{7 \times 1.39 \times 10^{15}}{60}$$

$$= 1.62 \times 10^{14} \text{ Btu per sec}$$

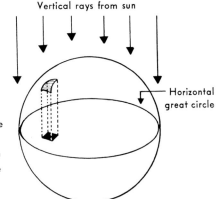

FIG. 12.21. Effective area of the earth for receiving radiant energy from the sun. The vertical direction is determined by the axis from the center of the earth to the center of the sun.

Vertical rays from sun

Horizontal great circle

$$\text{Weight of coal} = \frac{1.62 \times 10^{14}}{1.2 \times 10^4}$$

$$= 1.35 \times 10^{10} \text{ lb per sec}$$

$$= 6,750,000 \text{ tons per sec}$$

A capacitor has a capacitance of 620 μf. How much mechanical work must be done to charge this capacitor to a potential difference of 750 volts, assuming an efficiency of 78 per cent in the process?

$$\text{Stored energy} = \tfrac{1}{2} \times 620 \times 10^{-6} \times (750)^2$$

$$= 3.1 \times 10^{-4} \times 56 \times 10^4$$

$$= 174 \text{ joules or watt-sec}$$

$$\text{Work required} = \frac{174 \times 0.738}{0.78}$$

$$= 165 \text{ ft-lb}$$

A capacitor with a capacitance of 800 μf is charged to a potential difference of 1,200 volts. Suppose that its terminals are connected by a length of copper wire which weighs 0.14 lb. If all the energy goes into heating the wire and no heat is transferred into the surroundings, what will be the increase in temperature of the wire? The specific heat of copper may be taken to be 0.092 Btu per lb per °F.

$$\text{Stored energy} = \tfrac{1}{2} \times 800 \times 10^{-6} \times (1,200)^2$$
$$= 4 \times 10^{-4} \times 1.44 \times 10^6$$
$$= 576 \text{ watt-sec}$$

Since 1 watt-sec (joule) is equal to 9.48×10^{-4} Btu, we have

$$E = 9.48 \times 10^{-4} \times 576$$
$$= 0.544 \text{ Btu}$$

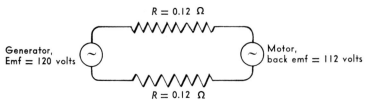

FIG. 12.22.

$$0.092 \times 0.14 \times \Delta t = 0.544$$
$$\Delta t = \frac{0.544}{0.092 \times 0.14}$$
$$= 42.2°F$$

An electric generator which produces an emf of 120 volts is in a circuit with an electric motor which has a back emf of 112 volts when running under full load (Fig. 12.22). The two copper conductors which connect the machines have a resistance of 0.12 ohm each. What is the rate at which heat is transferred from the conductors, assuming that there is a constant flow of heat from conductors to surroundings, i.e., there is no increase in temperature of the conductors?

The potential drop in each conductor is the same and is one-half of the difference between 120 volts and 112 volts. For each conductor

$$V = \frac{120 - 112}{2}$$
$$= 4 \text{ volts}$$

The current in the circuit is then

$$I = \frac{4}{0.12}$$

$$= 33.3 \text{ amp}$$

The power loss is

$$P = (33.3)^2 0.12$$

$$= 133 \text{ watts}$$

$$= 133 \times 0.0569$$

$$= 7.56 \text{ Btu per min}$$

A 25-henry inductor with an internal resistance of 0.4 ohm is placed in series in a d-c circuit with a conductor whose resistance is 4.0 ohms. If the emf is 110 volts, how many equivalent Btu of energy are stored in the inductor when the current has reached its final value?

The total resistance of the circuit is 4.4 ohms.

$$I = \frac{110}{4.4}$$

$$= 25 \text{ amp}$$

$$E = \frac{1}{2} \times 25(25)^2$$

$$= 7,810 \text{ watt-sec}$$

or

$$= 7,810 \times 9.48 \times 10^{-4}$$

$$= 7.40 \text{ Btu}$$

Suggested references

Burr W. Leyson, "The Miracle of Light and Power," E. P. Dutton & Co., Inc., New York, 1955. An interesting story of the development of our public services for electricity, gas, and steam, with a chapter on electricity and safety in the home.

Hugh H. Skilling, "Exploring Electricity," The Ronald Press, New York, 1948. Men of electricity, from Thales and his amber bead in 600 B.C. through Galvani, Volta, and Ampère to Meitner, Fermi, and the first atomic explosion.

FIG. 12.23. The fireboat *Fire Fighter* in a spectacular exhibition of the capacity of its monitors. *(Courtesy of the New York City Fire Department.)*

M. Brotherton, "Capacitors: Their Use in Electronic Circuits," D. Van Nostrand Company, Inc., Princeton, N.J., 1946. The introduction to this book on energy-storing devices is recommended for beginning students in engineering.

John Mills, "A Fugue in Cycles and Bels," D. Van Nostrand Company, Inc., Princeton, N.J., 1935. The impact of electricity upon music and the revolutionary influences it may have upon composers and directors.

Problems

12.1 A man weighing 165 lb carries a box weighing 130 lb up four floors in a building in 1 min.

a. If the floors are 11 ft apart, what power in kilowatts is he producing?

b. How many kilowatts of power would have to be produced by an electric motor to raise the box and man this same height in 4 sec?

12.2 A stevedore lifts 100-lb loads a height of 4 ft on an average of three loads per minute during an 8-hr day.

a. What would be the cost of doing this work by electric power if the rate is $0.04 per kwhr?

b. What reasons can you give to justify the use of manual labor rather than machinery?

12.3 The New York City fireboat *Fire Fighter* (Fig. 12.23) can deliver 20,000 gal of water per min at 150 psi. This pressure ideally would throw the streams of water almost 350 ft vertically upward were it not for air resistance.

a. How many kilowatts must be supplied by the electric motors which drive the pumps, neglecting friction losses in the motor-pump system?

b. The motors are supplied with electric power from generators which in turn are operated by two 2-cycle 16-cylinder diesel engines. Assuming 53 per cent efficiency for the engines, how many gallons of fuel oil are required per hour to supply the necessary power? The heat of combustion of fuel oil may be taken as 18,200 Btu per lb and its specific gravity as 0.89.

12.4 Assume that the flow of water over Niagara Falls on the American side is 266,000 cfs and the average drop over the falls is 168 ft.

a. If 9 per cent of the potential energy is dissipated as heat to the surrounding air and earth, what is the increase in temperature of the water after the fall?

b. If 60 per cent of the total available energy were converted to electrical energy, estimate how many homes it could supply with adequate electricity at 7 P.M. on a winter evening.

12.5 An electric motor which delivers 5 hp draws 18 amp on a 230-volt line when operating at full load and at the rated speed of 1,800 rpm.

a. What is its efficiency in per cent?

b. Assume that the motor is composed of 40 lb of iron with a specific heat of 0.109 Btu per lb per °F and 30 lb of copper with a specific heat of 0.092 Btu per lb per °F. How much would the temperature increase after 4 hr of steady operation if no heat were transferred away from the motor?

12.6 An electric crane is rated at 15 tons.

a. If it is to raise this load at a speed of 1 ft in 5 sec, what must be the horsepower of the motor?

b. If the motor efficiency is 89 per cent, how many amperes of current would it require on a 230-volt supply line?

12.7 A hydraulic turbine and housing in a field installation weighs 30 tons. The units are made of steel with a specific heat of 0.118 Btu per lb per °F. It is desired to dry out the installation, which contains

200 lb of water that could not be removed by draining it. Fourteen 1,000-watt incandescent bulbs are placed inside the installation for this purpose. How many hours will be required to remove all the water, assuming that the initial temperature of turbine, housing, and water is 62°F? Assume that the process is 30 per cent efficient and that the entire installation is brought to 212°F.

12.8 *a.* How many Btu per min are produced by six incandescent light bulbs each rated at 100 watts? The voltage in the circuits is 110 volts.

b. Suppose that these bulbs remain lighted in a room with the dimensions 14 by 12 by 9 ft. The air in the room is at a temperature of 72°F at the time the lamps are lighted. What will be the temperature of the air in the room after 12 hr if 28 per cent of the heat transferred from the lamps is lost through the walls, floor, and ceiling? The specific heat of air may be taken to be 0.24 Btu per lb per °F and its density 0.0763 pcf. Assume uniform distribution of heat throughout the air and constant specific heat.

c. Does the increase of temperature that was calculated in (*b*) seem reasonable? Why or why not?

12.9 Air-conditioning machines are rated in terms of "tons." The unit of capacity is the number of Btu absorbed by 1 ton of ice in melting at 32°F in 24 hr. For example, since the heat of fusion of ice is 144 Btu per lb, a 1-ton air-conditioning unit should be able to absorb 12,000 Btu per hr as determined by the following calculation:

$$P = \frac{2,000 \times 144}{24}$$

$$= 12,000 \text{ Btu per hr}$$

In practice this represents an average or nominal capacity because the heat which can be transferred by a unit depends upon a number of factors including the temperature of the air and its humidity.

a. A residence is being cooled by a 3-ton air-conditioning unit. What per cent of the capacity of the unit is required to remove the heat produced by four 100-watt bulbs, six 75-watt bulbs, four 40-watt bulbs, a 500-watt electric coil for heating coffee, and eight persons playing bridge? The average heat output of a person at rest is about 480 Btu per hr.

b. How many kilowatts of electric power would be needed to cool a large house during a reception at which 76 people were in attendance? Assume that the air-conditioning equipment is 69 per cent efficient and that the walls, floors, and ceilings of the house permit an additional 50 per cent increase in the heat load from the outside air under the given conditions. Assume also that persons moving around at a reception produce about 650 Btu per hr each.

12.10 Electric locomotives use electric motors to provide power to pull trains on level ground or up grades. However, these locomotives have an advantage over steam or diesel locomotives in going down long grades because the motors can be used as electric generators to provide dynamic braking and to feed power back into the system to help pull some other train up a grade.

A 50-car coal train is coasting down a 2 per cent grade (Fig. 12.24) at a constant speed of 45 mph due to the retarding action of the dy-

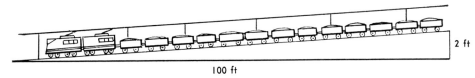

FIG. 12.24. Electric locomotives and coal cars coasting down a 2 per cent grade.

namic braking effect provided by using the motors as generators. The locomotives themselves weigh a total of 200 tons and each coal car weighs 35 tons.

How many kilowatts of power are fed back into the system, assuming that 23 per cent of the power is lost in friction, conversion, and transmission?

12.11 A thermionic converter (Fig. 12.25) is a device for converting heat energy directly into electrical energy. The principle is illustrated by the diagrammatic sketch in Fig. 12.26. How many cubic feet of acetylene gas per hour at standard conditions (heat of combustion may be taken as 1,350 Btu per cu ft) would be required to operate an ordinary flashlight bulb which is rated at 2.4 volts and draws 0.39 amp? Assume a conversion efficiency of 8.1 per cent.

12.12 Suppose that we have a constant d-c source of a potential difference of 110 volts. Assume that this is short-circuited by 1 ft of

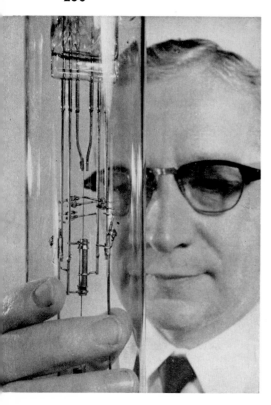

FIG. 12.25. Experimental thermionic converter for directly converting heat to electricity displayed by Dr. Volney C. Wilson, who developed it. *(Courtesy of the General Electric Company.)*

No. 14 copper wire. What time in seconds would elapse before the wire melts?

Assume no change in the voltage and no heat transferred from the wire. The specific heat of copper, 0.092 Btu per lb per °F, may be taken to be constant. The heat of fusion of copper is 50.6 Btu per lb and the melting point is 1,083°C.

The resistance of No. 14 wire is 2.52 ohms per 1,000 ft and may be assumed to be constant although it will actually increase with temperature; No. 14 wire weighs 12.43 lb per 1,000 ft.

12.13 A capacitor with a capacitance of 200 μf is charged to a potential difference of 15,000 volts. It is attached to a piece of copper wire weighing 0.095 lb submerged in 1.2 lb of water at 68°F in a glass beaker. What is the increase in temperature of the wire and water when the capacitor is discharged? Assume a 7 per cent loss of energy to the atmosphere and a specific heat of copper of 0.0918 Btu per lb per °F.

12.14   An inductor has an inductance of 38 henrys and is in a d-c circuit which is carrying a current of 140 amp. If the circuit is switched in such a way that the inductor is suddenly connected in a simple loop circuit only with a 0.04-μf capacitor, to what voltage will it charge the capacitor?

12.15   Estimate the area in acres over which solar energy would have to be collected during the time the sun shines in one day in order to supply the electrical energy used by a small community of 4,500 people in a 24-hr period. Assume an average rate of solar radiation of 5.2 Btu per sq ft per min and a conversion efficiency of 8 per cent.

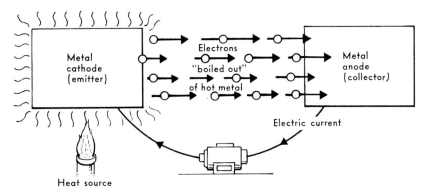

FIG. 12.26.   Principle of the thermionic converter. *(Courtesy of the General Electric Company.)*

12.16   A permanent horseshoe magnet is held vertically above a small steel plate weighing 0.052 lb. It lifts the plate to it from a distance of 2 in. with such force that the plate has acquired a velocity of 2.4 fps at the instant of impact.

a. Assuming that 80 per cent of the kinetic energy is absorbed by the plate, what is its increase in temperature? Assume a specific heat of 0.115 Btu per lb per °F.

b. What is the ratio of the change in potential energy of the plate to change in kinetic energy between its position at rest and its position just before impact?

c. Permanent magnets do not lose their magnetism as a result of attracting objects to themselves. The increase in potential energy of the steel plate and the loss of kinetic energy represent a loss of energy from the magnetic field. Explain in detail how this energy is restored.

The engineer in practice

The previous chapters have presented basic ideas, methods, and principles in engineering and also have provided some of the elementary knowledge used by the engineer. These topics have been treated individually and there has been no attempt as yet to bring them together. However, the engineer in practice calls upon all of these and more in performing the major function of his profession, the design function. How this function brings them together will be discussed in the first section of this chapter. One aspect of design, the economic aspect, is highly important. One of the major economic problems of the designer will be discussed next. These topics lead to the problems at the end of the chapter which are more comprehensive than the others in the book. The student should read the introduction to them before he begins his solutions.

Design

A dictionary definition of the word "design" is to map out in the mind, to plan, or to invent. Design is a synthetic process which brings together materials, methods, principles, and other resources to produce plans for an economical engineering product, be it diesel turbine, electric motor, steel bridge, chemical process, space satellite, or waffle iron. This is the essence of the work done by the engineer in practice. The term design and the idea of designer have too frequently been associated with those civil engineers who are doing structural design work over the drawing boards. This is not so. The word in its broadest sense applies to the *creative genius* of all engineers and is so used in the discussion in this chapter. Pencil and paper, whether they be used for calculating, sketching, or precise drafting, are simply aids to the design process which actually takes place in the mind and through the imagination of the engineer. He designs a crude-oil refining process (Fig. 13.1) or an automatically operated electronic control system just as much as he designs a reinforced-concrete building frame.

Furthermore, the good designer not only considers the design of a machine, for example, to perform a particular function satisfactorily, but he must also keep in mind the ease of maintenance and repair, the problems which will confront the manufacturer, and certainly the costs which are involved at all stages. Even this is not enough, for the machine must be durable, safe, and in many instances appealing to the eye.

We might also say that the designer is a pioneer in one sense of the word, a professional pioneer who has confidence in his ability to find a

FIG. 13.1. Fractionating columns and a reactor-regenerator of a catalytic cracking unit designed by chemical engineers for refining crude oil. *(Courtesy of the American Oil Company.)*

reasonable solution to a new problem. A statement contained in a report of the American Society for Engineering Education bears well upon this point:*

The capacity to design includes more than mere technical competence. It involves the willingness to attack a situation never seen or studied before and for which data are often incomplete; it also includes an acceptance of full responsibility for solving the problem on a professional basis.

What is involved in design? Perhaps the best answer to this question is to take a close look at something which the engineer has already designed and built and with which everyone is familiar. The electric oscillating fan which is shown in Fig. 13.2 illustrates very clearly a design process which included both theoretical and practical considerations. Most people take such a fan for granted without realizing the tremendous amount of time and effort which have been devoted to developing the design.

The principal elements are the motor, which is the local source of energy for operation, and the fan-blade assembly. The theory which must be used requires a knowledge of electricity and magnetism, fluid dynamics, mechanisms, and heat. The motor, which consists essentially of two parts, a stationary unit (the field) and a rotating unit (the armature), must be designed to have so many coils of wire of a certain

* Report of the Committee on Evaluation of Engineering Education, American Society for Engineering Education, June 15, 1955, p. 15.

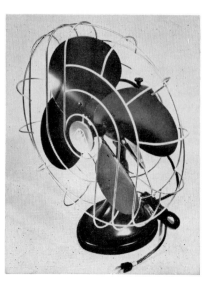 

size in these units, to deliver so much power at a certain speed of rotation at a certain amperage and at a standard voltage. It should also be designed so that it does not get hot enough to burn a human being, much less overheat and burn out the insulation surrounding the coils. The student may say that he will buy his motors from an electrical manufacturer and design only the other parts of the fan. True enough, but someone has to design and build these motors before he gets them. Not all designs are the product of the creative genius of a single engineer; in fact, very few are.

The fan blades (Fig. 13.3) must be given a certain size, shape, and pitch. They should move so many cubic feet of air per minute at the operating speed of the motor. This is a very complicated problem in fluid mechanics, a three-dimensional problem since the fan is in the open. If the fan were in a pipe or duct where the flow into the fan blades was essentially from one direction, it would be less difficult. The motor housing is streamlined for better aerodynamic flow. The student may say at first thought, "We shall use the air flowing over the motor housing to cool the motor." But this tends to defeat the purpose of the fan which is to circulate air for cooling people. If the motor heats the air, it is less effective for the fan's purpose.

The mechanism to produce oscillation of the fan (Fig. 13.4) poses a simple problem in machine design. The oscillation must be produced by power from the motor, as is the rotation of the fan blades. Note the use of worm gears to reduce the speed since it would be impracticable for the fan to oscillate at motor speed. This mechanism is placed in back of the fan and fits well into the streamlining of the motor housing. If it were placed below, it would disturb the symmetry of air flow and impede it. A linkage must also be designed (Fig. 13.5) between the motor housing and the pedestal. The designer must consider the angle of oscillation and also some device for disengaging the mechanism for steady air flow in one direction. And the angle of oscillation, shall it be 30°, 45°, 49°, or what? Here is one of the many places where the designer must make an arbitrary decision based upon his judgment, experience, and imagination.

The angle of oscillation is but one of many practical aspects of the

FIG. 13.2. A 16-in. oscillating electric fan. (Courtesy of the Hunter Division, Robbins and Myers, Inc.)

FIG. 13.3. View of the fan blades showing their shape, size, pitch, and mounting. (Courtesy of the Hunter Division, Robbins and Myers, Inc.)

FIG. 13.4. Interior view of the mechanism which produces oscillation (taken from above). *(Courtesy of the Hunter Division, Robbins and Myers, Inc.)*

design. How shall the fan-blade mounting be attached to the motor shaft? Shall it be welded, force-fitted, keyed, or held by a setscrew? Common sense argues against a permanent attachment, and the setscrew with a tapered point which fits a matched hole in the shaft (Fig. 13.6) is a satisfactory device.

Safety must always be considered. Not only must the motor remain relatively cool, but the fan blades must be guarded. The attachment of

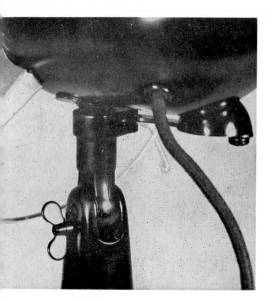

FIG. 13.5. View of the linkage mechanism and the swivel joint. *(Courtesy of the Hunter Division, Robbins and Myers, Inc.)*

the guard housing to the motor housing (Fig. 13.6) is another feature of the design. The guard itself must be sufficiently strong and yet offer as little resistance as possible to the passage of air through it. It is to be anticipated that someone is going to grab the guard to pick up the fan instead of using the handle for that purpose on the motor housing. The material of the guard must be protected from corrosion. There will be complaints if it soon becomes rusty.

The designer should not forget that the successful operation of the motor depends upon adequate lubrication. Provision must be made for lubricating the bearings easily and without having to remove any portion of the motor housing or guard assembly.

The upper portion of the pedestal must be attached to the motor housing so that the latter can rotate freely but cannot be lifted off the pedestal. It must also be located close to the combined center of gravity of the motor, fan blades, and guard assembly so that the fan will not have a tendency to fall forward or backward. A swivel joint connecting the upper and lower portions of the pedestal (refer back to Fig. 13.5) must be designed for ease and sureness of operation to permit tilting the fan upward or downward. Over-all consideration must be given to the swivel joint, the guard assembly, and the oscillating linkage to be sure

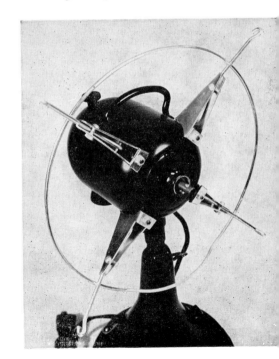

FIG. 13.6. View of the brackets which support the guard assembly and the tapered hole in the motor shaft. (*Courtesy of the Hunter Division, Robbins and Myers, Inc.*)

FIG. 13.7. The fan pedestal viewed from above, showing the switch location, the holes for wall or shelf mounting, and the shaping to indicate the front of the fan. (*Courtesy of the Hunter Division, Robbins and Myers, Inc.*)

that the guard assembly will not strike any portion of the pedestal and jam when the fan is tilted downward. Note the indentation in the back guard ring in Fig. 13.6.

The base of the pedestal itself is a design problem. If we make it quite large for the sake of stability, we may add unnecessarily to the weight and make the fan more unwieldy. The smaller we make it, the easier it is to knock the fan over. Somewhere between the extremes, the designer must make a choice. He must also consider the location of the switch, which is usually on the pedestal (Fig. 13.7), so that it may be reached by hand without danger of getting into the fan blades. He may also specify holes in the pedestal for wall or shelf mounting. Another detail which adds to the completeness of the design is the shaping of the pedestal to show the front of the fan. Note not only that the pedestal has a blunt point for this purpose but that this is accented by a slight ridge on the surface of the pedestal.

Throughout all these considerations, the designer must keep in mind the availability of materials, methods of fabrication, methods of assembly, and perhaps ways of packing and shipping, just as he has considered various aspects of the use and maintenance of the fan. And just as important, he must be continually "cost conscious." One might say that the integral sign and the dollar sign usually go hand in hand in engineering design. This brings us to one aspect of economics in design which merits further discussion and which is presented in the following section.

Economic balances

An economic balance arises in a design whenever there are some costs which increase and other costs which decrease with respect to one or more of the factors involved. The design of a 24-mile causeway across Lake Pontchartrain illustrates this situation very clearly. This structure consists of two component parts, pier units and deck slabs. An economic balance of the spacing of the piers (Fig. 13.8) was sought so that the over-all cost of the causeway would be a minimum. The student can well understand that if the piers are spaced very close together there will be too many of them even if they are made smaller. And if they are spaced very far apart, the deck slabs (Fig. 13.9) will not only have to be too large and expensive to span the long gap, but might have

FIG. 13.8. Construction of a 24-mile causeway across Lake Pontchartrain, Louisiana. The nearly constant depth of approximately 15 ft made it economical to prefabricate all components of the structure at a plant built on the shore near the north end and to transport them by barge to be erected. (*Courtesy of Palmer and Baker Engineers, Inc.*)

FIG. 13.9. View of the underside of a typical prefabricated deck slab of the Lake Pontchartrain causeway in which the beams and floor were cast integrally. *(Courtesy of Palmer and Baker Engineers, Inc.)*

to be replaced by even more expensive truss or arch structures. We may say that in general the cost of the piers per linear foot of the causeway decreases and the cost of the deck slabs increases as the span is increased. Somewhere between a very small span and a very large span there is a span of minimum cost per foot (Fig. 13.10).

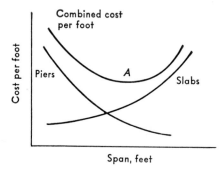

FIG. 13.10. Simple economic balance. Minimum point *A* is reached when the slopes of the two curves are equal in magnitude but opposite in sign.

The problems encountered in erecting such a structure as the causeway cannot be overlooked. Actually for this particular structure, the economic span was limited by the capacity of the floating crane which lifted the floor slabs from barges to the piers. The capacity of the crane was 200 tons.

Another economic balance in the design of the Lake Pontchartrain causeway had to be made in determining the height of the piers above the water and the number of raised portions and movable bridges to permit small and large craft to pass the causeway. The construction of one "hump" in the structure to permit the passage of small boats can be seen in progress in the background of Fig. 13.8. The higher the piers, the greater is their cost. On the other hand, if the piers are very low, there will be damage from waves during strong winds and stormy weather, and also serious interruption of automobile and truck traffic with the possibility that the causeway may be out of service much of the time. Too many movable bridges and humps increase the cost unduly. Too few add to the cost of operation of boats and barges which constantly ply the lake waters.

Another instance of this type of economic balance is seen in the design of transmission lines for electrical power which are constructed on land and in water (Fig. 13.11). What major elements are involved in the design of these systems? The size and weight of the wire conductors, the size and construction of the towers, the electric power to be transmitted, and the power losses in the conductors. The towers are designed to hold the conductors at a safe distance from the ground and to resist wind forces as well as to carry the weight of the conductors. The greater the span, the fewer the towers needed although the towers must be made higher because of the greater sag of the conductors. On the other hand, the greater the span, the more the weight on the conductor and the larger it must be to withstand the tensile stresses produced by its own weight and wind loads. The larger the conductor, the more power it can carry and the less the power loss. And so we see again the problem of the designer in reaching a solution which satisfies the technical requirements at a minimum cost.

Another such type of economic balance is found in highway location

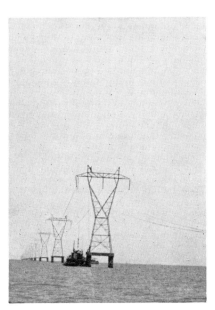

FIG. 13.11. Typical transmission lines for electric current. *(a)* Steel transmission-line towers constructed on concrete piers over water. *(b)* Wooden H frame transmission-line towers. *(Courtesy of the Louisiana Power and Light Company.)*

in hilly country. If the road is designed to be more or less level rather than to follow the ground slopes of the hills, it will be necessary to cut through the tops of the hills and to fill in the valleys. It is uneconomical to throw away the earth which is cut from the hill or to go to a borrow pit to dig up earth for the fills. Accordingly the elevation of the road is selected such that the amount of cut is approximately equal to the amount of fill (Fig. 13.12). Elevation *A* requires too much fill and elevation *B* too much cut. Elevation *C* is more nearly balanced.

Again we find an economic balance between cost and size of equipment to produce a certain product. The petroleum refineries use a wide variety of processing equipment, such as the catalytic cracker, a unit which is composed of a reactor, a regenerator, and fractionating columns. Its purpose is to refine crude oil into such products as naphthalene, benzene, kerosene, and gasoline. The refinery wishes to process a certain number of barrels of crude oil per day. Shall it use six small units, three of medium size, or one which is very large?

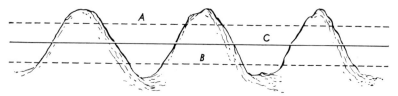

FIG. 13.12.   Cut and fill for highway location.

There are also types of economic balances which involve time as a factor. It is well known that the annual depreciation in the value of an automobile generally decreases with age but the cost of operation generally increases. In the first year or two, there is little increase in operating costs but the depreciation drops sharply, so that the combined annual cost is decreasing. After several years the depreciation reaches a relatively stable value which decreases slowly, but the cost of operation rises more sharply, so that the combined annual cost now climbs upward. The best time to sell, therefore, is just before the combined cost begins to increase. This is a problem in operation rather than in design although the latter is involved indirectly since the amount of maintenance and repair needed depends upon the design.

The design of a muffler and tail-pipe assembly for an automobile involves the time element. Shall the muffler be built out of relatively inexpensive sheet metal, using inexpensive manufacturing operations, or shall it be made from expensive stainless steel, which is much harder and more expensive to fabricate? The sheet metal will corrode rapidly compared with the stainless steel and an assembly made from it will have to be replaced more often. A component part of short life but low replacement cost not infrequently proves to be economical.

These are but a few of the many examples of economic balances which occur daily in the work of the professional engineer.

Introduction to the problems

The problems in this chapter are more comprehensive than most of those in the preceding chapters. They are designed to give the beginning student in engineering a chance to try his hand as a professional engineer in situations where he must use his judgment, experience, or imagination as well as some of the methods and elementary principles of engineering. Some are design problems and others might well be parts of such problems.

It is to be expected that in many cases every student will come up with a different answer and with different conclusions. There are some problems where unique answers are obtained for parts of the problem, but the student may be asked to indicate where variations in these answers might be expected in actual practice.

In some of the problems he must go through all steps from defining the problem to arriving at conclusions and making recommendations. There are problems that involve economic balances or the conversion of energy. Some are design problems and others might well be miscellaneous and intended simply to test the ingenuity and common sense of the student. Some are primarily problems of analysis and others involve both analysis and design.

The student should approach the problems in this chapter with the attitude of a practicing engineer who is called upon for an analysis or a design. The solutions to at least some of these problems can be drawn up in formal report form as if the student were an engineer submitting his findings to a client or to an associate. He should be careful to state all his assumptions, with justifications where possible, and to include all pertinent information. His reasoning should be clearly stated and his solutions should contain all significant steps so that they may be readily followed and checked. Finally, he should summarize his findings and draw conclusions, making recommendations wherever possible.

Suggested references

Eugene Von Fange, "Professional Creativity," Prentice-Hall, Inc., Englewood Cliffs, N.J., 1959. An explanation of creative thinking and what is behind it. The following chapters are of particular interest: 1. Understanding Creation; 4. Some Techniques; 7. Judgment and Reflection; 9. A Basic Plan; 12. Develop Methods.

W. J. King, The Unwritten Laws of Engineering, *Mech. Eng.*, May, June, July, 1944. Three excellent articles on the various facets of professional practice.

Dennistoun W. Ver Planck and B. Richard Teare, Jr., "Engineering Analysis," John Wiley & Sons, Inc., New York, 1954. Many fine examples of engineering design and analysis.

J. C. L. Fish, "Engineering Economics," 2d ed., McGraw-Hill Book Company, Inc., New York, 1923. Several chapters on methods and techniques of estimating and on the determination of various kinds of costs involved in construction, operation, and maintenance.

H. G. Thuesen, "Engineering Economy," Prentice-Hall, Inc., Englewood Cliffs, N.J., 1950. An extensive study of costs. Chap. 6, Some Concepts Useful in Economic Studies, is especially useful.

Clarence E. Bullinger, "Engineering Economy," 3d ed., McGraw-Hill Book Company, Inc., New York, 1958. Another extensive study of costs with an interesting chapter on the intangible analysis (chap. 13).

Problems

13.1 A manufacturer of cans buys tin-coated steel in strips to make the end units and sides of the cans. In making the end units (tops and bottoms), strips of the proper width are fed into a machine in which circular dies punch out a number of circular pieces in a straight line across the strip at one stroke. The dies are placed to leave a clearance of 0.05 in. between adjacent units as they are punched in a line across the strip and also a clearance of 0.05 in. between the outermost units and the sides of the strip. In this method, the centers of the units fall on the corners of squares.

Suppose it is suggested to the management that considerable saving could be made if the units were punched so that their centers fell on the vertices of equilateral triangles (or parallelograms composed of two equilateral triangles) with the same clearances of 0.05 in. (Fig. 13.13).

a. Neglecting waste at the sides and ends of a strip, what percentage of metal would be saved by so rearranging the dies?

b. Considering all waste, including that at sides and ends where the clearance is also 0.05 in., what percentage of metal is saved with this new arrangement if the diameter of the units is $2\frac{1}{2}$ in. and if six units are punched at each stroke (i.e., the gang punch is made of six dies)? The strips are 4 ft $0\frac{1}{2}$ in. long for each of the two arrangements.

c. In making this suggestion to management, point out two ways in which the change-over might be made. Which of these two ways is obviously the simpler and should be followed if conditions will permit?

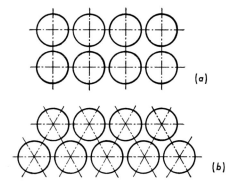

(a)

FIG. 13.13. Patterns for punching end units: (a) centers on squares; (b) centers on equilateral triangles.

(b)

d. Assume that the metal strip from which the units are punched is supplied from a large roll as a continuous strip. Neglect the wastage at the beginning and end of the strip. Derive an expression for the amount of metal saved per foot of length, i.e., an expression for the difference in width of the two strips w, in terms of the number of units n punched at one time, the diameter of each unit D, the uniform clearance c between units, and the cosine of 30°.

$$w = f(n, D, c, \cos 30°)$$

e. Comment on as many of the various factors which might affect this change-over as you can recognize, and indicate under what conditions the change-over might or might not be economical.

13.2 A can manufacturer wants to know something about the relative merits of various sizes and shapes of cans to hold 1 gal.

a. Make a comparative study of the total surface areas in square inches of the following solids which will give an approximate comparison of the net amount of sheet metal required for each shape. The volume of each of these solids is, of course, to be 1 gal: (1) cube; (2) right cylinder with height equal to the diameter of the base; (3) right cylinder with height equal to twice the diameter of the base; (4) sphere. Note which of these shapes requires the minimum amount of surface area.

b. Considering the practical aspects of manufacturing cans and of distributing various products in them, list reasons why you might select one of the preceding cans as the best to use even though it may not have the smallest surface area.

c. Derive the relationship between the diameter D and the height h for a cylindrically shaped can to give the least or minimum surface area to enclose a given volume.

d. A visit to a grocery store to inspect can shapes will indicate that the ratios of diameter to height for cylindrical cans vary over a wide range. Can you offer a reasonable explanation for this? It will help to consider the contents of the cans and also to plot, for cylindrical cans of equal volume, a curve showing the variation in surface area as a function of the ratio of height to diameter.

13.3 An automobile is purchased new. Make a study of the costs of owning and operating the automobile considering such decreasing annual costs as depreciation, and increasing annual costs as gas and oil consumption, replacements and repairs, to determine the best time at which to sell the automobile. Plot a curve for the total of the increasing costs, and a curve for combined total costs for a period of from 5 to 6 years.

13.4 Examine three or four types of fabric, metal, or paper lamp shades.

a. On the basis of your observations, give a report on the probable manufacturing processes and industrial problems involved, the probable per cent of wastage, and the probable relative costs for each.

b. Design a lamp shade of your own and indicate the probable method of manufacture, per cent wastage, and relative costs.

13.5 A long, low bridge across a relatively flat valley is to be designed with reinforced-concrete bents, steel beams, and reinforced-concrete roadway as shown in Fig. 13.14. The costs are as follows:

Roadway: $2.50 per sq ft (average including curbing and rails).

Steel beams: The cost of an entire beam varies as the square of its span length. A 50-ft beam costs $23 per ft of length.

Bents: $9,800 per bent, including foundations.

The costs above are all-inclusive, i.e., they include materials, labor, overhead, etc.

a. What is the most economical span for building this bridge on the basis of the given data, i.e., what span gives the least combined cost per foot?

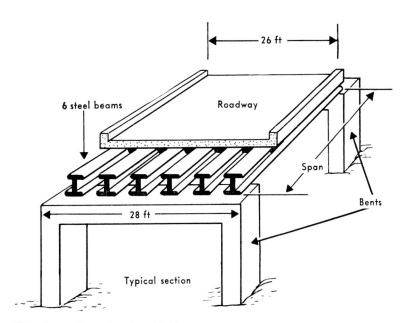

FIG. 13.14. Typical section of bridge.

b. Which of the three elements of cost might be considered slightly inaccurate in solving this problem with the given data? Can you give three reasons why this might be so?

c. What effect might the element of cost in (*b*), which is inaccurate, have on the probable design of the bridge if the valley were not flat but were three or four times as deep in the center as at the edges?

13.6 *a.* Compare the probable number of operations required in manufacturing an ordinary wooden porch chair with arms as compared with the manufacture of a modern metallic tube chair (Fig. 13.15).

FIG. 13.15. Wooden and metallic porch chairs. *(Courtesy of Maison Blanche, Inc.)*

b. Design a modern chair for a minimum number of manufacturing operations, listing the operations which are required and making an accurate sketch of your design.

13.7 *a.* Analyze and report on the system of forces which hold the trunk lid of an automobile open. Measure or calculate the weight of the trunk lid, compute the reacting forces, and sketch the system of forces to scale.

b. Design a system of your own for performing this function. This means to determine the over-all mechanical features of the system and the major reacting forces rather than to make detailed computations of stresses and strains within the various component parts.

13.8 Make a study of the horsepower which you can exert through the muscular efforts of your legs and arms. This can be done in several ways. Work done by the legs can easily be measured or estimated in running up stairs or in doing knee bends. Work done by the arms can be estimated by throwing different weights of objects in the air, by climbing ropes, by lifting weights from a standing position above the head, or by doing push-ups. Loads can be varied by carrying weights in addition to the weight of the body.

a. Determine the relationships (1) between horsepower and load and (2) between horsepower and time. Plot curves for these two relationships. Be sure to explain fully the assumptions made in each study, the methods used, and the limitations of the method, and give all data which are taken.

b. What conclusions can you draw from this study?

13.9 Make a study of the efficiency of a heating unit on a gas or electric stove in raising the temperature of water in a pot from room temperature to boiling. What suggestions can you make to improve this everyday process?

13.10 A flexible conveyor belt runs on rollers from a gravel pit a distance of three-quarters of a mile to a storage area close by a construction site where it deposits the gravel in separate stock piles which are in the shape of cones. Data are as follows:

The flexible *belt* is carried on three sets of rolls placed at suitable intervals, a center set of horizontal rolls and two sets of side rolls, one on each side at an angle of 30° with the horizontal. The belt is thus trapezoidal in cross section with the flat center portion 2 ft wide and the sides extending outward and upward at an angle of 30° with the horizontal to a vertical height of 8 in. above the top surface of the flat portion of the belt. The belt moves at a maximum speed of 4 fps.

Gravel stands on an angle of 30° with the horizontal when deposited in a pile on the ground. In other words, the sides of the pile will be on a 30° slope. But owing to the motion of the belt which introduces vibrations and also deflections as the belt passes over rolls and sags between rolls, gravel will stand on an angle of only 20° with the horizontal while being conveyed on the belt.

In order to be deposited in piles, the belt is carried upward along a *steel boom* or arm (Fig. 13.16). The boom in this case is self-supporting

FIG. 13.16. Conveyor belt transporting gravel up a boom supported by a tower and dumping it in a pile. *(Courtesy of the Goodyear Tire and Rubber Company.)*

and may be revolved horizontally about a swivel at its base and can be raised as high as 45° with the horizontal. The boom may be considered to be 100 ft in length from the ground to the point of discharge of the gravel at the top.

Assume that the boom may be represented by a straight line 100 ft long to avoid complicating the problem with the dimensions of the boom itself.

Assume that the gravel is piled continuously on the belt such that the outer edges of the pile come to within 4 in. of the top of the sides of the belt. This 4-in. distance is measured along the sloping sides of the belt, and *is not* a vertical distance.

Assume that the ground is level in the storage area.

a. How many hours will be required to build up one conical stockpile of gravel to its maximum height starting from the ground level with the belt operating at maximum speed?

b. What suggestion would you make for increasing storage capacity by improving the method of stockpiling with this same equipment?

c. Estimate the horsepower required to operate this belt at its maximum speed. Estimate what peak horsepower would be required to set the loaded belt in motion.

13.11 An elevator system consists of the cage itself, a driving motor geared to a drum over which the cables are wrapped, and a counterweight.

a. Determine the horsepower of the electric drive motor to raise the elevator loaded to capacity with 12 persons at a maximum upward acceleration of 7 fps². Neglect the weight of the cables and the torsional inertia of the drum.

b. What is the maximum downward acceleration if the power supply and brakes should fail? Neglect friction.

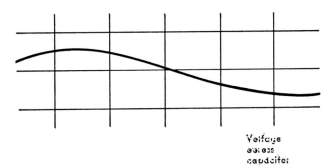

FOURTEEN

Submitting problems and reports

The engineer eventually has to present his work to someone, a client, a colleague, or his boss. These presentations may be either formal or informal and, in turn, each of these may be either verbal or written. Frequently, engineers write papers and then give them orally at meetings.

Stated in another way, the engineer is constantly communicating what he has done to someone else. The success of a particular piece of work, and indeed the success of his entire career, depends upon his effectiveness in communication. Time and time again alumni tell their former professors how they wish that they had realized the value of English and had made more of an effort while they were in college to develop their ability to speak and write clearly and effectively. The importance of this phase of educational experience cannot be over-emphasized to the student who is beginning the study of engineering. He should take full advantage of the many opportunities to communicate verbally and in writing during his years as an undergraduate.

It is not the purpose of this chapter to discuss all methods of communication but rather to make suggestions about presenting problem work and writing reports.

Problems

Problems should always be presented in a neat and orderly fashion. Since most problems are usually specific and limited in their scope, especially those submitted by engineering students to their professors in courses, it is usually not necessary to make a complete statement of the problem or to write an introduction and state formal conclusions. Problems in college are generally means of helping a student gain an understanding of concepts and techniques of specific parts of subject matter as he progresses through his courses. However, some professors may wish the student to make a complete statement of the problem at the beginning. If this is not the case, the presentation of the problem should include at least the data and assumptions and should indicate what is to be determined in the opening statements.

The following rules are offered as *highly desirable suggestions* rather than as being absolutely necessary. Variations may occur between professors and between engineers. However, it is believed that these rules represent good practice and will produce good presentations.

Format

1. *Always* put the *date* and your *name* on your problem. If more than one sheet is required, put the date and name on every sheet. It is surprising how frequently an engineer wishes to know the date on which work was done and how significant this can be.

2. Use good-quality paper, preferably engineering school problem sheets if they are available in your college. It is also desirable to use coordinate paper which is ruled in horizontal and vertical lines. There are many types of problem sheets available which do have these cross lines on them, most of them with the cross lines on the back so as not to interfere with easy reading of the problem. Such paper offers two advantages: (*a*) horizontal lines to guide the student in keeping his lettering or writing in line and (*b*) coordinate lines to aid him in plotting or drawing sketches, diagrams, and curves.

3. Print all the words and letters neatly in preference to writing unless the problem involves much English prose. Use regular engineering letters in preference to fancy lettering. Many students may prefer to write and may not be able to print neatly when they begin their college course. However, it is desirable for the student to develop a neat style of printing even though the letters may not be perfectly

formed and perfectly spaced. If writing is used, it should be above all legible and neat.

4. Use *pencil* only. Few engineers have the temerity to do their work in ink. Students may be interested to know that Albert Einstein is reputed to have done his derivations and calculations in ink. Keep an eraser handy and learn to use it efficiently. There is one exception to the use of an eraser. In taking data in the laboratory or field, it is general practice *not to erase* observations or readings when once recorded. If they are thought to be in error and additional readings are taken, draw a line through the original readings and insert the later ones. In this way both sets of readings are on record. Not infrequently, the first observations may prove to be the correct ones, or may have some bearing on the experiment or the field work which will later prove to be significant.

5. Use only one side of each sheet. If more than one sheet is used, be sure that all sheets are properly attached, unless the assignment is folded lengthwise.

6. Do not crowd the work but space it judiciously and do not be afraid of using additional sheets of paper. Nothing is more discouraging to the reader than to be confronted with a solid mass of work in which it is difficult to determine where one calculation ends and another begins. On the other hand, do not spread the work too far apart so that there are large blank spaces between the various steps.

7. Do not use short cuts or skip steps in presenting a solution. This does not mean to include scratch work but rather to be sure that every significant number or quantity in a calculation is included and that sufficient designations and explanations are made. The problem should be clearly understandable to anyone who is checking your work.

8. Use underlining, either black or in colors, to designate significant answers. This does not mean to underline the answers to every calculation which is made but only those which are the required answers to the problem. Other means may be used to designate an answer such as drawing a box around it. However, beware of fanciful designations.

Units and numbers

1. Units must be designated at every step in solving a problem where a numerical result appears. As has been indicated in a previous chapter, the number 35 by itself means nothing, since it could be gallons, foot-pounds, or feet per second.

2. Units may be abbreviated in accordance with the recommendations of the American Standards Association in Appendix D. For exam-

ple, feet per second may be abbreviated as *fps*. Some engineers may prefer to use the expanded form *ft per sec* and others *ft/sec*. Note that periods are not used at the end of the abbreviations except for inch (*in.*), barometer (*bar.*), and molecular (*mol.*).

3. Numerical fractions should usually be written with the numerator above the denominator, i.e., $\frac{7}{8}$ in. rather than 7/8 in. This is less likely to lead to confusion.

4. Be careful not to mix units; i.e., do not compute an area using one dimension in feet and another in inches.

5. Choose units in general so as to simplify numerical calculations and give practical answers; i.e., do not compute highway distances in inches.

6. A dot · is not normally used in engineering to indicate multiplication of numerical quantities. Use the multiplication sign ×. For example, write 13.6 × 12.2, but not 13.6 · 12.2.

7. Be careful to use the equals sign properly. Avoid running several calculations together on the same horizontal line, all joined by the equals sign. The following is an example of what should *not* be done:

$$V = 4 \times 5 = 20 \times 231 = 4{,}620 \text{ cu in.}$$

This could represent the calculation of a number of cubic inches contained in four 5-gal containers where the number of gallons is first computed and then multiplied by the conversion factor 231 cu in. per gal. It is obvious that 4 × 5 cannot equal 4,620. This problem could better be solved in two ways: (1) by determining first the number of gallons and then in converting this to cubic inches,

$$V = 4 \times 5 = 20 \text{ gal}$$
$$V = 20 \times 231$$
$$= 4{,}620 \text{ cu in.}$$

or (2) in one step by multiplying all three quantities together with the answer following on a separate line,

$$V = 4 \times 5 \times 231$$
$$= 4{,}620 \text{ cu in.}$$

The latter form is more direct and generally preferable. Many engineers follow this practice of not putting more than one equals sign on a line.

Arrangement of computations

1. Do not try to crowd too many numbers into a single computa-

tion. Conversely, do not use too few. In the extremes, a problem could be solved either in one complicated expression which contains all the numbers or it could be solved by multiplying or dividing no more than two numbers together at any one time. Neither of these is desirable. Break the problem into steps or parts that are logical subdivisions.

2. Use the method of tabulating wherever possible.

3. Work vertically in preference to working horizontally; i.e., set up a sum in column form rather than horizontally as

$$17.1 + 23.7 + 491.6 + 86.2$$

Language.   Engineering problems are presented with the aid of three "languages": (1) the English language, (2) the language of mathematics, and (3) the language of drawing. Each has its place. English is needed to explain and clarify. Mathematics is needed where numerical solutions are required or where theory is developed. Drawing is used to simplify and clarify both the English and mathematical presentations, and in many instances to substitute for them.

Diagrams and graphs.   It is difficult to overemphasize the importance of using diagrams and sketches in presenting problems. So much more can be transmitted quickly in a picture than in English prose. The student should take every opportunity to develop his ability to make neat, well-defined freehand sketches. Most engineering drawing books contain a chapter on the technique of freehand sketching and this should be studied carefully. These sketches should follow the conventions of engineering drawing, including proper dimensioning, cross sectioning, and the use of notations.

The plotting of graphs and curves is facilitated by the use of engineering coordinate paper, which has been previously mentioned. Most of this paper has the cross lines spaced about a quarter of an inch apart. If this is not sufficiently accurate for the plot, more precise paper having ten lines to the inch or twenty lines to the inch may be used for a plot on a separate sheet.

Parabolic or hyperbolic curves of the form

$$y = ax^b$$

plot as curves on rectangular coordinate paper but as straight lines on log-log paper, commonly called *double-log paper* (Fig. 14.1). If logarithms are taken of the above quantities, we obtain

$$\log y = \log a + b(\log x)$$

which represents a straight-line equation for the variables log y and log x.

Exponential equations of the type

$$y = e^x$$

$$y = ae^{bx}$$

$$y = 10^{bx}$$

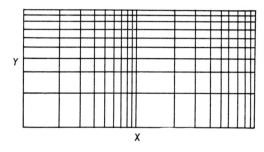

FIG. 14.1. Double-log paper. Both scales are logarithmic.

where e is the base of natural logarithms and 10 is the base of common logarithms, can be plotted as straight lines on semilog paper, which is a combination of arithmetic and logarithmic scales (Fig. 14.2). These equations reduce to the following form when logarithms are taken and

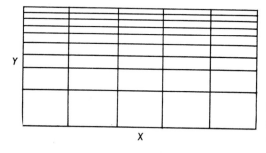

FIG. 14.2. Semilog paper. The ordinates are plotted logarithmically and the abscissas arithmetically.

are seen to be in the form of a straight line where the variables are ln y or log y and x:

$$\ln y = x$$

$$\ln y = \ln a + bx$$

$$\log y = bx$$

The choice of scales in plotting data in the form of curves or straight lines is important. The value of a subdivision between successive cross lines should be selected as 1, 2, 5, 10, 20, 50, 100, and so forth. The value of a subdivision should never be chosen as 3, 4, 6, 7, 8, or 9.

Typical problem presentations

The following examples are given to indicate satisfactory and unsatisfactory presentations of two types of problems, one a problem requiring the derivation of a formula from assumptions and basic principles, and the other the numerical calculation of a volume. These should be examined carefully before reading the criticisms of the poorly presented problems. Acceptable presentations are shown in Fig. 14.3 and Fig. 14.5.

The poorly presented derivation in Fig. 14.4 illustrates a number of faults.

1. There is mixed lettering in some of the words with capital and lower-case letters used indiscriminately.

2. In the diagram, x and y do not clearly designate the lengths which they are supposed to represent.

3. Mistakes have been carelessly scratched out rather than erased. Scratch work may be shown on the left-hand margin but should be done neatly and should be clearly separated.

4. The distance for y was chosen in such a way as to give a more complicated expression for x than in the better presentation.

5. The problem is poorly organized and presented on the sheet.

6. The final answer is not clearly designated.

7. The whole appearance of the sheet is sloppy and confusing.

The poorly presented computation of the volume of a water tank in Fig. 14.6 also has mixed capital and lower-case letters as well as the following faults:

1. The diagram is confusing. The reader cannot tell whether the 18-ft dimension is horizontal or vertical, and similarly for the 20-ft dimension.

2. Incorrect work is scratched out.

3. A dot is used to indicate multiplication instead of a multiplication sign or parentheses.

4. The equals sign is improperly used in several places.

5. There are no explanations of the calculations and no indications on the left-hand side of the equations as to what each equation represents.

6. The final answer is not underlined or otherwise designated.

7. No units are designated.

Problem No. 4
John Doe
Oct. 6, 1959

DERIVATION OF *VOLUME* OF RIGHT CONE

Let r = radius of base
x = radius of disc
element
h = height of cone

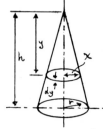

From similar triangles:

$$\frac{x}{y} = \frac{r}{h} \quad , \quad x = \frac{ry}{h}$$

dv = vol. of differential element
or disc

$$dv = (\pi x^2)\, dy$$
$$= \pi \left(\frac{ry}{h}\right)^2 dy$$

Vol. of cone = $V = \displaystyle\int_{0}^{h} \pi \left(\frac{ry}{h}\right)^2 dy$

$$= \frac{\pi r^2}{h^2} \int_{0}^{h} y^2\, dy$$

$$= \frac{\pi r^2}{h^2} \left[\frac{y^3}{3}\right]_{0}^{h}$$

$$= \frac{\pi r^2}{h^2} \times \frac{h^3}{3}$$

$$= \frac{1}{3} \pi r^2 h$$

FIG. 14.3.

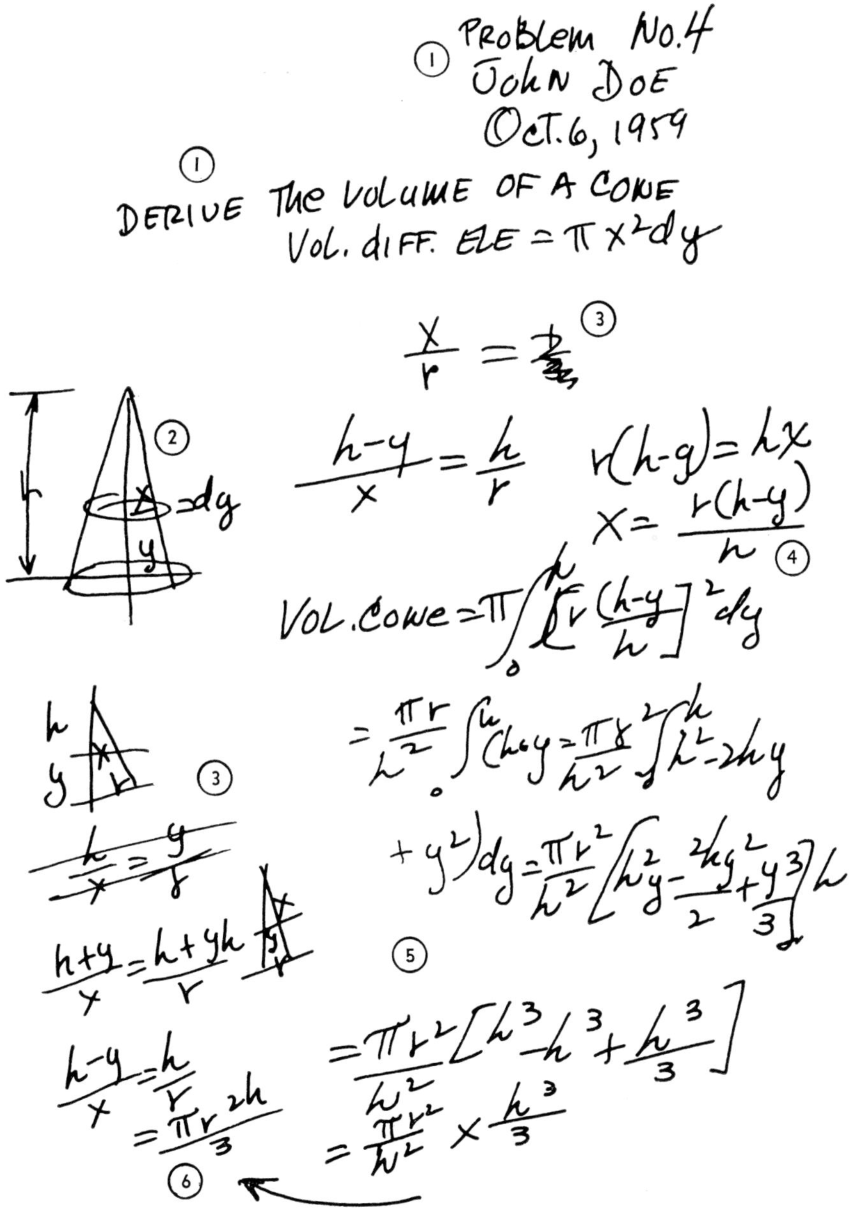

(1) PROBLEM No. 4
John Doe
Oct. 6, 1959

(1) DERIVE The VOLUME OF A CONE
Vol. diff. ELE $= \pi x^2 dy$

$\dfrac{x}{r} = \dfrac{?}{?}$ (3)

(2)

$\dfrac{h-y}{x} = \dfrac{h}{r}$ $r(h-y) = hx$

$x = \dfrac{r(h-y)}{h}$ (4)

VOL. CONE $= \pi \displaystyle\int_0^h \left[r \dfrac{(h-y)}{h} \right]^2 dy$

$= \dfrac{\pi r}{h^2} \displaystyle\int_0^h (h \cdot y = \dfrac{\pi x^2}{h^2} \int^h h^2 - 2hy$

$+ y^2) dy = \dfrac{\pi r^2}{h^2} \left[h^2 y - \dfrac{2hy^2}{2} + \dfrac{y^3}{3} \right]^h$

(5)

$= \dfrac{\pi r^2}{h^2} \left[h^3 - h^3 + \dfrac{h^3}{3} \right]$

$= \dfrac{\pi r^2}{h^2} \times \dfrac{h^3}{3}$

(3)

$\dfrac{h}{x} = \dfrac{y}{y}$

$\dfrac{h+y}{x} = \dfrac{h+yh}{r}$

$\dfrac{h-y}{x} = \dfrac{h}{r}$

$= \dfrac{\pi r^2 h}{3}$

(6)

FIG. 14.4.

Problem No. 3
John Smith
10/7/59

CALCULATION OF VOLUME OF WATER TANK
(SEE SKETCH)

V in gal
Dimensions are inside

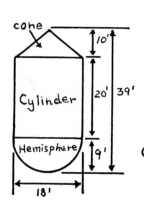

Cone: $V = \frac{1}{3} \pi r^2 h$

$$= \frac{\pi}{3}(9)^2 \times 10$$

$$= \qquad 848 \text{ cuft}$$

Cylinder: $V = \pi r^2 h$

$$= \pi (9)^2 \times 20$$

$$= \qquad 5090 \text{ cuft}$$

Hemisphere: $V = \frac{2}{3} \pi r^3$

$$= \frac{2\pi}{3}(9)^3$$

$$= \qquad \underline{1527 \text{ cuft}}$$

Total $V = \qquad 7465 \text{ cuft}$

Volume $= 7473 \times 7.48$
$= 55,900 \text{ gal}$

FIG. 14.5.

PRoblem No. 3
John Smith
10/7/59

Given: WATer tANK MAde up oF 3
Pieces, one a hemisphere, one a
cyLinder, and a cone.

What is volume in gaLs?

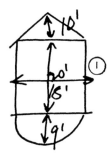

$\pi(9)^2 \cdot 20 = 2295 + \frac{1}{2} \cdot \frac{4}{3} \cdot \pi(9)^2$

$\frac{3}{4} \cdot \pi \cdot (a) \cdot r$

$= 3811 + \frac{1}{3} \cdot \pi(9)^2 \cdot 10 = 848$)

$= 3811 + 848 = 4659$

$= 4659 \times 7.48 = 34,800 \text{ gals.}$

FIG. 14.6.

Report writing

A report is basically the communication of information or counsel which someone wishes to use for a particular purpose. The *introduction* should give a clear statement of the subject, the purpose, and the plan of treatment in the body of the report. It may also include a brief statement of the conclusion, a recommendation, or findings. The *body* of the report should be carefully outlined and written with attention to detail as well as to over-all unity and coherence. The *conclusion* or summary of the report should be consistent with the introduction and the body. Above all, the report should be written with the point of view of the reader firmly in mind.

Books have been written on the subject of report writing and volumes could be written in this chapter. However, reading about report writing and actually writing a report are two different things. The aptitude of a student for report writing depends upon the capacity to organize material logically as well as to interpret and present it. Adequate attention to this subject can be given only in a full-fledged course devoted entirely to it. It is the purpose of this section of the chapter to present only some basic ideas with regard to report writing to guide the beginning student in his first efforts. If he learns these, he will acquire a foundation on which to build in later courses and in later years. These basic ideas are presented as four steps in the procedure to be followed in writing a report.

Preliminary study by author. The first stage is one in which the author himself attempts to crystallize his concept of the report as a whole. He is not thinking yet of how he will interpret it to the reader but rather asks himself the question, "Do I fully understand the subject of the report and its treatment from beginning to end?" It is helpful at the start to make a tentative outline of the material in the report. If the subject matter is rather complex and has many subdivisions, he might make notations on cards for each part so that he may spread these out before him and rearrange them to obtain a better understanding of the organization of the material.

Plan of presentation for reader. This stage involves organization for communication to the reader. The author must keep in mind the reader's point of view and the purpose for which he will use the report. These two should reach an early agreement on the purpose and extent of the report. The author should plan his presentation to treat the subject clearly and adequately. He should include all material which is pertinent and be particularly careful to avoid confusion in bringing out the essential points. The outline for the report should take rather definite form at this time. Three particular things should be kept in mind from the standpoint of the reader.

1. The report should have a good beginning. The introduction should give the subject of the report, state the purpose for which it is written, and outline the pattern to be followed in the report. First impressions are usually most vivid and the introduction is most important. Frequently, an abstract of the report is given at the very beginning.

2. The thread of continuity of the report should be maintained throughout the body. The division of the report into sections and paragraphs should be made with this in mind. Transitional comments and references to previous statements should be inserted in the proper places and especially in the opening of new sections. The reader should be kept abreast of the development of the report as he proceeds through it.

3. The final section of the report should include all important points, give proper emphasis to significant material, summarize results clearly and understandably, and present recommendations with a brief review of the reasons supporting them.

If the report is rather bulky and contains a mass of statistics and charts, it is frequently desirable to present these data in an appendix to avoid crowding the body of the report.

Rough draft. This is the actual writing stage of the report and should be done as rapidly as possible to maintain an easy and continuous flow of thought. Preferably, there should be a minimum of interruptions. Little attention should be given to defects of phrasing or awkward expressions. Precious few writers can sit down and dash off a finished report on the first writing. These few, we may be sure, are quite experienced. It is important that the trend of thought be maintained during this writing. The report can be polished and refined in the final step. The young writer is tempted to pause and review what he has just written sentence by sentence or paragraph by paragraph and consider ways of improving it. In doing this he keeps running back and forth through the report and interrupts the train of thought.

Final draft. The review and polishing of the rough draft constitute the final step in preparing a report. It is now that the writer looks back over what he has written to see that he has maintained continuity and has included all essential information. He should be sure that the introduction, the body of the report, and the final section are consistent. Now is the time to improve diction, correct errors, and look for omissions.

The problem of transmitting information by means of a report is similar to that of imparting knowledge by the lecture method. A humorous summary of the technique of report writing is quoted from Mrs. Josiah Royce, wife of the famous Harvard professor, who characterized his lecture methods as follows: *

> Oh, Professor Royce's method of lecturing is quite simple. He always tells his students at the begininng of the hour just what he is going to tell them, and how he is going to tell it to them; then he tells them exactly what he told them he would tell them in exactly the way he told them he would tell them; then, at the end of his lecture hour, he always takes time to tell them that he has told them what he told them he would tell them.

Several typical reports are included in Appendix F.

Reports in industry

Most major industries have rules, instructions, or suggestions for submitting reports within their various divisions. An example of instructions for the preparation of reports has been provided by the engineering department of E. I. du Pont de Nemours & Company. These instructions are issued in six items listed in the following order:

Introduction
Format
Elements of reports
Issuance of reports
Signatures required on reports
Distribution

The instructions are reproduced in full in Appendix G, but it may be well to point out some of the significant features of these instructions in a brief discussion. First, it should be noted that the instructions are only one part of a number of Sections of Standard Practice for the department.

---

* J. Raleigh Nelson, "Writing the Technical Report," 3d ed., pp. 27–28, McGraw-Hill Book Company, Inc., New York, 1952.

The introduction defines a report and comments on the various types. Note that reports are used either to exchange or to record information. Too many times, a report is written for what appears to be a present or immediate exigency, only to prove to be inadequate when it is read at some later date. It has been suggested that reports should be written to be *timeless*, to read the same today as fifteen years hence.

The format depends upon the nature of the material to be presented and the purpose of the report. This item gives suggestions to assist the author in deciding upon the details of presentation.

The elements of a report are listed and also rated as being optional or required for either a minimum report or an ultimate report. It is interesting to note that the minimum elements required are the *title, abstract, summary, discussion,* and *distribution list.*

Factors to be considered in the issuance of a report are the timing, serial numbering, and processing by the engineering information center. In considering the timing of a report, it may be desirable to issue a preliminary "hard core" report in advance of the final complete report, or it may be desirable to issue the report in several parts.

All reports should carry the author's signature and in general must be approved by someone "up the line." In many instances, reports should also be noted by particular persons. The item on signatures for the engineering department of Du Pont presents a table showing various types of reports and the signatures required.

A report is no good unless it gets to the persons who need it. In a large organization, a report can easily become lost like the proverbial needle in a haystack unless it is carefully directed into the proper offices. Hence a distribution list is an essential element in these circumstances. Frequently, only the minimum elements are sent around on distribution together with a request slip for the full report in the event that the minimum elements are not sufficient for a particular use.

Suggested references

J. Raleigh Nelson, "Writing the Technical Report," 3d ed., McGraw-Hill Book Company, Inc., New York, 1952. A very complete book on report writing, with numerous examples.

Fred H. Rhodes and Herbert F. Johnson, "Technical Report Writing," McGraw-Hill Book Company, Inc., New York, 1941. Brief treatment of report writing, including mathematical analysis of errors, graphical presentation of data, statistical methods, and dimensional analysis.

Ellen Johnson, "The Research Report: A Guide for the Beginner," The Ronald Press, New York, 1951. A simplified procedure for introducing the inexperienced student to the essentials of research.

Frank Kerekes and Robley Winfrey, "Report Preparation, Including Correspondence and Technical Writing," Iowa State College Press, Ames, Iowa, 1951. A carefully written and detailed book by engineers, replete with examples of every element in writing engineering reports.

Greek alphabet

Name	Capitals	Lower case
Alpha	A	α or α
Beta	B	β or β
Gamma	Γ	γ
Delta	Δ	δ or ∂
Epsilon	E	ϵ
Zeta	Z	ζ
Eta	H	η
Theta	Θ	θ or ϑ
Iota	I	ι
Kappa	K	κ or $\varkappa$
Lambda	Λ	λ
Mu	M	μ
Nu	N	ν
Xi	Ξ	ξ
Omicron	O	o
Pi	Π	π
Rho	P	ρ
Sigma	Σ	σ or ς
Tau	T	τ
Upsilon	Υ	υ
Phi	Φ	ϕ or φ
Chi	X	χ
Psi	Ψ	ψ
Omega	Ω	ω

Geometric figures

Plane rectilinear figures

Notation. Lines a, b, c, d; angles α, β, γ; altitude h; perimeter p; radius of inscribed circle r; radius of circumscribed circle R; area A.

Triangle:

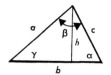

$$p = a + b + c$$

Let $s = \tfrac{1}{2}(a + b + c)$.

$$r = \frac{\sqrt{s(s-a)(s-b)(s-c)}}{s}$$

$$R = \frac{b}{2 \sin \beta} = \frac{abc}{4rs}$$

$$A = \frac{bh}{2} = \frac{ab \sin \gamma}{2}$$

Rectangle:

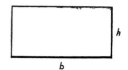

$$p = 2(b + h)$$
$$A = bh$$

Parallelogram:

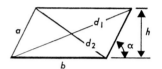

$$h = a \sin \alpha$$
$$p = 2(a + b)$$
$$d_1 = \sqrt{a^2 + b^2 + 2ab \cos \alpha}$$
$$d_2 = \sqrt{a^2 + b^2 - 2ab \cos \alpha}$$
$$A = bh$$

Trapezoid:

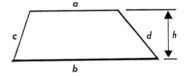

$$p = a + b + c + d$$
$$A = \frac{(a + b)h}{2}$$

Regular polygon:

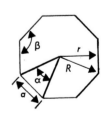

Let n = number of sides.

$$\text{Central angle} = \alpha = \frac{2\pi}{n} \quad \text{radians}$$
$$= \frac{360}{n} \quad \text{degrees}$$

$$\text{Vertex angle} = \beta = \frac{n-2}{n}\,\pi \qquad \text{radians}$$

$$= \frac{n-2}{n} \qquad 180°$$

$$p = na$$

$$r = \frac{a}{2}\cot\frac{\alpha}{2}$$

$$R = \frac{a}{2}\csc\frac{\alpha}{2}$$

$$A = \frac{nar}{2}$$

Plane curvilinear figures

Notation. Lines a, b, x, y; radius r; diameter d; perimeter p; circumference c; central angle in radians θ; arc s; chord l; rise h; area A.

Circle:

$$c = 2\pi r = \pi d$$

$$A = \pi r^2 = \frac{\pi d^2}{4}$$

Circular arc:

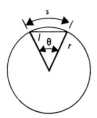

$$s = r\theta = \frac{d\theta}{2}$$

$$l = 2r\sin\frac{\theta}{2}$$

Circular segment:

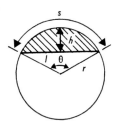

$$h = r\left(1 - \cos\frac{\theta}{2}\right) = \frac{l}{2}\tan\frac{\theta}{4}$$

$$A = \frac{r^2}{2}\left(\theta - \sin\theta\right)$$

Note: θ is in radians.

$$A \text{ (approx.)} = \frac{2lh}{3}$$

(For $h = r/4$, error is about 3.5 per cent.)

Circular sector:

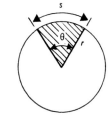

$$A = \frac{\theta r^2}{2} = \frac{sr}{2}$$

Annulus:

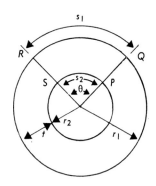

$$A \text{ (total)} = \pi(r_1^2 - r_2^2)$$

$$A \text{ (sector } PQRS) = \frac{\theta}{2}\left(r_1^2 - r_2^2\right)$$

$$= \frac{t}{2}\left(s_1 + s_2\right)$$

Ellipse:

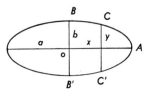

$$p = \pi(a + b)\left(1 + \frac{R^2}{4} + \frac{R^4}{64} + \frac{R^6}{256} + \cdots\right)$$

where $R = (a - b)/(a + b)$.

$$A = \pi ab$$

$$A \text{ (section } BCC'B') = xy + ab \sin^{-1}\frac{x}{a}$$

$$A \text{ (segment } ACC'A) = -xy + ab \cos^{-1}\frac{x}{a}$$

Parabola:

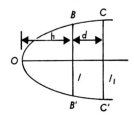

$$\text{Arc } BOB' \text{ (approx.)} = l\left(1 + \frac{8R^2}{3} - \frac{32R^4}{5} + \cdots\right)$$

where $R = h/l$.

$$A \text{ (segment } BOB') = \frac{2hl}{3}$$

$$A \text{ (section } BCC'B') = \frac{2d}{3}\left(\frac{l_1{}^3 - l^3}{l_1{}^2 - l^2}\right)$$

Solids with plane surfaces

Notation. Lines c, d; altitude h; slant height s; perimeter of base p or p'; perimeter of a right section p_r; area of base A or A'; area of right section A_r; total lateral area A_l; total surface area A_t; volume V.

Prism:

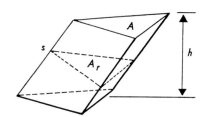

$$A = hp = sp_r$$
$$V = hA = sA_r$$

Prismatoid:

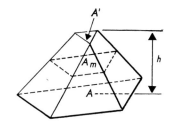

Let A_m = area of mid-section.

$$V = \frac{h}{6}(A + A' + 4A_m)$$

Pyramid:

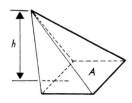

A_l = sum of areas of triangular sides

$$A_l \text{ (right regular pyramid)} = \frac{sp}{2}$$

$$V = \frac{1}{3} hA$$

Frustum of pyramid:

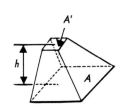

$$V = \frac{h}{3}(A + A' + \sqrt{AA'})$$

Tetrahedron: four faces, equilateral triangles.

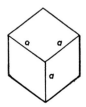

$$A_t = 1.732a^2$$
$$V = 0.118a^3$$

Cube: six faces, squares.

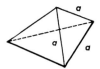

$$A_t = 6a^2$$
$$V = a^3$$

Octahedron: eight faces, equilateral triangles.

$$A_t = 3.464a^2$$
$$V = 0.471a^3$$

Dodecahedron: twelve faces, regular pentagons.

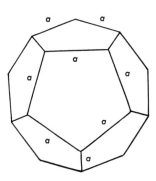

$$A_t = 20.65a^2$$
$$V = 7.66a^3$$

Icosahedron: twenty faces, equilateral triangles.

$A_t = 8.66a^2$

$V = 2.18a^3$

Solids with curved surfaces

Notation.   Lines a, b, c, d; altitude h or h_1; slant height s; radius R or r; diameter d; perimeter of base p; perimeter of a right section p_r; angle in radians θ; arc s; chord l; rise h; area of base A or A'; area of a right section A_r; area of lateral surface A_l; total surface area A_t; volume V.

Right cylinder:

$A_l = 2\pi rh = hp$

$A_t = 2\pi r(r + h)$

$V = \pi r^2 h = hA$

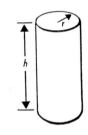

General cylinder:

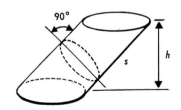

$A_l = hp = sp_r$

$V = hA = sA_r$

Right circular cone:

Cone:

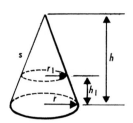

$$A_l = \pi r s$$

$$A_t = \pi r (r + s)$$

$$V = \frac{1}{3} hA$$

$$= \frac{1}{3} \pi r^2 h$$

Frustum:

$$s = \sqrt{h_1{}^2 + (r - r_1)^2}$$

$$A_l = \pi s (r + r_1)$$

$$V = \frac{\pi h_1}{3} (r^2 + r_1{}^2 + r r_1)$$

General cone:

Cone:

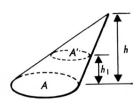

$$V = \frac{1}{3} hA$$

Frustum:

$$V = \frac{h_1}{3} (A + A' + \sqrt{AA'})$$

Sphere:

$$A_t = 4\pi r^2 = \pi d^2$$

$$V = \frac{4\pi r^3}{3} = \frac{\pi d^3}{6}$$

Spherical sector:

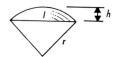

$$A_t = \frac{\pi r}{2}\ (4h + l)$$

$$V = \frac{2\pi r^2 h}{3}$$

Spherical zone:

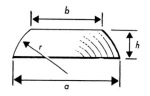

$$A_l = 2\pi r h$$

$$A_t = \frac{\pi}{4}\ (8rh + a^2 + b^2)$$

$$V = \frac{\pi h}{24}\ (3a^2 + 3b^2 + 4h^2)$$

Spherical segment:

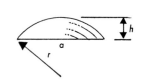

$$A = 2\pi r h$$

$$= \frac{\pi}{4}\ (4h^2 + a^2)$$

$$A_t = \frac{\pi}{4}\ (8rh + a^2)$$

$$= \frac{\pi}{2}\ (2h^2 + a^2)$$

$$V = \frac{\pi h}{24}\ (3a^2 + 4h^2)$$

$$= \pi h^2 \left(r - \frac{h}{3}\right)$$

Torus:

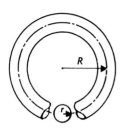

$$A_l = 4\pi^2 Rr$$

$$V = 2\pi^2 Rr^2$$

Ellipsoid and spheroid:

Ellipsoid:

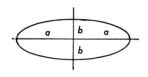

$$V = \frac{4}{3}\pi abc$$

Prolate spheroid:

$$c = b; \quad \text{let} \quad \frac{\sqrt{a^2 - b^2}}{a} = e$$

$$A_t = 2\pi b^2 + 2\pi ab \frac{\sin^{-1} e}{e}$$

$$V = \frac{4}{3}\pi ab^2$$

Oblate spheroid:

$$c = a; \quad \text{let} \quad \frac{\sqrt{a^2 - b^2}}{a} = e$$

$$A_t = 2\pi a^2 + \frac{\pi b^2}{e} \ln \frac{1+e}{1-e}$$

$$V = \frac{4}{3}\pi a^2 b$$

Paraboloid of revolution:

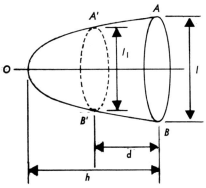

$$A \text{ (segment } AOB) = \frac{2\pi l}{3b^2}\left[\left(\frac{l^2}{16}+b^2\right)^{3/2}-\left(\frac{l}{4}\right)^3\right]$$

$$V \text{ (segment } AOB) = \frac{\pi b l^2}{8}$$

$$V \text{ (segment } AA'B'B) = \frac{\pi d}{8}\left(l^2+l_1^2\right)$$

Hyperboloid of revolution:

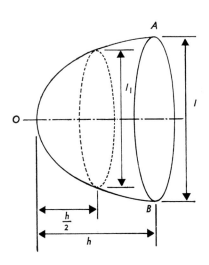

$$V \text{ (segment } AOB) = \frac{\pi h}{24}\left(l^2+4l_1^2\right)$$

Dimension systems

Mechanical quantities

Symbol	Quantity	Dynamical or physical	Gravitational or technical	Energetical
L *	Length	L	L	L
t	Time	T	T	T
m	Mass	M	$FL^{-1}T^2$	$EL^{-2}T^2$
V	Velocity	LT^{-1}	LT^{-1}	LT^{-1}
a	Acceleration	LT^{-2}	LT^{-2}	LT^{-2}
F	Force	MLT^{-2}	F	EL^{-1}
p	Pressure	$ML^{-1}T^{-2}$	FL^{-2}	EL^{-3}
M	Momentum	MLT^{-1}	FT	$EL^{-1}T$
E	Energy	ML^2T^{-2}	FL	E
P	Power	ML^2T^{-3}	FLT^{-1}	ET^{-1}
T	Torque	ML^2T^{-2}	FL	E

* Brackets are omitted for simplicity.

Thermal quantities

Symbol	Quantity	Thermo-physical	Thermo-technical	Energetical
	Mechanical dimensions	M, L, T	F, L, T	E, L, T
θ	Temperature	θ	θ	θ
H	Quantity of heat (enthalpy)	ML^2T^{-2}	FL	E
c	Thermal capacity (specific heat)	$L^2T^{-2}\theta^{-1}$	$L^2T^{-2}\theta^{-1}$	$L^2T^{-2}\theta^{-1}$
k	Thermal conductivity	$MLT^{-3}\theta^{-1}$	$FT^{-1}\theta^{-1}$	$EL^{-1}T^{-1}\theta^{-1}$
U	Transmittance	$MT^{-3}\theta^{-1}$	$FL^{-1}T^{-1}\theta^{-1}$	$EL^{-2}T^{-1}\theta^{-1}$
s	Entropy	$ML^2T^{-2}\theta^{-1}$	$FL\theta^{-1}$	$E\theta^{-1}$

Electromagnetic quantities

Symbol	Quantity	Electro-physical	Practical	Definitive
L	Length	L	L	L
t	Time	T	T	T
m	Mass	M	$I^2RL^{-2}T^3$	$PL^{-2}T^3$
F	Force	MLT^{-2}	$I^2RL^{-1}T$	$PL^{-1}T$
E	Energy	ML^2T^{-2}	I^2RT	PT
P	Power	ML^2T^{-3}	I^2R	P
Q	Electric charge	Q	IT	Q
Ψ	Displacement flux	Q	IT	Q
D	Displacement	QL^{-2}	$IL^{-2}T$	QL^{-2}
E	Electric field intensity	$MQ^{-1}LT^{-2}$	IRL^{-1}	$PQ^{-1}L^{-1}T$
C	Capacitance	$M^{-1}Q^2L^{-2}T^2$	$R^{-1}T$	$P^{-1}Q^2T^{-1}$
I	Current	QT^{-1}	I	QT^{-1}
V	Voltage	$MQ^{-1}L^2T^{-2}$	IR	$PQ^{-1}T$
R	Resistance	$MQ^{-2}L^2T^{-1}$	R	$PQ^{-2}T^2$

Abbreviations *

Term	Abbreviation	Term	Abbreviation
absolute	abs	center to center	c to c
acre	spell out	centimeter	cm
acre-foot	acre-ft	chemical	chem
alternating-current (as adjective)	a-c	chemically pure	cp
		circular	cir
ampere	amp	coefficient	coef
Angstrom unit	A	conductivity	cond
atmosphere	atm	constant	const
average	avg	cosecant	csc
avoirdupois	avdp	cosine	cos
azimuth	az or α	cotangent	cot
barometer	bar.	coulomb	spell out
barrel	bbl	counter electro-motive force	cemf
Baumé	Bé		
board feet (feet board measure)	fbm	cubic	cu
		cubic centimeter	cu cm, cm³ (liquid,
boiler pressure	spell out		meaning
boiling point	bp		milliliter,
brake horsepower	bhp		ml)
British thermal unit	Btu or B		
calorie	cal	cubic foot	cu ft
candlepower	cp	cubic feet per min-ute	cfm
cent	c or ¢		

* Adapted from recommendations of the American Standards Association.

Term	Abbreviation	Term	Abbreviation
cubic feet per second	cfs	greatest common divisor	gcd
cubic inch	cu in.	henry	h
cubic meter	cu m or m³	high-pressure (adjective)	h-p
cubic millimeter	cu mm or mm³	horsepower	hp
cubic yard	cu yd	horsepower-hour	hp-hr
cycles per second	spell out or c	hour	hr
cylinder	cyl	hundred	C
day	spell out	hyperbolic cosine	cosh
decibel	db	hyperbolic sine	sinh
degree	deg or °	hyperbolic tangent	tanh
degree centigrade	C	inch	in.
degree Fahrenheit	F	inch-pound	in-lb
degree Kelvin	K	inches per second	ips
degree Réaumur	R	indicated horsepower	ihp
diameter	diam		
direct-current (as adjective)	d-c	indicated horsepower-hour	ihp-hr
dozen	doz	inside diameter	ID
efficiency	eff	intermediate-pressure (adjective)	i-p
electric	elec		
electromotive force	emf		
elevation	el	internal	int
equation	eq	joule	j
external	ext	kilocycles per second	kc
farad	spell out or f		
feet board measure (board feet)	fbm	kilogram	kg
		kilogram-calorie	kg-cal
feet per minute	fpm	kilograms per cubic meter	kg per cu m or kg/m³
feet per second	fps		
feet per second per second	fps²	kilograms per second	kgps
fluid	fl	kilometer	km
foot	ft	kilometers per second	kmps
foot-pound	ft-lb		
freezing point	fp	kilovolt	kv
frequency	spell out	kilovolt-ampere	kva
fusion point	fnp	kilowatt	kw
gallon	gal	kilowatthour	kwhr
gallons per minute	gpm	lambert	L
gallons per second	gps	latitude	lat or φ
gram	g	least common multiple	lcm
gram-calorie	g-cal		

Term	Abbreviation	Term	Abbreviation
linear foot	lin ft	pounds per cubic foot	lb per cu ft or pcf
liquid	liq		
liter	l	pounds per square foot	psf
logarithm (common)	log		
logarithm (natural)	$\log_e$ or λ	pounds per square inch	psi
low-pressure (as adjective)	l-p		
		pounds per square inch absolute	psia
mass	spell out		
mathematics(ical)	math	power factor	spell out or pf
maximum	max		
mean effective pressure	mep	quart	qt
		radian	spell out
megacycle	spell out	reactive kilovolt-ampere	kvar
megohm	spell out		
melting point	mp	reactive volt-ampere	var
meter	m		
mho	spell out	revolutions per minute	rpm
micron	μ or mu		
mile	spell out	revolutions per second	rps
miles per hour	mph		
miles per hour per second	mphps	rod	spell out
		root mean square	rms
milliampere	ma	secant	sec
milligram	mg	second	sec
milliliter	ml	second (angular measure)	″
millimeter	mm		
million	spell out	shaft horsepower	shp
million gallons per day	mgd	sine	sin
		specific gravity	sp gr
millivolt	mv	specific heat	sp ht
minimum	min	square	sq
minute	min	square centimeter	sq cm or cm²
minute (angular measure)	′	square foot	sq ft
		square inch	sq in.
mole	spell out	square kilometer	sq km or km²
molecular weight	mol. wt	square meter	sq m or m²
month	spell out	square micron	sq μ or sq mu or μ^2
ohm	spell out or Ω		
ounce	oz	square millimeter	sq mm or mm²
outside diameter	OD		
parts per million	ppm	square root of mean square	rms
pint	pt		
potential	spell out	standard	std
pound	lb	tangent	tan

Term	Abbreviation	Term	Abbreviation
temperature	temp	volt	v
tensile strength	ts	volt-ampere	va
thousand	M	volt-coulomb	spell out
thousand foot-pounds	kip-ft	watt	w
		watthour	whr
thousand pounds	kip	week	spell out
ton	spell out	weight	wt
ton-mile	spell out	yard	yd
versed sine	vers	year	yr

APPENDIX E

Conversion factors

Length [L]

1 cm = 0.3937 in.
1 fathom = 6 ft
1 ft = 12 in.
    = 30.48 cm
1 furlong = 660 ft
1 in. = 2.540 cm
1 km = 1,000 m
    = 0.6214 mile
    = 3,281 ft
1 m = 3.281 ft
    = 39.37 in.
1 mil = 0.001 in.
1 mile = 5,280 ft
    = 1.609 km
    = 1,760 yd
1 nautical mile = 1.152 statute
                        miles
1 yd = 3 ft
    = 36 in.
    = 91.44 cm

Area [L^2]

1 acre = 43,560 sq ft
1 cir mil = 7.854×10^{-7} sq in.
1 sq cm = 0.1550 sq in.
1 sq ft = 144 sq in.
    = 929.0 sq cm
1 sq in. = 6.452 sq cm
    = 1.273×10^6 cir mils
1 sq m = 10.76 sq ft
1 sq mile = 640 acres
    = 2.788×10^7 sq ft
    = 2.590 sq km
1 sq yd = 9 sq ft
    = 1,296 sq in.

Volume [L^3]

1 cu ft = 1,728 cu in.
    = 7.481 gal
    = 28.32 liters
1 cu in. = 16.39 cu cm

Volume [L^3] (Cont.)

```
1 cu m = 35.31 cu ft
       = 1.308 cu yd
1 cu yd = 27 cu ft
1 gal (liq) = 231 cu in.
           = 0.1337 cu ft
           = 3.785 liters
           = 8 pt (liq)
           = 4 qt (liq)
1 liter = 1,000 cu cm
        = 1.057 qt
        = 61.02 cu in.
1 pint (liq) = 28.87 cu in.
1 qt (liq) = 2 pt (liq)
          = 57.75 cu in.
          = 0.9464 liter
```

Linear velocity [LT^{-1}]

```
1 fps = 30.48 cps
      = 0.6818 mph
1 kmph = 0.6214 mph
1 knot (nautical mph) = 1.152 mph
1 m per sec = 2.237 mph
1 mph = 1.467 fps
      = 1.609 kmph
      = 0.8684 knot
60 mph = 88 fps
```

Angular velocity [T^{-1}]

```
1 radian per sec = 57.30 deg
                         per sec
1 rps = 6.283 radians per sec
      = 360 deg per sec
1 rpm = 0.1047 radian per sec
      = 6 deg per sec
```

Weight [MLT^{-2}]*

```
1 kg = 2.205 lb
1 oz (avdp) = 28.35 g
1 lb (avdp) = 16 oz
           = 0.4536 kg
           = 7,000 grains
```

Weight [MLT^{-2}]* (Cont.)

```
1 ton (short) = 2,000 lb
             = 907.2 kg
1 ton (long) = 2,240 lb
1 cu ft of water (fresh) = 62.4 lb
1 cu ft of water (sea) = 64.0 lb
1 gal of water (fresh) = 8.34 lb
```

Force [MLT^{-2}]

```
1 g = 980.7 dynes
    = 2.205 × 10⁻³ lb
```
$$1 \ g = 980.7 \ \text{dynes}$$
$$= 2.205 \times 10^{-3} \ \text{lb}$$
$$1 \ \text{lb} = 4.448 \times 10^{5} \ \text{dynes}$$
$$= 453.6 \ \text{g}$$
$$= 32.17 \ \text{poundals}$$

Pressure or force per unit area [$ML^{-1}T^{-2}$]

```
1 atm = 76.00 cm of mercury
             at 0°C
      = 29.92 in. of mercury
             at 0°C
      = 33.9 ft of water at 4°C
      = 14.70 psi
1 ft of water at 4°C
             = 2.950 × 10⁻² atm
             = 0.4336 psi
1 psi = 0.0680 atm
      = 2.307 ft of water
1 ton (short) per sq ft
             = 0.9450 atm
             = 32.04 ft of water
```

Energy [ML^2T^{-2}] or [FL]

$$1 \ \text{Btu} = 778.3 \ \text{ft-lb}$$
$$= 3.929 \times 10^{-4} \ \text{hp-hr}$$
$$= 2.930 \times 10^{-4} \ \text{kwhr}$$
$$= 0.2520 \ \text{kg-cal}$$
$$1 \ \text{cm-g} = 980.7 \ \text{ergs}$$
$$= 7.233 \times 10^{-5} \ \text{ft-lb}$$
$$1 \ \text{erg (cm-dyne)} = 1.020 \times 10^{-3} \ \text{cm-g}$$
$$= 7.367 \times 10^{-8} \ \text{ft-lb}$$

---

* These same conversion factors apply to the units of mass having the same names: 1 slug (mass) = 32.17 lb (mass).

Energy [ML^2T^{-2}] or [FL] (Cont.)

1 ft-lb = 1.356 joules
= 1.356 w-sec
1 hp-hr = 2,545 Btu
= 1.98 × 10⁶ ft-lb
= 0.7457 kwhr
1 joule (w-sec) = 9.480 × 10⁻⁴ Btu
= 10⁷ ergs
= 0.7376 ft-lb
1 kg-cal = 1,000 g-cal
= 3.969 Btu
1 kwhr = 3,413 Btu
= 2.655 × 10⁶ ft-lb
= 1.341 hp-hr

Power (ML^2T^{-3}) or (FLT^{-1})

1 Btu per min = 778.3 ft-lb per min
= 0.02357 hp
= 0.01758 kw
1 hp = 42.41 Btu per min
= 550 ft-lb per sec
= 33,000 ft-lb per min
= 0.7457 kw
1 kw = 56.89 Btu per min
= 737.6 ft-lb per sec
= 44,260 ft-lb per min
= 1.341 hp

APPENDIX F

Examples of reports

Type I—Mathematical analysis

NATIONAL ADVISORY COMMITTEE FOR AERONAUTICS
Technical Note 2062 *

Dynamic Similitude between a Model and a Full-scale Body for Model Investigation at Full-scale Mach Number

By Anshal I. Neihouse and Philip W. Pepoon

Summary

An analysis is given for interpreting results of dynamic tests of a model investigated at full-scale Mach number in terms of the corresponding full-scale body. This analysis shows that dynamic similarity for such a condition can be closely approximated although the effect of gravity is not to scale. Thus an error is introduced which, however, should be small if the time period of model action is short.

* Courtesy of the National Aeronautics and Space Administration, Washington, D.C.

Introduction

When geometrically similar systems move under the action of forces in such a manner that the relative positions of the parts of one system after a certain time are geometrically similar to those of another system after a proportional period of time, the systems are said to be dynamically similar. When geometrical similarity of the paths of motion of corresponding points is associated with geometrical similarity of the parts, constant-scale ratios of force, mass, and time must be maintained in addition to that of length.

In model testing, full-scale conditions cannot be completely duplicated in every respect and some compromise is generally necessary, the nature of the compromise depending upon the end result required. In simulating equal flow patterns, the Reynolds number, or the ratio of inertia to frictional or viscous forces, is maintained constant between the model and its counterpart. For dynamic testing such as model spin tests, the Froude number, or the ratio of inertia to gravity forces, is maintained constant. If compressibility is believed to be involved in the flow, the Mach number, or the ratio of inertia to elastic forces, is kept constant.

With the advent of high-speed missiles and rocket-propelled airplanes, an increasing amount of dynamic testing is conducted at full-scale Mach numbers on scale models of flight vehicles. Proper ballasting of the model and corresponding interpretation of the results should be of interest for such tests as well as for tests in which parts of the airplane, such as pilot-escape capsules or bombs, are jettisoned at high speeds.

This paper presents a special application of dynamic similarity for an investigation in which a scale model would be tested dynamically at the actual Mach number of the corresponding full-scale body.

Symbols

V velocity
V_c velocity of sound
Ω angular velocity

l linear dimension

F force

m mass

W weight (mg)

g acceleration due to gravity

I moment of inertia

a linear acceleration

ρ density of air surrounding test vehicle

S area of surface

C coefficient

α angular acceleration

t time

$$K = \frac{V_{c_{alt}}}{V_{c_{SL}}}$$

$$R = \frac{l_{fs}}{l_m}$$

Subscripts:

fs full scale

m model

alt   altitude

SL sea level

Analysis

If the Mach number for the model tests and that for the airplane are to be equal, the ratio of the velocity of the airplane to the velocity of sound at the flight altitude must be equal to the ratio of the velocity of the model to the velocity of sound at its test altitude. If it is assumed that the model tests made at sea level represent flight of the airplane at altitude,

$$\frac{V_{fs}}{V_{c_{alt}}} = \frac{V_m}{V_{c_{SL}}}$$

Then the ratio of the velocity of the full-scale body to the velocity of the model is

$$\frac{V_{fs}}{V_m} = \frac{V_{c_{alt}}}{V_{c_{SL}}} = K \tag{1}$$

For dynamic similitude between airplane and model, the helix angles of corresponding points due to any rotary motion must be equal (reference 1); that is,

$$\frac{\Omega_{fs} l_{fs}}{V_{fs}} = \frac{\Omega_m l_m}{V_m}$$

Therefore,

$$\frac{\Omega_{fs}}{\Omega_m} = \frac{V_{fs}}{V_m} \frac{l_m}{l_{fs}}$$

Since $l_{fs}/l_m = R$, then the ratio of the angular velocity for the full-scale body to the angular velocity for the model can be written as

$$\frac{\Omega_{fs}}{\Omega_m} = \frac{K}{R} \qquad (2)$$

As pointed out in reference 1, the ratio of inertia forces to aerodynamic forces must also be equal for airplane and model. Since

$$F = ma = C \frac{1}{2} \rho V^2 S$$

then

$$\frac{m_{fs} a_{fs}}{C_{fs} \frac{1}{2} \rho_{fs} V_{fs}^2 S_{fs}} = \frac{m_m a_m}{C_m \frac{1}{2} \rho_m V_m^2 S_m}$$

If the assumption is made that $C_{fs} = C_m$,

$$\frac{a_{fs}}{a_m} = \frac{m_m}{m_{fs}} \left(\frac{\rho_{fs}}{\rho_m} \frac{V_{fs}^2}{V_m^2} \frac{l_{fs}^2}{l_m^2} \right)$$

$$= \frac{m_m}{m_{fs}} \left(\frac{\rho_{fs}}{\rho_m} K^2 R^2 \right)$$

(The term ρ_{fs}/ρ_m was omitted in reference 1 because it was assumed that $\rho_{fs}/\rho_m = 1$.)

If a difference in altitude between airplane and model tests is considered, it follows from reference 1 that

$$\frac{m_{fs}}{m_m} = R^3 \frac{\rho_{fs}}{\rho_m}$$

and

$$\frac{m_{fs}}{\rho_{fs} l_{fs}^3} = \frac{m_m}{\rho_m l_m^3}$$

Therefore the ratio of the linear acceleration for the full-scale body to the linear acceleration for the model can be written as

$$\frac{a_{fs}}{a_m} = \frac{\dfrac{\rho_{fs}}{\rho_m} K^2 R^2}{R^3 \dfrac{\rho_{fs}}{\rho_m}} = \frac{K^2}{R} \tag{3}$$

Since $t = \dfrac{V}{a}$ and $\dfrac{t_{fs}}{t_m} = \dfrac{V_{fs}}{a_{fs}} \dfrac{a_m}{V_m} = \dfrac{R}{K^2} K$, the relation between t_{fs} and t_m is

$$\frac{t_{fs}}{t_m} = \frac{R}{K} \tag{4}$$

Also, inasmuch as $a = l\alpha$, the necessary relation between the angular acceleration for the full-scale body and for the model is

$$\frac{\alpha_{fs}}{\alpha_m} = \frac{a_{fs}}{a_m} \frac{l_m}{l_{fs}}$$
$$= \frac{K^2}{R} \frac{1}{R} = \frac{K^2}{R^2} \tag{5}$$

Also, in reference 1 the ratio of the moments of inertia is shown to be

$$\frac{I_{fs}}{I_m} = R^5 \frac{\rho_{fs}}{\rho_m} \tag{6}$$

Discussion

When the Mach number for the model equals the Mach number for the full-scale body and the model undergoes rotation, ballasting of the model as indicated in the foregoing analysis leads to an interpretation of the measured values in the manner indicated. [See equations (1) to (6).] Because the acceleration due to gravity cannot be altered, the vertical acceleration (due to gravity) for the model tests is too small for dynamic similarity by the scale ratio R. The acceleration of the model vertically downward, therefore, is not sufficient, or in other words, the vertical downward acceleration of the flow is too great, for dynamic similarity. Thus an error is introduced that does not permit complete dynamic similarity, but if the time period of model action is short, the deviation from dynamic similarity should be small. For longer time periods, this effect can be computed and added to the model motion.

For a condition in which the model does not undergo rotation or is rotating at constant speed about one principal axis only, dynamic similarity could be obtained by varying the ratio m_{fs}/m_m in such a manner that $a_{fs} = a_m$. Since

$$\frac{m_{fs}a_{fs}}{m_m a_m} = \frac{\rho_{fs} V_{fs}^2 l_{fs}^2}{\rho_m V_m^2 l_m^2}$$

and since $a_{fs} = a_m$ and $V_{fs} = V_m K$,

$$\frac{m_{fs}}{m_m} = \frac{\rho_{fs}}{\rho_m} K^2 R^2$$

This equation can be written

$$\frac{W_{fs}/g l_{fs}^2}{W_m/g l_m^2} = \frac{\rho_{fs}}{\rho_m} K^2$$

If both the model and the airplane are considered to be operating at sea level, their sea-level wing loadings would therefore be the same.

Concluding remarks

An analysis is given for interpreting results of dynamic tests of a model investigated at full-scale Mach number in terms of the corresponding full-scale body. This analysis shows that dynamic similarity for such a condition can be closely approximated although the effect of gravity is not to scale. Thus an error is introduced which, however, should be small if the time period of model action is short.

Langley Aeronautical Laboratory
National Advisory Committee for Aeronautics
Langley Air Force Base, Va., January 23, 1950

Reference

1. Max Scherberg and R. V. Rhode, Mass Distribution and Performance of Free Flight Models, *NACA TN* 268, 1927.

Type 2—Experimental design

NATIONAL ADVISORY COMMITTEE FOR AERONAUTICS
Technical Note 3620 *

The Design of a Miniature Solid-propellant Rocket

By Robert H. Heitkotter

Summary

A miniature rocket motor was designed and developed to produce 3 ounces of thrust for a duration of 2 seconds. The rocket is simply designed, safe to operate, easily handled, and gives reproducible performance. Standard solid-propellant-rocket design techniques were found to be not wholly applicable to the design of miniature rockets because of excessive heat losses.

Introduction

Free-flying dynamic scale models are used frequently for securing aerodynamic research data. These models generally use movable aerodynamic surfaces in order to furnish disturbing or restoring forces and moments for purposes of investigating the response of the model. Often, these aerodynamic surfaces are in unsteady or unknown flow fields; consequently, the magnitudes of forces or moments being applied are not accurately known. The use of small rockets to produce the required disturbing forces or moments minimizes these difficulties. Rocket motors have been used with good results to disturb the flight of rocket-powered research models in pitch and yaw. Recently, a requirement for the disturbance of a free-spinning model in the Langley 20-foot free-spinning tunnel resulted in the development of a miniature

* Courtesy of the National Aeronautics and Space Administration, Washington, D.C.

rocket producing 3 ounces of thrust for 2 seconds. (See ref. 1.) Inasmuch as presently known solid-propellant-rocket techniques were inadequate for the design of miniature rockets, the engineering methods necessary to produce the desired characteristics and the steps of research and design necessary to fabricate such a rocket are presented herein.

Symbols

A	area, sq in.
C_d	discharge coefficient, per sec
C_F	thrust coefficient
d	diameter, in.
F	thrust, oz or lb
I_{sp}	specific impulse, lb-sec/lb or sec
I_t	total impulse, oz-sec or lb-sec
K	restriction ratio, S/A_t
p	static pressure, lb/sq in. abs
r	propellant burning rate, in./sec
S	propellant burning surface, sq in.
t	time, sec
w	mass discharge rate, lb/sec
γ	ratio of specific heats

Subscripts:

a	atmospheric
c	rocket combustion chamber
e	exit
t	rocket throat

Design procedure

According to the design requirements specified for the miniature rocket of reference 1, the rocket motor was to produce 3 ounces of thrust for a duration of 2 seconds and was to weigh less than 20 grams. No commercially manufactured rocket motor was available or could

be modified to meet these requirements. The weight requirement stipu-
lated a miniature rocket having a propellant that would operate at low
pressures in order to keep the weight of the metal parts to a minimum.
Cordite SU/K, a double-base extruded propellant of British origin, was
selected because of its desirable ballistic properties at relatively low
operating pressures and because it could be easily machined. A design
chamber pressure of 315 lb/sq in. abs was chosen because past experience had shown that rocket motors using Cordite SU/K propellant will
sometimes enter an unstable burning period referred to as "chuffing" if
lower operating pressures occur. (See ref. 2.)

An end-burning charge in the shape of a circular cylinder was chosen
to study the parameters of surface area and length necessary to produce
the desired results and to give a reasonable shape to the rocket motor.
The propellant charge was to be inhibited on all lateral surfaces and at
one end in order to produce end burning along the axis of the propellant. A simple orifice-type nozzle with an area ratio A_e/A_t of 1 was
selected. For preliminary design purposes standard internal-ballistic
equations were used to determine the initial propellant size. These equations may be found in reference 2. Since the ratio of nozzle exit area
to nozzle throat area was 1, the exit pressure p_e was equal to the throat
pressure p_t. The exit pressure p_e was computed from the following
equation, by using the assumed value of chamber pressure p_c of
315 lb/sq in. abs:

$$p_e = p_t = p_c \left(\frac{2}{\gamma+1}\right)^{\frac{\gamma}{\gamma-1}} = 315 \times 0.555 = 175 \text{ lb/sq in. abs}$$

where the value of γ was determined to be 1.25 for Cordite SU/K
propellant. Since the values for A_e/A_t, p_c, p_e, γ, and required thrust are
known, a value for thrust coefficient C_F and required nozzle throat
area A_t may be calculated as follows:

$$C_F = \sqrt{\frac{2\gamma^2}{\gamma-1}\left(\frac{2}{\gamma+1}\right)^{\frac{\gamma+1}{\gamma-1}}\left[1-\left(\frac{p_e}{p_c}\right)^{\frac{\gamma-1}{\gamma}}\right]} + \left(\frac{p_e-p_a}{p_c}\right)\left(\frac{A_e}{A_t}\right)$$
$$= 1.20$$

$$A_t = \frac{F}{C_F p_c} = \frac{0.1875}{378} = 0.000496 \text{ sq in.}$$

The propellant burning area S is determined from the restriction
ratio $K = S/A_t$. The restriction ratio required is a function of design
chamber pressure and must be determined from experimental data.

Figure 1 shows the variation of restriction ratio K and burning rate r with chamber pressure p_c for full-scale rocket firings of Cordite SU/K propellant. These data were obtained from previous static firing tests of many full-scale Cordite rocket motors. Figure 1 shows that, for a design chamber pressure p_c of 315 lb/sq in. abs, the restriction ratio required is 207. The propellant burning surface area, therefore, must be 0.102 square inch. Figure 1 also shows the burning rate to be 0.227 inch per second. Therefore, for a 2-second duration, the propel-

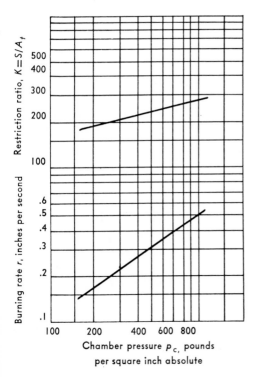

FIG. 1.

lant length must be 0.454 inch. By using the above calculated size, a charge in the shape of a right circular cylinder was machined from propellant stock.

An inhibiting material was needed that would withstand the high temperature and erosive effects of the propellant gas and would cause the propellant to burn progressively rearward in order to maintain a constant burning area and the desired burning rate. This in turn would cause the pressure level to remain constant and thereby produce the required 3 ounces of thrust. Also, the inhibiting material should not cause a change in the ballistic properties of the propellant. The propellant was wrapped with several layers of cellulose acetate tape as an inhibitor for initial tests.

An igniter was made by utilizing a commercially manufactured match-type squib which consists of a cardboard tube containing two insulated wires with a match head at the end and having a sulfurized compound as a filler and insulating material. The squib was held in place by a metal nut in the igniter holder which was placed at right angles to the propellant chamber. The original test rocket was constructed of SAE 1020 steel with a removable head cap.

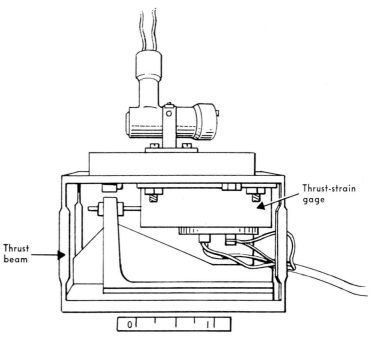

Thrust-strain gage

Thrust beam

FIG. 2.

Test procedure and analysis of results

Instrumentation. The thrust stand used in the experimental rocket tests consisted of a deflected table which transmitted the thrust load to a small strain-gage force pickup. An electrical strain-gage pressure pickup was connected to a pressure probe installed in the rocket chamber wall. These instruments, in conjunction with a recording oscillograph, gave continuous records of thrust and pressure as a function of time. A miniature rocket is shown mounted on the thrust stand in Figure 2.

Results of preliminary tests.   Figure 3 shows a thrust-time history obtained from one of the initial miniature-rocket-motor tests. Several static firings of the rocket motor revealed the following conditions: improper ignition characteristics, low thrust and pressure particularly during initial burning, and unsatisfactory inhibiting of the propellant. These conditions were attributed to a lack of igniter flammability, severe heat losses immediately after ignition, and insufficient propellant burning surface necessary to sustain 3 ounces of thrust.

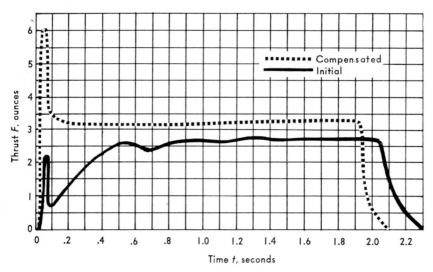

FIG. 3.

In order to increase the flammability of the igniter, the match-head end of the squib tube was filled with a fine-grained black powder cemented in place with an acetone adhesive. In order to improve the inhibitor and to maintain a constant burning rate, a method was devised to fabricate a phenolic shell, which was then bonded to the propellant by a coating of an epoxy adhesive on the inside of the shell and lateral propellant surface.

A study of the test results revealed that the propellant experienced a severe heat loss to the chamber walls immediately after ignition. This heat loss in miniature rockets is much greater than the heat loss occurring in larger rockets because the propellant gives off heat to the chamber walls at a rate proportional to the cube of the scale factor, and the metal parts absorb the heat at a rate proportional to the square of the scale factor.

In order to compensate for the heat loss the propellant grain was modified by the addition of an uninhibited cylindrical protrusion 0.25 inch in diameter and 0.05 inch long. This protrusion also compensated for the low thrust immediately after ignition. Static firing tests using the new charge design with increased surface area were made. The results of these tests disclosed that the additional surface area compensated for the heat loss and maintained the required thrust.

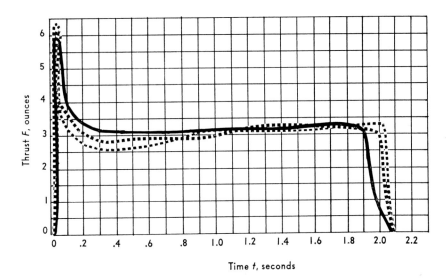

FIG. 4.

However, this also resulted in a higher chamber pressure (353 lb/sq in. abs) and a higher propellant burning rate. Consequently, it was also necessary to increase the length of the propellant charge in order to achieve a 2-second burning time. A thrust-time curve obtained from the static firing of this compensated propellant design is shown by the dashed-line curve in Figure 3. The results show that solid-propellant-rocket design techniques, taken from full-scale firings, can be applied in the initial design of miniature rockets but compensatory methods must be utilized because of excessive heat losses encountered.

Results of tests of revised rocket design. Many static firings of the revised rocket design were made to determine its ballistic characteristics and serviceability. Figure 4 shows thrust-time curves for several static firings of the miniature rocket. These data show the rocket to have close repeatability of performance.

The igniter design proved to be satisfactory. However, after several firings a phenolic nut instead of a metal nut was fabricated to hold the igniter squib because this type of construction provided an inexpensive reliable igniter that affords a pressure-relief device in the event the chamber pressure becomes high enough to cause a possible rupture of the case and danger to the users of the rocket or damage to the models. The phenolic nut was sealed in place with the same epoxy

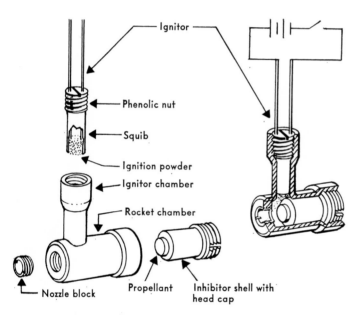

FIG. 5.

adhesive used as the inhibiting material. The inhibitor was completely satisfactory in that it caused no variation in the ballistic properties of the propellant. In order to simplify the design and insure positioning of the propellant in the chamber, the head cap was made an integral part of the inhibitor shell; thus, the design provides an inexpensive expendable unit consisting of propellant, inhibitor, and head cap all in one piece. Repeated static firings of the reusable rocket case revealed a loss of thrust caused by an enlarged orifice created by erosive propellant gas flow during burning. In order to avoid this problem the rocket case was modified to incorporate a replaceable nozzle block as shown by a cutaway sketch of the miniature rocket and components in Figure 5. The miniature rocket incorporating these modifications proved to be simply designed, safe to operate, easily handled, and to give reproducible performance. Performance characteristics of the miniature rocket are compiled in table 1.

Table I. Weights and performance characteristics of the miniature rocket motor

Weight of rocket motor components in grams:	
Rocket motor case	14.17
Inhibited propellant and shell	2.44
Cordite SU/K propellant	1.16
Igniter assembly	1.95
Rocket motor and components	18.56
Experimentally determined performance parameters (average values at 3 ounces of thrust):	
Nozzle discharge coefficient, C_d, per sec	0.00745
Thrust coefficient, C_F	1.08
Specific impulse, I_{sp}, sec	145
Total impulse, I_t, oz-sec	6.50
Discharge rate, w, lb per sec	0.0013
Adiabatic flame temperature, °F	3,800
Chamber pressure, p_c, psia	353
Restriction ratio, K	205
Nozzle exit pressure, p_e, psia	196
Burning time, t, sec	2

Concluding remarks

A miniature rocket motor was designed and developed to produce 3 ounces of thrust for a duration of 2 seconds. Standard solid-propellant rocket design techniques were found to be inadequate for the design of a miniature rocket because of excessive heat losses.

Langley Aeronautical Laboratory
National Advisory Committee for Aeronautics
Langley Field, Va., November 25, 1955

References

1. Sanger M. Burk, Jr., and Frederick M. Healy, Comparison of Model and Full-scale Spin Recoveries Obtained by Use of Rockets, *NACA TN* 3068, 1954.
2. R. N. Wimpress, "Internal Ballistics of Solid Fuel Rockets," McGraw-Hill Book Company, Inc., New York, 1950.

APPENDIX G

Instructions for the preparation of reports *

Item 101: Introduction

A report is a factual presentation of data or information directed to a particular reader or audience for a specific purpose. Reports are needed to exchange and record information. The facts contained in a report may be a record of past accomplishments, a release of new information, an account of conditions, an analysis of conditions for determining future policies, or a recommendation of a course of action to be followed. These facts must be accurate, complete, and arranged for easy comprehension and reading.

These instructions establish the minimum "hard core" elements (Title, Summary, Discussion) which Engineering Department reports will contain. Within these minimum elements the author is permitted considerable flexibility in the amount of detail used to present the material.

Brevity, consistent with clear coverage of information, is a principal objective.

* Issued by the Engineering Department of E. I. du Pont de Nemours & Company as part of its Standard Practice.

By permission of the Engineering Department, E. I. du Pont de Nemours & Company, Wilmington, Delaware.

Item 201: Format

The format (general shape in which information is presented) should be based on the attributes of the material. In good report writing there is only one basic framework in which material is presented. Variation within this framework is permissible to provide flexibility to meet the needs peculiar to the material and the situation.

All the elements which may be incorporated into a report are outlined in Item 301. The minimum elements which a report will contain are a Title, Summary Section, and Discussion Section. The depth (and consequently length) to which the author wishes to go in the Summary and Discussion Sections is dependent upon conditions surrounding the report. A one or two paragraph summary and limited discussion may be adequate, or extended treatment of the material may be judged necessary. Conclusions and Recommendations are to be succinctly stated in the Summary Section. The extent to which they are further amplified in the Discussion Section is left to the author's judgment. Other prefatory and supplementary elements may be included at the author's discretion, subject to the approval of his supervision.

In deciding upon the format and depth of treatment of the material, the author should consider:

1. Breadth of interest and/or application of the material
2. Purpose and objective to be accomplished
3. Performance and/or reference value
4. Formality of the situation
5. Preparation time which material justifies.

Guidance on the specific details of format may be found in "Guide for Preparing Reports," Accession Number _____.

Item 301: Elements of reports

Elements of Reports	Minimum	Ultimate
Cover	—	Required
Title	Required	Required
Title page	—	Required
Abstract	Required	Required
Letter of transmittal	—	Optional
Foreword	—	Optional
Table of contents	—	Optional
Table of illustrations, figures, etc.	—	Optional
Summary	Required	Required
Statement of problem	Each report will contain a summary to permit the reader to get significant facts without reading the entire report. It may vary in length from a few sentences to two or three pages. Brevity, consistent with clarity, is essential.	
Significant facts		
Conclusion(s)		
Recommendation(s)		
Discussion	To extent appropriate	To extent justified
Introduction	The subject or problem will be amplified only to the extent necessary: to give background information needed by the reader to understand the report; to describe unusual aspects of data collection; to relate the results or findings; to analyze, interpret, and discuss data; and to state basis for conclusion and recommendations.	
Text (detail of study and results)		
Basis for conclusion(s)		
Basis for recommendation(s)		
Appendix	—	Optional
Figures	—	Optional
Tables	—	Optional
Exhibits	—	Optional
Bibliography	—	Optional
Index	—	Optional
Distribution list (see item 601)	Required	Required

Item 401: Issuance of reports

Timing. The value of a report is, among other considerations, a function of time. Therefore, preparation of the report should proceed during the course of the study and the report issued immediately upon completion. Where the need for a lengthy report and/or considerable delay is foreseen, the author should issue a Part One preliminary "hard core" report. This preliminary report should be a condensation of material to be contained in the full report, if a Part Two is to be issued.

The utility of the findings is enhanced by early issuance in condensed form.

Serial numbering. Reports, which in the judgment of supervision are conclusive, important or significant enough to be considered for inclusion in the Engineering Department ED Report series will bear an ED serial number which is identical with the accession number assigned for retrieval purposes. Other reports may be assigned a division number such as DED-X-58-10, in addition to the accession number.

Engineering information center. *Inclusion.* All reports will be processed through the Engineering Information Center for inclusion in the index system.

Accession numbers. Accession numbers will be obtained from the Engineering Information Center by telephone. Assignment of an accession number is to be requested after the report is approved for final typing. The accession number should appear on the title page and cover, or first page if there is no cover. It will be used as the Coordinate Index serial number for identification and retrieval. At the time an accession number is requested, the following information should be provided to the Engineering Information Center:

a. Title of report
b. Author of report
c. Date report was approved for final typing
d. Study or project number, if any

Abstract. An abstract of 75 words or less will be prepared by the author for each report. The abstract should state the specific problem in the over-all field (scope), the facts revealed, and conclusions reached. It should be written in the style of the report and in a manner so it can be used separately from the report. The abstract is the primary means of briefly revealing the report's contents, and is of considerable importance for coordinate indexing.

Index terms. A list of proposed key words for indexing will be prepared by the author for each report and entered on the Title Page of one of the four copies going to Administrative Record Center 12. These key words should present a word picture of the principal and pertinent information in the report. This list will be used as a basis for establishing the terms for incorporating the report into the Coordinate Index, but should not be made a part of the report.

Item 501: Signatures required on reports

All required signatures are placed at the end of the summary section in the report. The required signatures are tabulated below.

Reports	Chief engr.	Div. mgr.	Super-vision	Author
Recommending expenditures based on OME or CCE:*				
Exceeding $150,000	A	N		P
Not exceeding $150,000		A	N	P
Not exceeding $ 50,000		A**	N	P
Not exceeding $ 10,000			A	P
Recommending expenditures based on evaluation estimate				
Not exceeding $ 50,000		A**	N	P
Containing studies of major importance or establishing policy	A	N		P
Directed to department heads	A	N		P
Distribution outside the company	A	N		P
Containing results of experimental or test work				
No expenditures recommended			A	P
Containing results of engineering studies				
No expenditures recommended			A	P

Code: A = approved by; N = noted by; P = prepared by.
* Reference should be made to Part 2, Item 506, for reports incorporating estimates inasmuch as certain statements are required.
** Or his authorized delegate.

Item 601: Distribution

A distribution list is a part of every report. Supervision should use discrimination in report distribution. The majority of Industrial Department personnel located in the Wilmington offices prefer to receive only the report title page or "Part One" report (minimum elements) when issued and their respective department's distribution list, together with a request slip for the full report.

Required distribution of reports include four copies to Administrative Record Center 12, and one copy of all research reports to Head of Intelligence Division, Central Research Department.

Index